AQA (A)

AS

Biology

Steve Potter

AS

AQA (A)

Biology

Steve Potter

Philip Allan Updates
Market Place
Deddington
Oxfordshire
OX15 0SE

Tel: 01869 338652
www.philipallan.co.uk

© Philip Allan Updates 2006

ISBN-13: 978-1-84489-217-4
ISBN-10: 1-84489-217-4

This textbook has been written specifically to support students studying AQA (A) AS Biology. The content has been neither approved nor endorsed by AQA and remains the sole responsibility of the author.

Design by Neil Fozzard

Printed in Great Britain by CPI Bath

Contents

Introduction

About this book

This textbook is written specifically for students following the AQA (specification A) AS biology course. Generally, the topics are in the same order as in the specification. However, where appropriate, some have been re-ordered.

The first four chapters deal with the key topics of:
- cell structure
- biological molecules
- transport across membranes
- the nature and properties of enzymes

These chapters cover many of the core principles that will underpin much of the biology found in later topics. For example, the structure of biological molecules (Chapter 2) and the nature and properties of enzymes (Chapter 4) are both important in the understanding of the A2 topic of digestion.

Chapters 5–7 relate to the way cells are organised in organisms, and the physiology of the circulatory and respiratory systems.

Chapters 8–14 focus on some of the ways in which we make use of biology in society.

Each chapter begins with an outline and a brief introduction. Margin comments accompany the text. Some of these provide extra information to help clarify a point without interrupting the flow of text. These are identified by a ◀ symbol. Others are examiner's hints on what to do and what not to do in unit tests. These are identified by an 🄔 symbol.

Feature boxes are included to provide extra detail or to give information about applications of a topic. In some cases, the boxes give information on classic experiments in biological research.

The main content of each chapter is followed by a comprehensive summary; this would be a good place to start your revision of that topic.

Each chapter ends with some multiple-choice questions, designed to test your understanding of the main ideas, followed by a set of examination-style questions, designed to give you an indication of how well you might perform in the unit tests.

The unit tests

Terms used in the unit tests

You will be asked precise questions in the examinations, so you can save a lot of valuable time as well as ensuring you score as many marks as possible by knowing what is expected.

Terms most commonly used are explained below.

Describe
This means exactly what it says — 'tell me about…' — and you should not need to explain why.

Explain
Here you must give biological reasons for why or how something is happening.

Complete
You must finish off a diagram, graph, flow chart or table.

Draw/plot
This means that you must construct some type of graph. For this, make sure that:
- you choose a scale that makes good use of the graph paper (if a scale is not given) and does not leave all the plots tucked away in one corner
- you plot an appropriate type of graph — if both variables are continuous variables, then a line graph is usually the most appropriate; if one is a discrete variable, then a bar chart is appropriate
- you plot carefully using a sharp pencil and draw lines accurately

From the…
This means that you must use only information in the diagram/graph/photograph or other forms of data.

Name
This asks you to give the name of a structure/molecule/organism etc.

Suggest
This means 'give a plausible biological explanation for' — it is often used when testing understanding of concepts in an unfamiliar situation.

Compare
In this case, you have to give similarities *and* differences.

Calculate
This means add, subtract, multiply, divide (do some kind of sum!) and show how you got your answer — always show your working!

'Do's and 'don't's

When you finally open the test paper, it can be quite a stressful moment. For example, you may not recognise the diagram or graph used in question 1. It can be quite demoralising to attempt a question at the start of an examination if you are not feeling very confident about it. So:

- *do not* begin to write as soon as you open the paper
- *do not* answer question 1 first, just because it is printed first (the examiner did not sequence the questions with your particular favourites in mind)
- *do* scan all the questions before you begin to answer any
- *do* identify those questions about which you feel most confident
- *do* answer first those questions about which you feel most confident, regardless of order in the paper
- *do* read the question carefully — if you are asked to explain, then explain, don't just describe
- *do* take notice of the mark allocation and don't supply the examiner with all your knowledge of osmosis if there is only 1 mark allocated (similarly, you will have to come up with four ideas if 4 marks are allocated)
- *do* try to stick to the point in your answer (it is easy to stray into related areas that will not score marks and will use up valuable time)
- *do* take care with:
  - drawings — you will not be asked to produce complex diagrams, but those you do produce must resemble the subject
  - labelling — label lines must touch the part you are required to identify; if they stop short or pass through the part, you will lose marks
  - graphs — draw small points if you are asked to plot a graph and join the plots with ruled lines or, if specifically asked for, a line or smooth curve of best fit through all the plots
- *do* try to answer all the questions

Chapter 1

Cell structure

This chapter covers:

- the concepts of scale, magnification and resolution
- the way optical microscopes, transmission electron microscopes and scanning electron microscopes work
- how to interpret micrographs
- the limitations of light and electron microscopes
- the ultrastructure of cells, including the appearance and main functions of the nucleus, chloroplasts, mitochondria, lysosomes, Golgi body, ribosomes, plasma membrane and endoplasmic reticulum
- cell fractionation as a technique for obtaining pure samples of different organelles for further study

In 1665, Robert Hooke used one of the first compound microscopes to examine cork. He found that it consisted of small units, which he called **cells**. Following this discovery, other researchers began to use microscopes to examine organisms — mainly plants. By 1839, two German botanists, Schleiden and Schwann, were so convinced by their findings that they put forward the **cell theory**. This states that all organisms are composed of cells.

Micrographs of (a) a cell in the root tip of a maize plant, (b) a mammalian cell, (c) a *Salmonella* bacterium, (d) *Vorticella*

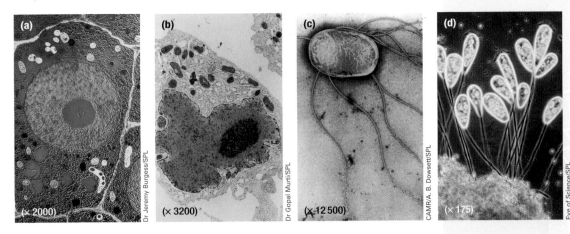

(a) (× 2000) Dr Jeremy Burgess/SPL
(b) (× 3200) Dr Gopal Murti/SPL
(c) (× 12 500) CAMR/A. B. Dowsett/SPL
(d) (× 175) Eye of Science/SPL

A modern version of the cell theory states that:

- a cell is the smallest independent unit of life — anything smaller than a cell is incapable of independent existence
- all organisms are cellular — some consist of just one cell; others contain billions
- cells arise from other cells by cell division — they cannot arise by spontaneous generation (be created from non-living materials)

Scale, magnification and resolution

You should appreciate the range of size of living organisms. The largest single organism in the world at the moment is the giant redwood tree, which can grow up to 100 m in height. The largest animal is the blue whale, which can be up to 30 m long. Adult humans can be 2 m tall. Domestic cats are about 0.3 m long and goldfish 0.1 m. A housefly is about 0.01 m long. One of the largest human cells is an oocyte (egg cell), which has a diameter of 0.0002 m. Most animal cells are smaller than this, with a diameter of 0.00005 m. Typical bacterial cells have a length of 0.000005 m.

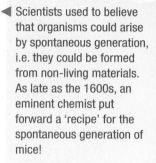

◀ Scientists used to believe that organisms could arise by spontaneous generation, i.e. they could be formed from non-living materials. As late as the 1600s, an eminent chemist put forward a 'recipe' for the spontaneous generation of mice!

Figure 1.1 The range of sizes of living organisms and their components

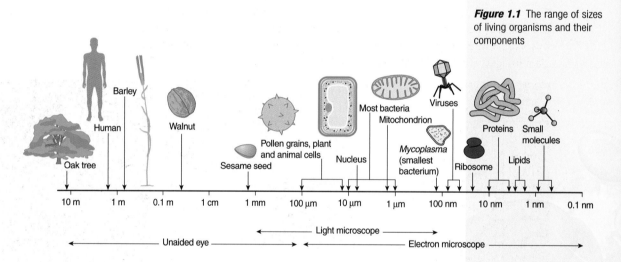

All these zeros can be confusing. To make the numbers more manageable, different, but related, units are used. For example, it is easier to think of a housefly having a length of 1 cm rather than 0.01 m. Similarly, we can visualise an oocyte having a diameter of 0.2 mm more easily than 0.0002 m.

In biology (as in other sciences), the units used for measurement of length are based on the metre (m). Smaller units are obtained by dividing by 1000. For example:

- 1 millimetre (mm) = 1/1000 m
- 1 micrometre (μm) = 1/1000 mm (1/1000 000 m)

Larger units are obtained by multiplying by 1000. For example:

- 1 kilometre (km) = 1000 m

Another derived unit that is used frequently is the centimetre (cm). One centimetre is 1/100 of a metre, or 10 millimetres.

Magnification describes any process that makes an object appear larger than it is. The early microscopes used by Hooke did not magnify greatly. Today, a photograph of an image produced by such a microscope could be further magnified by placing it on a photocopier and selecting 'enlarge'. However, this would merely produce a bigger version of a rather blurred image. There would not be any more detail.

This is a matter of resolution. Resolution is the ability of an instrument to distinguish between two points that are close together. If they cannot be resolved, they will be seen as one point and the detail seen will be limited.

Microscopy

Optical microscopes

Optical microscopes have come a long way since the days of Hooke. The best ones can now produce clear, detailed images magnified up to 1250 times. The images can be viewed directly or, in some cases, through a computer-aided projection system on a screen. The microscopes that you use will not be quite of this standard! Nonetheless, standard microscopes used at A-level can produce clear images with magnification up to 400 times.

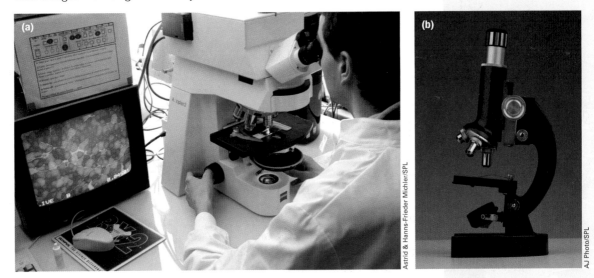

(a) A modern optical research microscope with a computer-aided projection system
(b) A standard microscope used at A-level

An optical microscope passes rays of light through a specimen. As the light passes through, different parts of the specimen absorb varying amounts and wavelengths of light. Light that is not absorbed is transmitted to the eye through two lenses — the objective lens and the eyepiece. Each lens refracts the light and, as a result, magnifies the image. The overall magnification of the microscope is the product of the magnification of the objective and eyepiece lenses. For example, an eyepiece with a magnification of 10 times and an objective with a magnification of 40 times produce an overall magnification of 400 (10 × 40).

You need to have an idea of the size of organisms and cells. You may be asked to calculate the size of, for example, a bacterium from a drawing or photograph. It is easy to press the wrong button on a calculator and produce an answer that suggests a bacterium is 50 m long, rather than 5 μm long! If you understand the range of size of organisms, a moment's thought will tell you that the first answer is wrong.

However, there is a limit to the resolving power of an optical microscope. No matter how good the lenses, the resolution is limited by the wavelength of light itself. The best optical microscopes have a resolving power of 0.2 μm. This means that anything smaller than 0.2 μm is not visible with an optical microscope. Electron microscopes were developed to improve resolution.

Box 1.1 Preparing slides for light microscopy

To prepare a specimen for viewing under a light microscope, the specimen is placed on a glass slide. It can be stained to reveal subcellular structures, such as nuclei or starch grains. To view detail of cells under high magnification, the specimen should be no more than one cell thick (thinner if possible) to allow maximum transmission of light. You have probably prepared a slide of onion epidermis, which is a convenient way of obtaining tissue that is only one cell thick.

Specimens on commercially prepared slides (particularly of animal tissue) have frequently been:

- dehydrated
- stained
- embedded in wax
- sectioned (sliced) using a microtome (a device that produces slices of uniform thickness)

Electron microscopes

An electron microscope uses a beam of electrons, rather than light. Electrons have a shorter wavelength than light, so these microscopes have a higher resolving power than optical microscopes. There are two main kinds of electron microscope:

- the **transmission electron microscope** (TEM) passes a beam of electrons through a specimen (rather like a beam of light passing through a specimen in an optical microscope)
- the **scanning electron microscope** (SEM) directs a beam of electrons at a specimen and creates an image from the electrons that are *reflected* from the surface, rather than from those that pass through

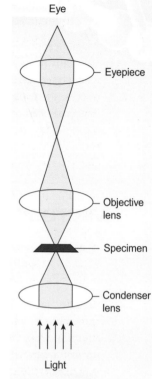

Figure 1.2 How an optical microscope produces an image

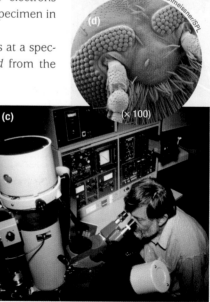

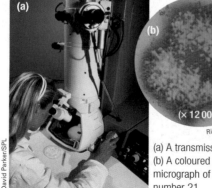

(a) A transmission electron microscope
(b) A coloured transmission electron micrograph of human chromosome number 21

(c) A scanning electron microscope
(d) A scanning electron micrograph of the head of an insect

Today's transmission electron microscopes can magnify up to 500 000 times and have a resolving power of 0.001 μm. This can reveal the internal structure of cell organelles and even produce outlines of large molecules, such as DNA.

A specimen for examination using a transmission electron microscope must be prepared in such a way that electrons can pass through it. Electrons are much more easily blocked than light, so the specimen must be exceptionally thin. One-cell thick would be much too thick — very few electrons would pass through. The specimen must also be examined in a vacuum as atoms and molecules in the air would limit transmission of electrons. Preparation involves using chemicals (often the salts of heavy metals) to fix the specimen. However, there are negative consequences that may arise. For example, the preparation techniques may:
- alter the specimen from its original condition
- introduce 'artefacts' — structures not originally present

Despite this, it is believed that the images produced by transmission electron microscopes do show the true internal structure of cells and organelles. The images are consistent and are supported by other evidence. Therefore, it is reasonable to conclude that they are accurate.

Interpretation of micrographs

Micrographs are photographs taken through a microscope. Electron micrographs are taken through an electron microscope; light micrographs are taken through an optical microscope.

> 🅮 You will probably only have to interpret light micrographs and transmission electron micrographs.

Interpretation micrographs taken through an optical microscope and a transmission electron microscope uses similar principles.

Different shades
One of these principles involves interpreting the opacity of the image that is produced. Different shades can mean different composition. **Optically dense** material allows little light to pass through; **electron-dense** material allows few electrons to pass through. As a result, these types of material appear dark when viewed through the eyepiece of an optical microscope or on the fluorescent screen of a transmission electron microscope.

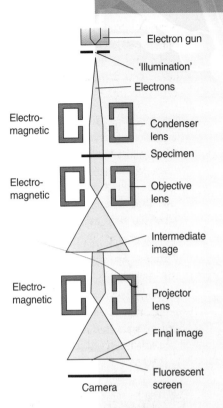

Figure 1.3 How a transmission electron microsope produces an image

A red blood cell consists almost entirely of haemoglobin. Therefore, it has uniform electron density and uniform brightness. The various structures in the nucleus of the liver cell have different compositions and electron densities, so there are different shades of light and dark.

(a) Electron micrograph of red blood cells
(b) Electron micrograph of the nucleus of a liver cell

If a micrograph is of uniform brightness/darkness, the same amount of light (or number of electrons) must be passing through all regions of the section. All regions must, therefore, have the same optical (or electron) density and are likely to have the same composition.

Different shapes

The appearance of a specimen under a microscope depends on a number of factors. First, from what angle is the specimen being viewed? Second, are we viewing the whole specimen? Red blood cells are often described as 'biconcave discs'. When viewed through an optical microscope, they usually appear round and are pale in the centre. When seen from the side, the biconcave aspect of their shape is apparent — they are thinner in the middle, which accounts for the 'paleness' here, when viewed from the front.

◀ Red blood cells are disc-shaped when seen from the front and biconcave when seen from the side.

However, red blood cells examined by a transmission electron microscope do not appear as biconcave discs. Why is this? When specimens are prepared for a transmission electron microscope, very thin sections are cut. Many sections are taken through a single cell. Different sections will have different shapes, depending on the angle at which each was cut. In addition, the red blood cells may be squashed or bent during the preparation, further distorting their shape.

◀ Distortion can occur when red blood cells are squeezed through tiny blood vessels.

Figure 1.4 Sections can have different shapes, depending on the angle at which each was cut

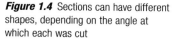

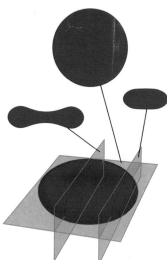

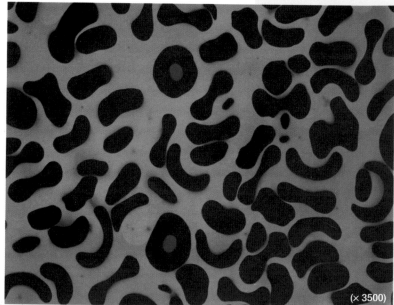

(× 3500)

Dr Gopal Murti/SPL

Red blood cells viewed through an electron microscope

How big is it really?

If the size of the image on the micrograph (the apparent size) and the magnification are known, then the actual size of the specimen can be calculated. For example, if a photograph of an object (the apparent size) is ten times bigger than the object (the actual size), then the object must be one-tenth the size of its picture. For example, if the length in the photograph is 5 cm, the actual length of the object must be one-tenth of this — 0.5 cm. The equation relating actual size, apparent size and magnification can be written in three ways:

$$\text{actual size} = \frac{\text{apparent size}}{\text{magnification}}$$

$$\text{magnification} = \frac{\text{apparent size}}{\text{actual size}}$$

$$\text{apparent size} = \text{actual size} \times \text{magnification}$$

The apparent size and actual size must be in the *same units*.

In a question, if the apparent size and actual size are given in different units, you have to convert one of the measurements so that they are both the same.

Worked example

The diameter of a cell in a micrograph is 3.5 cm. The magnification is 450. What is the actual size of the cell in micrometres (μm)?

Answer

Information given:

- apparent size (diameter of cell in micrograph)
- magnification

The relevant form of the equation is:

$$\text{actual size} = \frac{\text{apparent size}}{\text{magnification}}$$

The answer is required in micrometres. Therefore, the apparent size (cm) must first be converted to micrometres:

1 cm = 10 mm; 1 mm = 1000 μm, so 1 cm = 10 000 μm
3.5 cm = (3.5 × 10 000) μm = 35 000 μm

The apparent size is 35 000 μm. Substituting into the equation:

$$\frac{\text{apparent size}}{\text{magnification}} = \text{actual size}$$

$$\frac{35\,000}{450} = 77.8\,\mu m$$

The diameter of the cell is 77.8 μm.

Which part of the specimen is being observed?

When using an optical microscope, depth of focus is an issue. Remember, specimens may be up to one cell thick. The organelles are not distributed uniformly within cells so, by altering the depth of focus slightly, you can alter the appearance of the image.

Limitations of microscopes

Both optical microscopes and transmission electron microscopes have particular uses and limitations. For example, to see how cells are organised in a tissue or organ, it is better to use an optical microscope. The magnification and resolution are not as great as with a transmission electron microscope, but the field of view is wider and the cells can be viewed alive. However, to study the **ultrastructure** of cell organelles, a transmission electron microscope is needed — an optical microscope does not have the necessary magnification and resolution. The properties of optical microscopes and transmission electron microscopes are compared in Table 1.1.

Table 1.1

Property	Optical microscope	Transmission electron microscope
Magnification	Maximum 1250 times	Maximum 500 000 times
Focusing	Glass lenses: eyepiece (ocular lens) and objective lens	Electromagnetic lenses
Resolution	Maximum 0.2 μm	Maximum 0.001 μm
Specimen preparation	Can be mounted in water or aqueous solution; can be alive; may be stained	Specimen is fixed with salts of heavy metals and viewed in a vacuum
Image	Viewed directly through the eyepiece	Viewed on a fluorescent screen
Limitations	Low resolution does not allow much subcellular detail to be observed	Specimens are always dead and may contain artefacts as a result of preparation techniques
Advantages	Can be used to view live whole specimens under low magnification	Can produce high-magnification, high-resolution images of cells and organelles

Ultrastructure of cells

There are two main types of cell — **prokaryotic** and **eukaryotic**. Prokaryotic cells are the most primitive. They are thought to resemble the first cells formed. Bacterial cells, including those of blue-green bacteria, are prokaryotic. Eukaryotic cells are more complex and contain more organelles. The cells of plants, animals, protoctistans and fungi are eukaryotic.

◀ Organelles are subcellular structures with a specific function.

Figure 1.5 Generalised diagrams of (a) an animal cell and (b) a plant cell

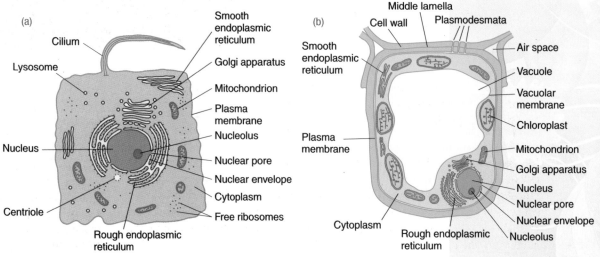

Eukaryotic cells

Animal cells

Nucleus

The **nucleus** typically occupies about 10% of the volume of a cell. It has several components:

- The **nuclear envelope** is a double membrane that surrounds the nucleus. There are many **nuclear pores**, which allow the passage of some molecules between the nucleus and the cytoplasm.
- The **nucleolus** is an organelle within the nucleus. It is not membrane-bound. Its function is to synthesise the components of ribosomes, which then pass through the nuclear pores into the cytoplasm.
- **Chromatin** consists of DNA molecules bound with proteins called histones. For most of the cell cycle, the chromatin fibres are loosely dispersed throughout the nucleus. Just before a cell is about to divide, the chromatin condenses into distinct, recognisable structures called **chromosomes**.

Mitochondria

Mitochondria are the sites of most of the reactions of aerobic respiration. They are surrounded by two membranes. The inner membrane is folded into **cristae** to increase the available surface area.

Figure 1.6 Structure of a mitochondrion

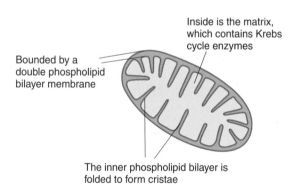

Inside is the matrix, which contains Krebs cycle enzymes

Bounded by a double phospholipid bilayer membrane

The inner phospholipid bilayer is folded to form cristae

Nucleotides (the building blocks of DNA and RNA) and some proteins can pass from the cytoplasm into the nucleus.

◀ Messenger RNA molecules pass from the nucleus into the cytoplasm. DNA molecules are too large to pass through the nuclear pores. DNA directs the synthesis of all types of protein (e.g. structural proteins and enzymes) inside cells.

Transmission electron micrograph of a mitochondrion

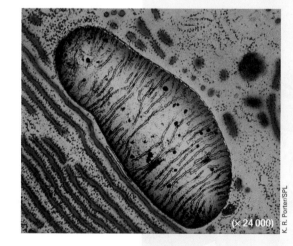

(× 24 000)

Some of the reactions of aerobic respiration take place in the **fluid matrix**. The folded inner membrane provides a large surface area for the electron-transport system, which produces most of the ATP.

Ribosomes

Ribosomes are the sites of protein synthesis. They can be found free in the cytoplasm, but are also bound to the membrane system of the **endoplasmic reticulum**, forming rough endoplasmic reticulum. Each ribosome comprises two subunits that are made from ribosomal RNA and protein. The subunits are manufactured in the nucleolus. They leave the nucleus through nuclear pores and combine in the cytoplasm.

ATP is the 'energy storage molecule' of cells. Energy released in respiration is stored in ATP molecules, to be released and used when needed. Cells that are very active (such as muscle cells or epithelial cells that absorb molecules from the gut) use a great deal of ATP and, therefore, contain many mitochondria.

Endoplasmic reticulum

Endoplasmic reticulum (ER) is a membrane system found throughout the cytoplasm of eukaryotic cells. There are two types of endoplasmic reticulum:

- **Rough ER** has ribosomes on its surface and is responsible for the manufacture and transport of proteins. Protein molecules manufactured by the ribosomes pass through small pores into the lumen of the ER. They are then moved in a vesicle to the Golgi body. Rough ER is extensive in cells that manufacture a lot of protein, such as secretory cells. Rough ER is usually close to the nucleus and is continuous with the outer membrane of the nuclear envelope.
- **Smooth ER** has no ribosomes on its surface. It is concerned with the synthesis of lipids. It is also associated with carbohydrate metabolism and detoxification. Smooth ER is, therefore, particularly extensive in brain and liver cells.

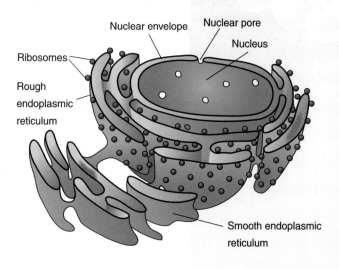

Figure 1.7 Rough ER and smooth ER are continuous with each other and with the outer membrane of the nuclear envelope

Golgi complex

The **Golgi complex** is sometimes called the Golgi apparatus or Golgi body. It consists of a number of flattened membrane-bound sacs in which proteins, formed in the ribosomes of the rough ER, are modified. For example, they may be converted into glycoproteins. The Golgi complex receives the unmodified proteins in vesicles formed from the rough ER. The modified proteins are also released from the Golgi complex in vesicles. These modified proteins can be used within the same cell. However, they frequently pass out of the cell by exocytosis (see Chapter 3) to be used elsewhere. Golgi complexes are most extensive in secretory cells.

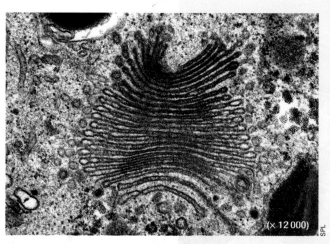

The Golgi complex

Lysosomes

Lysosomes have no specialised internal structure and are surrounded by a single membrane. They are formed in the Golgi complex and contain digestive enzymes (produced in the rough ER) that break down cellular waste and debris. All eukaryotic cells contain lysosomes, but they are particularly abundant in phagocytic cells. Here, enzymes from the lysosomes digest foreign cells that have been engulfed.

Plasma membrane

The plasma membrane is the boundary membrane of all eukaryotic cells. It controls what passes into and out of the cell. There have been several models of membrane structure. The model currently thought to be the best representation is the fluid mosaic model. The basic structure is a **phospholipid bilayer** — a double layer of phospholipid molecules. Different types of protein molecule are embedded in this bilayer:

- **ion-channel proteins** allow certain ions to pass through
- **transport proteins** carry molecules into or out of the cell
- **glycoproteins** act as cellular markers to allow the cell to be recognised

The structure of the plasma membrane and the role of the various proteins in transporting substances in and out of the cell are discussed in more detail in Chapter 3.

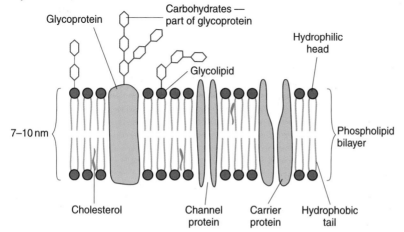

Figure 1.8 The fluid mosaic model of plasma membrane structure

In some cells, the plasma membrane is folded into structures called **microvilli**. These greatly increase the surface area of the cell; improving its ability to absorb substances. They occur on cells that absorb large mounts of substances, such as the epithelial cells that line the small intestine and those that line nephrons in the kidney.

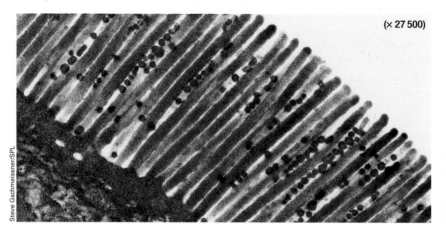

(× 27 500)

False-colour transmission electron micrograph of microvilli on the lining of the gut.

Steve Gschmeissner/SPL

Plant cells

All the structures found in animal cells are also found in plant cells. In addition, plant cells have cellulose cell walls, chloroplasts and a central vacuole.

Cellulose cell wall

The cell wall is made from cellulose fibrils. A **fibril** consists of many molecules of cellulose bonded together by hydrogen bonds. Many fibrils join to form larger structures called **fibres**. These are arranged in the cell wall in a criss-cross manner. This provides resistance in all directions to stress and tension.

Although the cell wall provides support for the cell, it is fully permeable to all molecules.

Besides this primary cell wall made from cellulose, some plant cells have extra layers of other materials that form a secondary cell wall. Xylem vessels, for example, have a secondary cell wall made from lignin, which gives additional support.

Electron micrograph showing the cellulose fibres in a plant cell wall

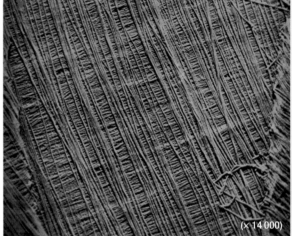

(×14 000)

Biophoto Associates/SPL

Chloroplasts

Chloroplasts occur in some plant cells. After the nucleus, they are the largest organelles.

◀ Chloroplasts can be seen with a standard optical microscope used at A-level.

Like mitochondria, chloroplasts are surrounded by a double membrane. However, the inner membrane is not folded. All the reactions of photosynthesis take place in the chloroplasts:

- The absorption of light energy and its use to create ATP take place on the thylakoid **membranes**.
- The synthesis of glucose takes place in the fluid **stroma**.

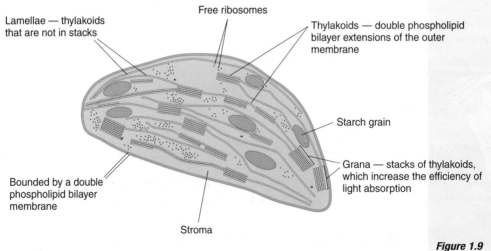

Lamellae — thylakoids that are not in stacks

Free ribosomes

Thylakoids — double phospholipid bilayer extensions of the outer membrane

Starch grain

Grana — stacks of thylakoids, which increase the efficiency of light absorption

Bounded by a double phospholipid bilayer membrane

Stroma

Figure 1.9
Structure of a chloroplast

Vacuole

Although some animal cells contain small vacuoles, only plant cells contain a large, central vacuole. This vacuole is surrounded by a membrane, called the **tonoplast**. Vacuoles are filled with solutions of various chemicals. Some contain pigments that give the cells their colour — for example, the cells in the petals of many flowers and the cells of beetroot. Vacuoles also contain the waste products of cell metabolism. Ordinarily, the vacuole is full of this mixture of solutions and exerts an outward **turgor pressure** on the cell wall. This helps to support the plant. When the plant loses water, the vacuole shrinks, turgor is lost and the plant wilts or droops.

Prokaryotic cells

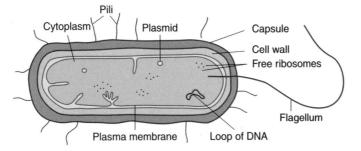

Figure 1.10 Generalised diagram of a bacterial cell

The prokaryotic cells of bacteria differ from eukaryotic cells in a number of ways:
- The DNA is not associated with protein to form true chromosomes. It is often referred to as naked DNA.
- The DNA is *circular*. The two 'ends' of the double helix of DNA are linked.
- Prokaryotes contain **plasmids**. These are small, circular pieces of DNA that can carry genes that confer resistance to antibiotics.
- The ribosomes are smaller.
- The cell wall is made from **peptidoglycan**. (Plant cell walls are made from cellulose; fungal cell walls from chitin.)
- There may be a **capsule** outside the cell wall. This prevents desiccation and provides some protection from digestion by enzymes in the gut of animals.
- They may possess **flagella** (singular flagellum).
- They may have small projections from the outer cell surface, called **pili** (singular pilus).
- They do *not* contain membrane-bound organelles such as mitochondria, chloroplasts and lysosomes.

e If you are asked to describe the features of a prokaryotic cell, list those that are present (peptidoglycan cell wall, small ribosomes, circular DNA) rather than those that are absent (e.g. membrane-bound organelles, nuclear envelope). If something is not there, how can it be a feature? However, if you are asked for *differences*, you can include structures that are absent.

Cell fractionation

Although much of the ultrastructure of organelles has been discovered from micrographs of whole cells, the functioning of the organelles requires experimental study.

The organelles can be separated by **cell fractionation**. The technique is based on the fact that the masses of organelles vary and depend on their size. When a mixture of organelles is spun in a centrifuge, the various types settle out at different speeds. The large nucleus requires a relatively low centrifuge speed to make it settle out; the much smaller ribosomes require a much higher speed.

The technique is carried out as follows:

- The cell sample is stored in a suspension that is:
  - buffered — the neutral pH prevents damage to the structure of proteins, including enzymes
  - isotonic (of equal water potential) — this prevents water gain or loss by the organelles
  - cool — this reduces the overall activity of enzymes released later in the procedure
- The cells are homogenised in a blender and filtered to remove debris.
- The homogenised sample is placed in an ultracentrifuge and spun at low speed — nuclei settle out, forming a pellet.
- The supernatant (the suspension containing the remaining organelles) is spun at a higher speed — chloroplasts settle out.
- The supernatant is spun at a higher speed still — mitochondria and lysosomes settle out.
- The supernatant is spun at an even higher speed — ribosomes, membranes and Golgi complexes settle out.

The ribosomes, membranes and Golgi complexes can be separated by another technique, called **density-gradient centrifugation**.

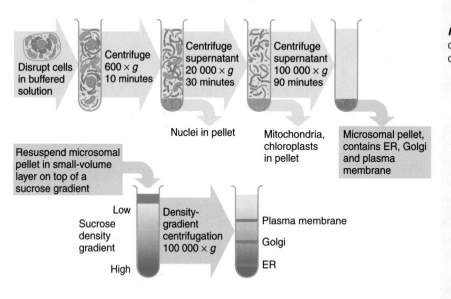

Figure 1.11 How differential centrifugation separates cell components

> 🄴 You may be asked to explain the reason for storing the cell sample in an isotonic solution. Candidates frequently make the mistake of suggesting that this will prevent osmotic damage to the *cells*. It is the *organelles* that are protected from osmotic damage. The cells themselves are burst open in the blender.

Summary

Cell theory

- A cell is the smallest unit of life capable of independent existence.

Scale, magnification and resolution

- Dimensions are measured in metres or units derived from the metre, including:
  - kilometre, km = 1000 m
  - millimetre, mm = 0.001 m
  - micrometre, μm = 0.000 001 m (0.001 mm)
- Magnification produces an enlarged image of an object.
- Resolution is the ability to distinguish between two points that are close together.
- $\text{magnification} = \dfrac{\text{apparent size}}{\text{real size}}$

Apparent and real size must be measured in the same units.

Microscopes

- An optical microscope passes a beam of light through the specimen, which may be alive or dead, a small whole organism or a section.
- A transmission electron microscope passes a beam of electrons through a specimen, which must be a very thin section of either a cell or a small organism.
- A scanning electron microscope forms an image from electrons reflected from the surface of a specimen.
- Optically and electron-dense regions of a specimen allow little light or few electrons to pass through, respectively. Therefore, they appear as dark regions in the image.
- Transmission electron microscopes have higher magnification and better resolution than light microscopes. However, preparation of the specimen may introduce artefacts.

Cell ultrastructure

- The two types of cell are prokaryotic and eukaryotic:
  - All eukaryotic cells contain a nucleus, mitochondria, lysosomes, ribosomes, ER (rough and smooth) and Golgi bodies, all enclosed within a plasma membrane.
  - Plant cells contain the above organelles and, in addition, have a large central vacuole and, in some cells, chloroplasts. They are enclosed by a cellulose cell wall.
  - Prokaryotic cells do not contain any membrane-bound organelles (nucleus, mitochondria, lysosomes, chloroplasts). They are smaller than eukaryotic cells and have smaller ribosomes. They have peptidoglycan cell walls and contain naked, circular DNA.

Cell fractionation

- Cell fractionation separates the components of a cell by centrifugation, heavier organelles being isolated at lower centrifuge speeds. Prior to homogenisation followed by centrifugation, the tissue is refrigerated (to reduce the rate of metabolic reactions) in an isotonic solution (to prevent osmotic damage to the organelles following homogenisation) which is pH buffered (to prevent damage to the tertiary structure of cell proteins, including enzymes).

Questions

Multiple-choice

1 To convert millimetres to micrometres:
   A multiply by 1000
   B divide by 100
   C divide by 1000
   D multiply by 100

2 The resolving power of a microscope is its ability to:
   A produce an enlarged image
   B separate two nearby points
   C show a large field of view
   D reduce the depth of view

3 Actual size, apparent size and magnification are related by the formula:
   A actual size = apparent size × magnification

   B apparent size $= \dfrac{\text{actual size}}{\text{magnification}}$

   C magnification = apparent size × actual size
   D apparent size = actual size × magnification

4 In comparison with optical microscopes, transmission electron microscopes have:
   A higher resolution but lower magnification
   B lower resolution but higher magnification
   C lower resolution and lower magnification
   D higher resolution and higher magnification

5 In comparison with eukaryotic cells, prokaryotic cells are generally:
   A smaller, with membrane-bound organelles and circular DNA
   B larger, with membrane-bound organelles and linear DNA
   C larger, with no membrane-bound organelles and with linear DNA
   D smaller, with no membrane-bound organelles and with circular DNA

6 The functions of the rough endoplasmic reticulum and the Golgi body are related because:
   A proteins synthesised by the rough endoplasmic reticulum are modified by the Golgi body
   B proteins synthesised by the Golgi body are modified by the rough endoplasmic reticulum

C lipids synthesised by the Golgi body are modified by the rough endoplasmic reticulum

D lipids synthesised by the rough endoplasmic reticulum are modified by the Golgi body

7 In cell fractionation, the purpose of keeping the tissue sample in an isotonic solution in a refrigerator prior to homogenisation is:

A to prevent osmotic damage to the cells and to reduce the metabolic activity of the cells

B to prevent osmotic damage to the cells and to increase the metabolic activity of the cells

C to prevent osmotic damage to the organelles and to reduce the metabolic activity of the cells

D to prevent osmotic damage to the organelles and to increase the metabolic activity of the cells

8 Chloroplasts and mitochondria both have:

A a double membrane surrounding the organelle

B a fluid substance inside the organelle

C both **A** and **B**

D neither **A** nor **B**

9 The plasma membrane provides:

A structural support for the cell and regulates which substances enter and leave

B structural support for the cell but does not regulate which substances enter and leave

C no structural support for the cell and does not regulate which substances enter and leave

D no structural support for the cell but regulates which substances enter and leave

10 The principle behind separating cell organelles by ultracentrifugation is that:

A the various organelles have different masses

B the various organelles have different volumes

C the various organelles have different shapes

D the various organelles have different widths

Examination-style

1 (a) Copy and complete the table. Use a tick or cross to show if the feature is present or absent.   *(3 marks)*

Type of cell	Feature		
	Chromosome	**Cell wall**	**Mitochondrion**
Red blood cell			
Photosynthesising cell from leaf			
Liver cell			
Bacterial cell			

(b) A red blood cell is viewed under an optical microscope with a magnification of 750 times. It appears round but paler in the centre than at the edges. The diameter of the red blood cell is measured as 6 mm.

   (i) Explain the difference in colour between the edge and the centre of the cell. *(1 mark)*

   (ii) Calculate the actual diameter of the cell. Express your answer in micrometres (μm). *(2 marks)*

Total: 6 marks

2 The drawing below is from a photograph taken through a transmission electron microscope. It shows a cell organelle.

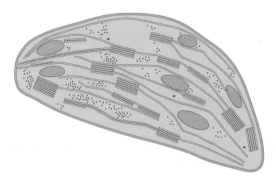

(× 30 000)

(a) Explain the evidence that shows that the photograph was *not* taken through:

   (i) an optical microscope *(1 mark)*

   (ii) a scanning electron microscope *(1 mark)*

(b) Calculate the length of the organelle. Express your answer in micrometres (μm). *(2 marks)*

(c) Describe the function of the organelle. *(2 marks)*

Total: 6 marks

3 The drawing below is taken from a transmission electron micrograph of a cell from the pancreas.

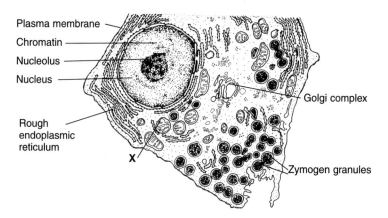

(a) Name the organelle labelled X. *(1 mark)*

(b) Explain why the nucleolus is not a uniform colour. *(2 marks)*

(c) The cell contains many zymogen granules, each of which contains inactive enzymes (which are proteins). Describe the features of the cell that allow it to synthesise large amounts of protein. *(2 marks)*

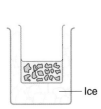

Tissue cut into small pieces and placed in a pH-buffered isotonic solution

Ice

Tissue put into blender/homogeniser

Mixture filtered to remove debris

Filtrate spun in centrifuge

Total: 5 marks

4 The following procedure was used to obtain different organelles from a sample of eukaryotic cells:

(a) Explain why:

    (i) the tissue sample was placed in a pH-buffered solution *(1 mark)*

    (ii) the tissue was homogenised in a blender *(1 mark)*

(b) The organelles separated from the sample were: chloroplasts, nucleus, mitochondria, Golgi bodies, lysosomes, ribosomes and endoplasmic reticulum.

    (i) Beginning with the first to settle out, list the organelles in the order in which they would have been separated by this process. *(1 mark)*

    (ii) From where might the tissue sample have been obtained? *(1 mark)*

    (iii) Which of the organelles do *not* occur in a prokaryotic cell? *(1 mark)*

Total: 5 marks

Chapter 2

Biological molecules

This chapter covers:

- the range of biological molecules that occur within living organisms
- the structure and function of some biological molecules:
  - carbohydrates (monosaccharides, disaccharides and polysaccharides)
  - proteins
  - lipids (triglycerides and phospholipids)
- methods of identifying biological molecules:
  - biochemical tests and ways of quantifying them
  - one-dimensional and two-dimensional chromatography
  - gel electrophoresis

The foods that make up our diet supply the nutrients needed by our bodies. What, then, are nutrients and why do we need them?

The main classes of nutrient are carbohydrates, lipids, proteins, vitamins, mineral ions, water and dietary fibre. Foods are made from parts of other organisms and the nutrients are contained within the cells of those organisms. To obtain nutrients, food is first chewed to break open the cells. The contents are then digested and the products of digestion are absorbed.

Many nutrients are the biological molecules that we need to build our own cells. Some are respiratory substrates — they are respired, aerobically or anaerobically, to release energy that is used to synthesise ATP. The energy held in ATP molecules is used to 'drive' the many reactions that occur within a cell, including the synthesis of large molecules and cell components. Other nutrients are not used directly in synthesis or as respiratory substrates. For example, many vitamins act as coenzymes and help to

◀ Many types of biological molecule are essential to build our bodies and to keep them functioning properly.

catalyse reactions. Dietary fibre is a mixture of several complex carbohydrates, none of which is digested or absorbed. Yet dietary fibre is essential in our diet; among other functions, it helps to protect against colon cancer.

Carbohydrates

Carbohydrates contain the elements carbon, hydrogen and oxygen. The hydrogen and oxygen atoms in a carbohydrate molecule are present in the ratio of two hydrogen atoms to one oxygen atom (e.g. glucose, $C_6H_{12}O_6$ and maltose, $C_{12}H_{22}O_{11}$). Carbohydrates range from very small molecules containing only 12 atoms, to very large molecules containing thousands of atoms.

Carbohydrates have a range of functions:
- Glucose is the main respiratory substrate of most organisms.
- Storage carbohydrates include:
  - starch in plants
  - glycogen in animals
- Structural carbohydrates include:
  - cellulose, which is the main constituent of the primary cell wall of plants
  - chitin, which occurs in the cell walls of fungi and in the exoskeletons of insects
  - peptidoglycan, which occurs in bacterial cell walls

In plasma membranes, carbohydrates are found combined with proteins to form glycoproteins. Glycoproteins often have antigenic properties. They act as markers for the immune system, which can differentiate between 'self' antigens (those that are normally found in the body) and foreign or 'non-self' antgens. The presence of 'non-self' antigens stimulates an immune response, such as the production and secretion of antibodies to destroy the antigen. More detail on the immune response can be found in Chapter 12.

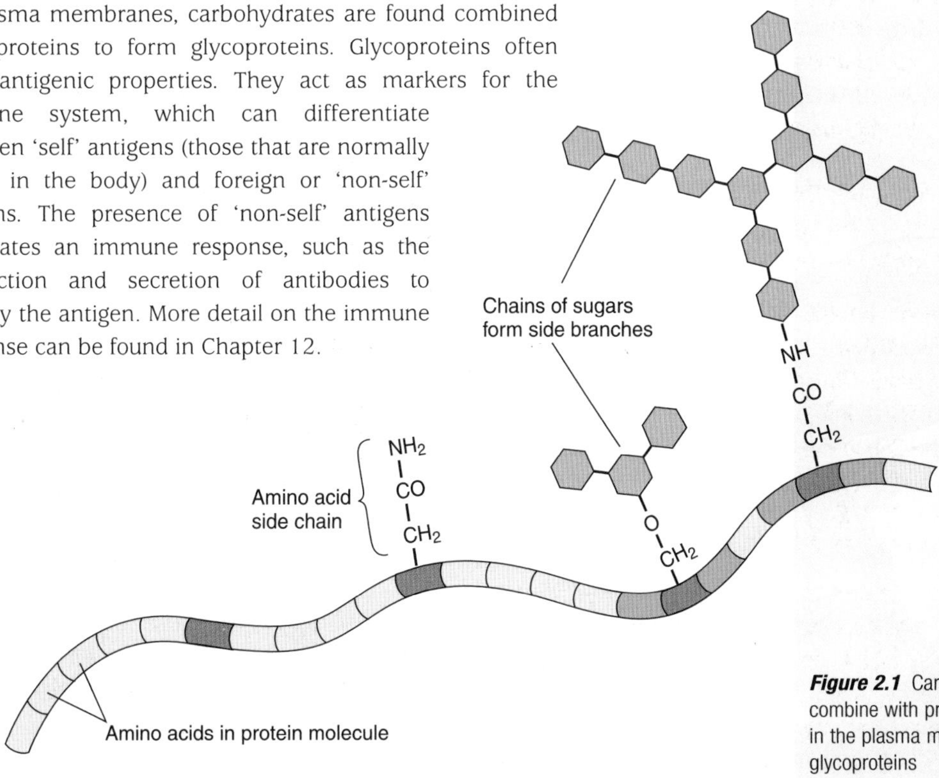

◀ The biological molecules that make up our bodies are organic molecules. All organic molecules contain both carbon and hydrogen. For example, glucose ($C_6H_{12}O_6$) and glycine ($C_2H_5O_2N$, an amino acid) are organic. Carbon dioxide (CO_2) contains carbon, but not hydrogen, and so is an inorganic molecule.

Chains of sugars form side branches

NH
CO
CH₂

NH₂
CO
CH₂

Amino acid side chain

O
CH₂

Amino acids in protein molecule

Figure 2.1 Carbohydrate chains combine with protein molecules in the plasma membrane to form glycoproteins

Monosaccharides

Monosaccharides are the simplest carbohydrates. A monosaccharide molecule can be thought of as a single unit. Other, more complex, carbohydrates have two or more such units joined together.

Monosaccharides are classified according to how many carbon atoms are present in the molecule:

- a **triose** molecule has three carbon atoms
- a **tetrose** molecule has four carbon atoms
- a **pentose** molecule has five carbon atoms
- a **hexose** molecule has six carbon atoms

Figure 2.2 shows the structures of four hexose sugars — α-glucose, β-glucose, galactose and fructose.

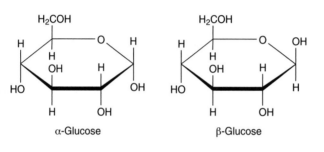

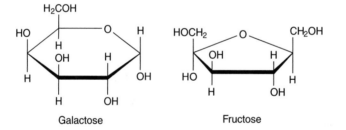

You do have to be able to recall the structures of α-glucose and β-glucose. However, you do not have to remember the position of every hydrogen and oxygen atom, only the simplified structures shown in Figure 2.3. These show the overall shape of the molecule, the position of each carbon atom and the hydrogen and oxygen atoms attached to carbon atoms 1 and 4.

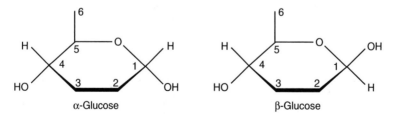

Note that the only difference between the two forms of glucose is the position of the hydroxyl (OH) group on carbon atom 1. Although you only need to be able to recall the structures of α-glucose and β-glucose, simplified structures of galactose

Sedoheptulose is a monosaccharide with seven carbon atoms in its molecule. It is an intermediate in the reactions of the Calvin cycle in the light-independent reactions of photosynthesis. D-glycero-d-manno-octulose has a molecule containing eight carbon atoms. It is found only in avocados and its function is uncertain.

Figure 2.2 The ring forms of α-glucose and β-glucose, galactose and fructose — carbon atoms are found at the 'angles'

It is easy to think that all the atoms of ring molecules lie in the same plane, but this is not so. The diagram below shows a three-dimensional representation of the atoms in α-glucose.

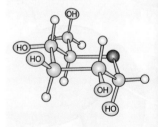

Figure 2.3 A simplified representation of the structures of α-glucose and β-glucose

and fructose are shown in Figure 2.4. Being aware of these will help you to understand the structures of some disaccharide sugars.

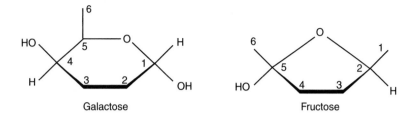

Galactose

Fructose

Figure 2.4 A simplified representation of the structures of galactose and fructose

Disaccharides

A **disaccharide** molecule is made by the reaction of two monosaccharide molecules. For example, a molecule of:

- **maltose** is derived from two α-glucose molecules
- **sucrose** is derived from an α-glucose molecule and a fructose molecule
- **lactose** (milk sugar) is derived from a β-glucose molecule and a galactose molecule

◀ Glucose, galactose and fructose are known as reducing sugars. They reduce the copper ions (Cu^{2+}) in Benedict's solution to form copper(I) oxide (Cu_2O). This is insoluble and forms a red precipitate — the recognisable result of the test.

Figure 2.5 The structures of three disaccharides

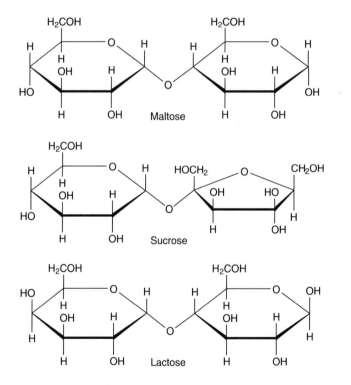

Maltose

Sucrose

Lactose

In each of these examples, two hexose monosaccharides react to form a disaccharide molecule. As the formula of a hexose is $C_6H_{12}O_6$, you might expect the formula of the disaccharides to be $C_{12}H_{24}O_{12}$. In fact, the formula is $C_{12}H_{22}O_{11}$. A molecule of water (H_2O) is formed from a hydroxyl group from one monosaccharide and a hydrogen atom from the other (Figure 2.6). This allows a bond to be formed between the two monosaccharide units to make a disaccharide.

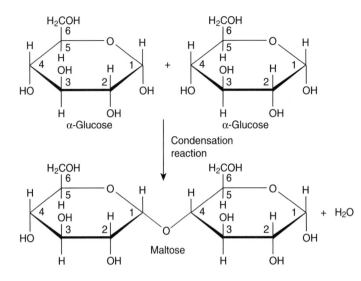

Figure 2.6 Two molecules of α-glucose are joined to form a molecule of maltose (a disaccharide)

The process shown in Figure 2.6 is called **condensation**. The bond formed is called a **glycosidic bond**. It is formed between carbon atom number 1 of one α-glucose molecule and carbon atom number 4 of another α-glucose molecule. The full name of the bond is, therefore, an α-1,4-glycosidic bond.

The reverse process is **hydrolysis** of the disaccharide (or other molecule). This involves 'putting back' the water that was removed during condensation and splitting the molecule into its component, smaller molecules (Figure 2.7).

◀ Condensation does not just occur in the formation of disaccharides, but also in the formation of poly-saccharides and other large molecules.

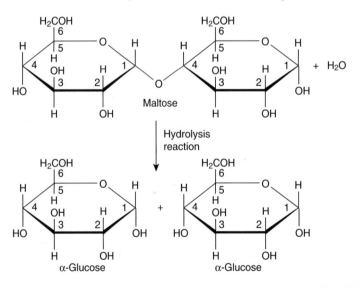

Figure 2.7 Hydrolysis of maltose

◀ Hydrolysis involves the addition of a molecule of water to break the bond formed during condensation.

ℯ The specification does not require you to know disaccharide structures in detail. However, you are required to know about polysaccharide structure and the processes of condensation and hydrolysis. The structures of some disaccharides are included to illustrate these processes and to help you to understand the process of digestion, which is studied at A2.

Polysaccharides

Polysaccharides are complex carbohydrates. Their molecules are derived from many hundreds of monosaccharide molecules joined together by condensation links. Starch and glycogen are made from α-glucose, while cellulose is made from β-glucose. This has a significant impact on their structures, which dictate their functions.

Box 2.1 Macromolecules, polymers and monomers

A macromolecule is just what the name suggests — it is a big molecule. Examples include proteins, starch, cellulose, glycogen and DNA. A polymer is also a large molecule — but it is not *just* large. A polymer molecule is made from many smaller, often identical, molecules called monomers. Besides being macromolecules, starch, glycogen, cellulose and proteins are polymers. Starch and glycogen are polymers of α-glucose, cellulose is a polymer of β-glucose and proteins are polymers of amino acids.

Starch

Starch is not a single compound but a mixture of **amylose** and **amylopectin**. Both are polymers of α-glucose, but the arrangement of the α-glucose monomers in these compounds is different. Amylose is a linear molecule containing many hundreds of α-glucose molecules joined by α-1,4-glycosidic bonds (as in maltose). As it is being formed, this long chain winds itself into a helix.

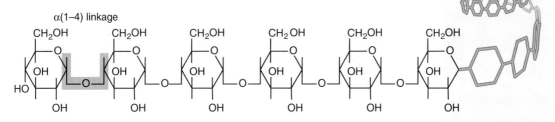

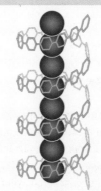

Figure 2.8 Linkages in amylose and the amylose helix

Box 2.2 Starch stains blue or black or blue-black with iodine

The helical structure of amylose allows a reaction between starch and iodine solution to occur. Rows of iodine atoms sit inside the amylose helix and interact with it, changing the light absorbing properties of both, so that the complex appears blue. Starches in different plants have different proportions of amylose and amylopectin. This results in different shades of blue-black with the iodine test, because only the amylose reacts with iodine.

Amylopectin also has a linear 'backbone' of α-glucose molecules joined by α-1,4-glycosidic bonds. In addition, there are side branches. At certain points along the chain, a glucose molecule forms an α-1,6-glycosidic bond with another glucose molecule. This bond is formed by condensation between carbon atom 1 of one glucose molecule and carbon atom 6 (the one *not* actually part of the ring) of another. The result is the beginning of a side branch, which is then extended by more α-1,4 bonds forming between glucose molecules.

◀ An enzyme that digests proteins is a *protease*; one that digests lipids is a *lipase*. An enzyme that digests starch is an *amylase* because starch is made from *amyl*ose and *amyl*opectin.

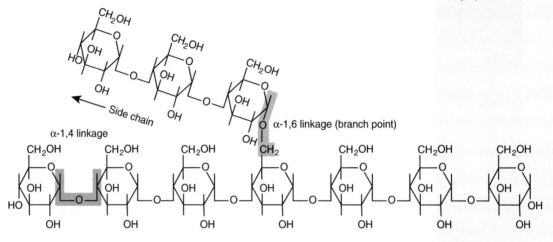

Figure 2.9 Structure of amylopectin

Starch is a plant storage carbohydrate. Since both amylose and amylopectin are compact molecules, many α-glucose molecules can be stored in a small space, without affecting cell metabolism. If glucose were stored without being converted to starch, it would create a negative water potential within the cytoplasm. This would draw water, by osmosis, from neighbouring cells and from organelles within the cell. Starch is insoluble and produces none of these effects. In addition, because starch is insoluble, the molecules cannot move out of cells — they remain in storage organs. The branched nature of amylopectin means that there are many 'ends' to the molecule. Therefore, starch can be quickly hydrolysed (by enzymes acting at the ends of the chains) to release glucose for respiration.

Glycogen

Glycogen is a storage carbohydrate in animal cells. The molecular structure is similar to that of the amylopectin component of starch but there are more α-1,6 links, so the molecule is more highly branched. Glycogen molecules can therefore be hydrolysed to release glucose more quickly than starch. This is important because animals have a higher metabolic rate than plants and need to release energy more quickly to 'drive' their metabolic processes.

In mammals, the main organs that store glycogen are the liver and the skeletal muscles.

Figure 2.10 Structure of a glycogen molecule

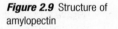

○─○ α-1,6 linkage
○─○ α-1,4 linkage

Inner branch

Outer branch

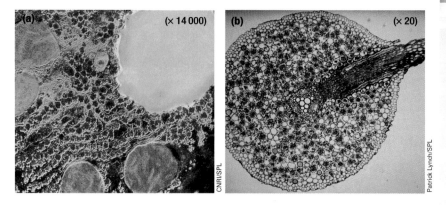

(a) False-colour transmission electron micrograph of a section through a liver cell containing stored glycogen. The glycogen appears red
(b) Light micrograph of starch grains (stained purple) in buttercup root cells

Cellulose

Cellulose is a structural carbohydrate found in plants. It is the main component of plant cell walls. Cellulose is a polymer derived from β-glucose molecules. Therefore, cellulose molecules have a different shape from starch molecules and have different properties.

Cellulose molecules are easily distinguished from starch and glycogen.
◄ In cellulose, alternate carbon-6 atoms in the chain point in opposite directions and the chain of β-glucose residues is unbranched.

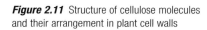

Cellulose fibre

Microfibril

Micelle

Figure 2.11 Structure of cellulose molecules and their arrangement in plant cell walls

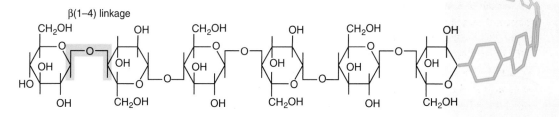

β(1–4) linkage

Figure 2.11 shows that cellulose molecules are aligned to form microfibrils, which then form the larger fibres that make up the cell wall. The microfibrils are formed as a result of **hydrogen bonding** between adjacent molecules.

The fibres form layers aligned in different directions (see p. 12). This gives extra strength as well as some elasticity, which is necessary to allow the cell wall to expand slightly when the cell takes in more water by osmosis. Although the cellulose cell wall gives support to the cell, it does not form any kind of barrier to the entry of molecules.

Box 2.3 Hydrogen bonds

A hydrogen bond forms between a hydrogen atom that is already bonded to some other atom (such as an oxygen atom in an OH group) and an oxygen atom (or sometimes a nitrogen or sulphur atom) that is also already bonded to another atom.

Hydrogen bond

Molecule of water

Hydrogen bonds are important in conforming many large biological molecules into specific shapes.

There are large 'gaps' between adjacent microfibrils that even large molecules can pass through.

The functions and properties of the more important carbohydrates are summarised in Table 2.1.

Table 2.1 The properties and functions of important carbohydrates.

Carbohydrate	Nature of molecule	Function	Significant property related to function
α-glucose	Monosaccharide; hexose	Principal respiratory substrate; monomer of starch	Glucose is the most stable of the hexose sugars
β-glucose	Monosaccharide; hexose	Principal respiratory substrate; monomer of cellulose	Glucose is the most stable of the hexose sugars
Starch	Polysaccharide	Storage carbohydrate in plants	Insoluble (does not affect water potential of cell); compact molecule (many molecules stored in a cell)
Glycogen	Polysaccharide	Storage carbohydrate in animals	Insoluble (does not affect water potential of cell); compact molecule (many molecules stored in a cell)
Cellulose	Polysaccharide	Component of primary cell wall of plants	Adjacent molecules hydrogen bond with each other to form fibrils that aggregate into fibres, giving strength and elasticity

Proteins

Protein molecules contain the elements carbon, hydrogen and oxygen (as do carbohydrates), but they also contain nitrogen and most contain sulphur. Protein molecules are polymers of amino acids and are, therefore, macromolecules. Even so, they vary enormously in size. The smallest protein molecules contain fewer than 100 amino acids; the largest contain several thousand. Proteins have a range of functions — for example, they are important in:

- the structure of **plasma membranes** — protein molecules form ion channels, transport proteins and surface receptors for hormones, neurotransmitters and other molecules
- the **immune system** — antigen and antibody molecules are proteins (Chapter 12)
- the **enzymic control** of metabolism — all enzymes are proteins (Chapter 4)
- the structure of **chromosomes** — DNA is wound around molecules of the protein histone to form a chromosome (Chapter 10)

Although proteins are referred to as polymers, this is not strictly true. In a true polymer, all the monomers (molecules making up the polymer) are identical. This is true of amylose and amylopectin in starch (all the monomers are α-glucose) and of cellulose (all the monomers are β-glucose). In proteins, although all the monomers are amino acids, there are different amino acids in any given protein molecule. However, since all amino acids have the same basic structure, it is acceptable to refer to a protein molecule as a polymer.

All amino acid molecules are built around a carbon atom to which is attached:
- a hydrogen atom
- an amino group (–NH$_2$)
- a carboxyl group (–COOH)
- an 'R' group, which represents the other atoms in the molecule, such as a single hydrogen atom, a hydrocarbon chain or a more complex structure

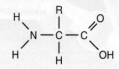

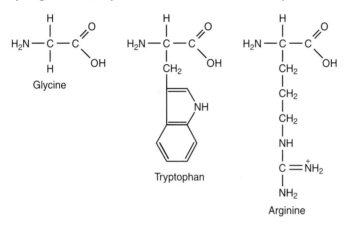

Figure 2.12 The general structure of an amino acid

e You may be asked to draw the general structure of an amino acid

Figure 2.13 Structures of three amino acids

Two amino acids can be joined together by condensation to form a **dipeptide**. A dipeptide can be enlarged into a **polypeptide** by condensation with more amino acid molecules. The bonds formed by condensation can be broken by hydrolysis.

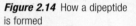

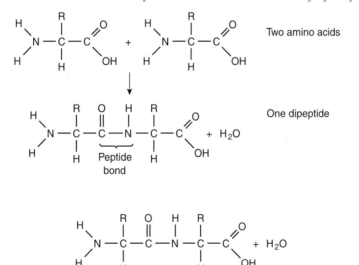

Figure 2.14 How a dipeptide is formed

Figure 2.15 Hydrolysis of a dipeptide

Levels of organisation in protein molecules

The sequence of amino acids in a polypeptide chain is the **primary structure** of the protein. Once formed, the polypeptide chain is then organised into a **secondary structure**, which is either an α-helix or a β-pleated sheet. The structures are held in place by hydrogen bonds that form between peptide bonds in adjacent parts of the amino acid chain. Both types of secondary structure can exist in different regions of the same polypeptide chain.

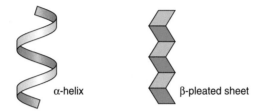

Figure 2.16 The secondary structure of proteins — sections of the amino acid chain fold into either an α-helix or a β-pleated sheet

A protein molecule can have a **tertiary structure**. This involves further folding of the secondary structure and the formation of new bonds to hold the tertiary structure in place. These new bonds include:

- more hydrogen bonds — between the R-groups of some amino acids
- disulphide bridges — between amino acids with R-groups that contain sulphur
- ionic bonds — between amino acids with positively charged R-groups and amino acids with negatively charged R-groups

Figure 2.17 The different levels of structure in a protein molecule

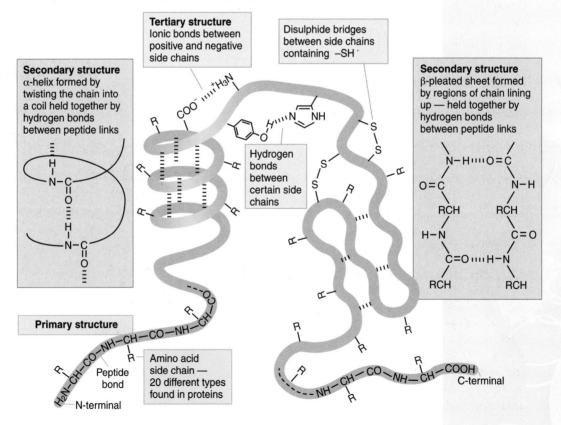

Each protein has a unique tertiary structure and, therefore, a unique three-dimensional shape:

- The primary structure of each protein is controlled genetically (Chapter 9). This determines the type and position of each amino acid in the polypeptide chain.
- The secondary structure of the molecule is the consequence of its primary structure. Some sections of the primary structures form α-helices; others form β-pleated sheets.
- The nature of the secondary structure determines where ionic and hydrogen bonds and disulphide bridges form, i.e. it determines the tertiary structure and shape of the protein molecule.

Figure 2.18 The tertiary structure of a protein molecule

Because the tertiary structure of each protein is unique, each has a specific function. Some functions of proteins are described in Table 2.2.

Table 2.2 How a unique tertiary structure determines the properties of proteins

Protein molecule	Effect of specific shape	Consequence
Enzyme	Active site binds only with certain molecules	Enzyme is specific — it will only catalyse a particular reaction
Insulin receptor in plasma membrane	Only insulin binds with this receptor	Insulin targets only cells with the receptor
Receptor in 'sweet' taste bud	Only binds with molecules with a shape that fits	These molecules taste sweet

e You may be asked to explain how the primary structure of a protein determines its final function.

Proteins are classified into two main groups, according to their molecular shapes. A **fibrous protein** has a tertiary structure that resembles a long string or fibre. Fibrous proteins are usually structural. Two examples are collagen (found in bone, cartilage and many other structures) and keratin (found in skin and nails).

A **globular protein** has a tertiary structure that resembles a globule or ball. The proteins involved in controlling cellular metabolism — for example, enzymes and receptor proteins — are globular.

A few proteins have a **quaternary structure**. In these cases, two or more polypeptide chains are bonded together to form the final protein molecule. Haemoglobin consists of four polypeptide chains, two α-chains and two β-chains. A molecule of collagen consists of three polypeptide chains wound around each other.

Figure 2.19 The quaternary structure of haemoglobin

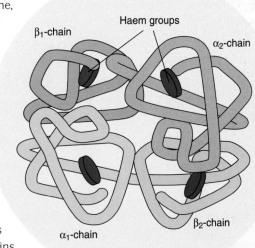

β₁-chain

Haem groups

α₂-chain

α₁-chain

β₂-chain

Lipids

Lipids are a varied group of compounds that include triglycerides, phospholipids and waxes. Unlike proteins and polysaccharides, lipids are *not* polymers. Their molecules are relatively quite small. The feature they share is that they are all esters of fatty acids and alcohols. Waxes are formed from fatty acids and long-chain alcohols. This structure makes them so insoluble in water that they can act as water repellents — for example, in coating birds' feathers. **Phospholipids** are one of the basic components of cell membranes. **Triglycerides** have several functions including:

- **respiratory substrate** — a molecule of triglyceride yields over twice as many molecules of ATP as a molecule of glucose
- **thermal insulation** — the cells of adipose tissue found under the skin contain large amounts of triglycerides and give good thermal insulation
- **buoyancy** — lipids are less dense than water (oil floats on water) and large amounts of lipid reduce the density of an animal
- **waterproofing** — the oils secreted by some animals onto their skin are triglycerides

Nearly all lipids contain only carbon, hydrogen and oxygen. A lipid molecule contains much less oxygen than a carbohydrate molecule of similar molecular mass. Therefore, more oxygen is needed to respire the lipid molecule.

Some of the lipids found in the myelin sheath that surrounds nerve cells are sphingolipids. These lipids contain nitrogen as well as carbon, hydrogen and oxygen.

Triglycerides

A triglyceride molecule is an ester formed from one molecule of **glycerol** (an alcohol containing three carbon atoms) and three **fatty acid** molecules.

A fatty acid molecule consists of a covalently bonded **hydrocarbon chain**, at the end of which is a carboxyl group, which has acidic properties. The hydrocarbon chain is non-polar. This means that it has no charge. The carboxyl group is ionic and dissociates in solution to form COO^- and H^+ (hydrogen ion). The hydrogen ions released make the solution acidic.

Glycerol is a polyhydroxy alcohol — it contains more than one hydroxyl (–OH) group. Ethanol, the alcohol in beer and wine, has the formula C_2H_5OH. It is a monohydroxy alcohol — it contains only one hydroxyl group:

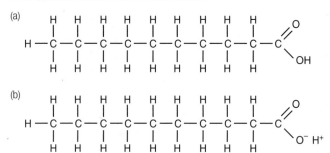

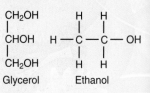

Glycerol   Ethanol

Figure 2.20
(a) The structure of a typical fatty acid molecule
(b) The acidic nature of fatty acids

The nature of the hydrocarbon chains in fatty acids can differ in two main ways:
- The number of carbon atoms in the chains can vary.
- Hydrocarbon chains with the same number of carbon atoms can have different numbers of hydrogen atoms. This is because of the nature of the bonding between the carbon atoms in the chain. If all the carbon–carbon bonds in the hydrocarbon chain are single bonds, the fatty acid is a **saturated**

fatty acid. If one of the carbon–carbon bonds is a double bond, then it is a **monounsaturated fatty acid**. If more than one carbon–carbon bond is a double bond, then the fatty acid is a **polyunsaturated fatty acid**. For example, the hydrocarbon chain in stearic acid contains no double carbon–carbon bonds. It is a saturated fatty acid (Figure 2.21 (a)). Oleic acid has the same number of carbon atoms as stearic acid, but is monounsaturated (Figure 2.21(b)); linoleic acid has the same number of carbon atoms as stearic acid but is polyunsaturated (Figure 2.21(c)).

Figure 2.21
(a) Stearic acid
(b) Monounsaturated oleic acid
(c) Polyunsaturated linoleic acids
(d) The generalised structure of a fatty acid; 'R' represents the hydrocarbon chain

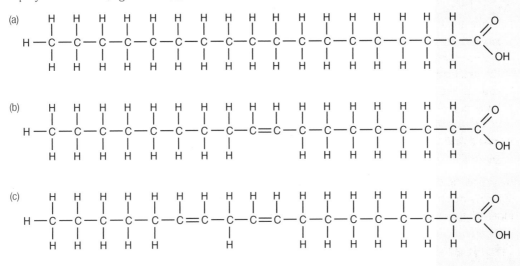

Atherosclerosis in an artery; eating polyunsaturated fatty acids can help to prevent this

Box 2.4 High in polyunsaturates

You may have seen cooking oils, margarines and other spreads advertised as 'high in polyunsaturates'. This means that the lipids in the product contain a high proportion of polyunsaturated fatty acids. Polyunsaturated fatty acids help to prevent cholesterol being laid down in the linings of arteries (atherosclerosis) and so help to prevent heart disease.

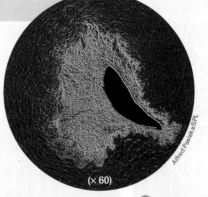

Alfred Pasieka/SPL

(× 60)

These products contain a high proportion of polyunsaturated or monounsaturated fatty acids

You may be asked to distinguish between saturated and unsaturated fatty acids or to complete diagrams showing saturated or unsaturated fatty acids

In the synthesis of a triglyceride molecule, condensation reactions take place to join three fatty acid molecules to a glycerol molecule. As with the bonds formed between monosaccharides and amino acids, the ester bonds formed by condensation of fatty acids and glycerol can be broken by hydrolysis.

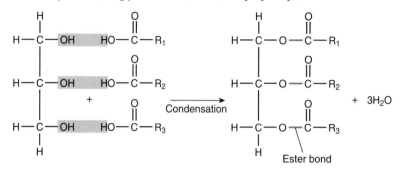

Figure 2.22 Synthesis of a triglyceride

Phospholipids

Phospholipids, like triglycerides, are based on the glycerol molecule. However, only two fatty acid molecules are bonded to the glycerol — the third is replaced by a phosphate group.

Since the phosphate group is ionic and the hydrocarbon chains of the two fatty acids are covalently bonded, there are two distinct regions to a phospholipid molecule:

- a **hydrophilic** (water-loving) region, consisting of the phosphate 'head'
- a **hydrophobic** (water-hating) region, consisting of the hydrocarbon 'tails'

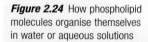

Figure 2.23 Structure of a phospholipid molecule

This is why, when placed in water, phospholipids become organised into a **bilayer**, in which the hydrophilic heads face outwards into the water and the hydrophobic tails face inwards, away from the water. Phospholipid bilayers are the basis of plasma membranes (Chapter 3).

Figure 2.24 How phospholipid molecules organise themselves in water or aqueous solutions

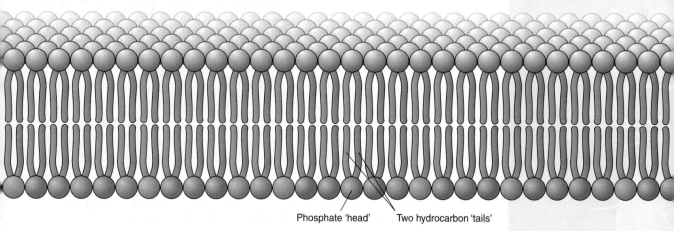

Phosphate 'head'   Two hydrocarbon 'tails'

Identifying biological molecules

Biochemical tests

There are biochemical tests for a range of biological molecules. You need to know the tests for:

- starch
- reducing sugars
- non-reducing sugars
- lipids
- proteins

Testing for starch

Starch reacts with a solution of iodine in potassium iodide to give a blue-black colour. The basis of this reaction is explained in Box 2.2, page 25. It is a straight-forward procedure:

- Place the solution or food to be tested in a spotting tray/test tube.
- Add a few drops of iodine solution.
- Look for a blue-black colour.

Testing for reducing sugars and non-reducing sugars

Both of these tests use **Benedict's solution**. When heated to 85°C with a reducing sugar, the Cu^{2+} ions in Benedict's solution are reduced to form red copper(I)oxide (Cu_2O), which is insoluble and precipitates out.

All monosaccharides are reducing sugars, as are some disaccharides — for example, lactose and maltose. However, sucrose and some other disaccharides are non-reducing sugars.

It is easy to show whether or not a test sample contains a reducing sugar. The sample is heated with Benedict's solution in a water bath for 5 minutes at 85°C and the colour noted. A yellow/orange/red colour shows that a reducing sugar is present.

However, to show that a test sample contains a non-reducing sugar is not quite so straightforward:

- First, it has to be established that no reducing sugars are present. The test is carried out as described above. A negative result is that the solution remains blue.
- The test sample is then is boiled with hydrochloric acid to hydrolyse molecules of non-reducing sugar.
- The acid is then neutralised by the addition of sodium carbonate, because Benedict's solution does not react in acidic conditions.
- The mixture is then re-tested with Benedict's solution. If a non-reducing sugar was present in the test sample, a red precipitate is formed, i.e. reducing sugars are now present (formed by the hydrolysis of the original non-reducing sugar).

A positive starch test result

Benedict's test for reducing sugars. From no sugar (left), increasing to 3% reducing sugar (right)

The tests are summarised in Table 2.3.

Step in test	Reducing sugar	Non-reducing sugar
Heat with Benedict's solution	Red precipitate; reducing sugar present — no further steps needed	No change; solution remains blue; reducing sugar absent — proceed
Boil with hydrochloric acid for 5 minutes		Acid hydrolyses non-reducing sugar molecules
Neutralise with sodium carbonate solution		Benedict's solution reacts only in neutral or alkaline conditions
Re-test with Benedict's solution		Red precipitate
Conclusion	Reducing sugar present originally	Non-reducing sugar present originally; reducing sugars now present were formed by acid hydrolysis of a non-reducing sugar

◀ When carrying out the test, the test sample should be heated with Benedict's solution in a water bath at 85°C or higher.

Table 2.3 Testing for reducing and non-reducing sugars

It is important to note that the Benedict's test does not distinguish between different reducing sugars. It is *not* a test for glucose — or galactose or any individual sugar. To distinguish between sugars, enzyme-based tests are used (Chapter 8).

Testing for lipids

The test for a lipid is based on the fact that lipids are soluble in organic solvents such as ethanol, but insoluble in water. This test is called the **emulsion test** and is carried out as follows.

- Shake the test sample with ethanol, in a clean, dry test tube.
- Filter the mixture (if necessary).
- Pour the filtrate into water.

Any lipid in the filtrate will not dissolve in the water. It will form an emulsion that makes the liquid appear milky white.

Testing for proteins

There are several biochemical tests for proteins, but the simplest, and often the most reliable, is the **Biuret test**. In this test, a protein in an alkaline solution reacts with copper ions to produce a mauve/purple colour. There are two ways of carrying out the test:

- Method 1:
  - The test solution is mixed with sodium hydroxide solution in a test tube.
  - A few drops of 1% copper(II) sulphate solution are added.
  - The mixture is allowed to stand for a few minutes to allow the colour to develop fully.

Lipids produce a milky white emulsion when dispersed in water

Andrew Lambert Photography/SPL

- Method 2:
  - The test solution is mixed with Biuret solution (which contains copper ions in an alkaline solution).
  - The mixture is allowed to stand for a few minutes to allow the colour to develop fully.

The Biuret test can be made semi-quantitative in the following way:
- Add $2\,cm^3$ Biuret solution to $5\,cm^3$ $0.1\,mol\,dm^{-3}$ protein solution in a test tube.
- Leave for 10 minutes.
- Transfer a sample to a cuvette.
- Insert the cuvette into a colorimeter and measure the percentage transmission of light.
- Repeat with protein solutions of different concentrations (0.2, 0.4, 0.6, 0.8, $1.0\,mol\,dm^{-3}$) and with distilled water.
- Plot a graph of percentage transmission against concentration. This is called a **calibration curve**.
- Repeat with the test solution.
- Estimate the concentration of protein in the test solution from the calibration curve.

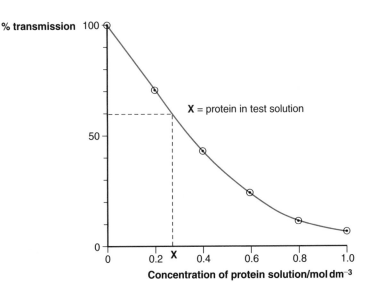

Figure 2.25 Estimating the percentage of protein in a test solution from the calibration curve

Box 2.5 How a colorimeter works

The principle behind a colorimeter is that when a sample of liquid is illuminated, not all the light is transmitted (passes through) — some is absorbed. A small container (cuvette) containing the test liquid is placed in the colorimeter and illuminated. The light that passes through the liquid is detected by a photocell. The instrument converts this into one of two readings:
- percentage transmission — the percentage of the light that passes through the sample
- absorbance — a measure (but *not* a percentage) of how much light is absorbed by the sample

Separating and identifying substances in a mixture

Sometimes it is necessary to separate a mixture of molecules and to identify the components. There are several possible techniques, but you only need to know about chromatography and electrophoresis.

Chromatography

This technique of separating and identifying substances requires that the substances in the mixture can be transported along chromatography paper by a solvent. Different substances move different distances (in the same time) and this can be used to identify each substance in the mixture.

◀ Chromatography paper is like high-grade filter paper; often, filter paper can be substituted.

The technique is carried out as described below:
- Place the solvent to be used to a depth of 2 cm in a boiling tube.
- Draw a pencil line 2 cm from the end of a piece of chromatography paper and mark a spot in the centre of this line.
- Place several small drops of the mixture on the pencil spot, allowing each to dry fully before adding the next. This allows a small, concentrated spot of the mixture to be built up.
- Suspend the chromatography paper in the boiling tube as shown in Figure 2.27, with the tip submerged in the solvent. Note that the spot must be above the surface of the solvent, otherwise the substances will simply dissolve into it.
- 'Run' the chromatogram until the solvent has travelled about 80–90% of the way up the paper. It must not reach the end of the paper. At the end of the run, mark the position of the solvent front.

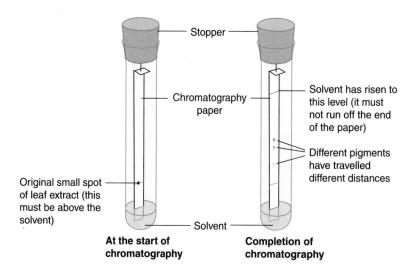

Figure 2.26 How to carry out one-dimensional paper chromatography

If the chromatogram was of, say, pigments from a leaf, then several coloured spots would be seen. However, some substances are colourless. If the original mixture was of amino acids resulting from the digestion of a protein, then the 'spots' would be invisible. In such cases, the chromatogram must be 'developed' using an appropriate dye to reveal the position of the spots.

The substances are identified by calculating the **R_f value**, which is a measure of how far the substance has moved relative to the solvent front. It is calculated in the following way:

$$R_f = \frac{\text{distance moved by substance}}{\text{distance moved by solvent front}}$$

The R_f value of a substance in a particular solvent under controlled conditions is unique. The substance can be identified by referring to a table of R_f values.

The technique described above is correctly called one-dimensional chromatography, because the solvent has moved in one dimension — upwards. Although each substance has a unique R_f value, sometimes these values are similar and separation is not always obvious. In such cases, better separation is obtained by using **two-dimensional chromatography**. In two-dimensional chromatography, the chromatogram is run twice, in different directions and with different solvents.

Figure 2.27 Two-dimensional chromatography can separate substances that are not well separated by one-dimensional chromatography

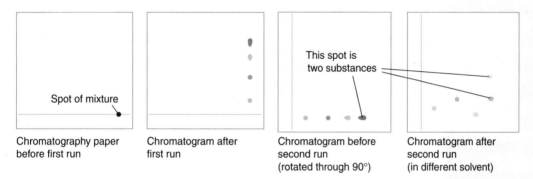

Spot of mixture

Chromatography paper before first run

Chromatogram after first run

This spot is two substances

Chromatogram before second run (rotated through 90°)

Chromatogram after second run (in different solvent)

Electrophoresis

Electrophoresis is a technique used to separate charged particles. It is based on the principle that in an electric field, charged particles in solution migrate towards either the positive electrode or the negative electrode. Negatively charged ions migrate towards the positive electrode; positively charged ions

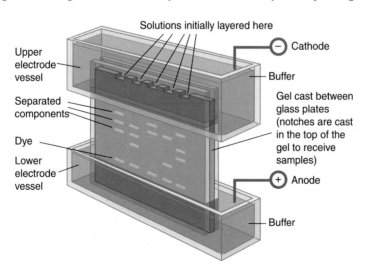

Solutions initially layered here

Upper electrode vessel

Separated components

Dye

Lower electrode vessel

— ⊖ Cathode

Buffer

Gel cast between glass plates (notches are cast in the top of the gel to receive samples)

⊕ Anode

Buffer

Figure 2.28 In gel electrophoresis, the large charged particles are separated according to their molecular mass

migrate towards the negative electrode. In electrophoresis, the electric field moves the charged particles towards the electrodes through a supporting medium; this may be paper or a gel. Paper electrophoresis is used to separate small charged particles. Gel electrophoresis is used in biology to separate the large molecules found in biological systems. For example, it is used to produce the patterns of DNA fragments that make up a '**genetic fingerprint**'. Use of a marker dye, which moves more quickly than nearly all biological macromolecules, enables the experimenter to track how far the molecules have moved.

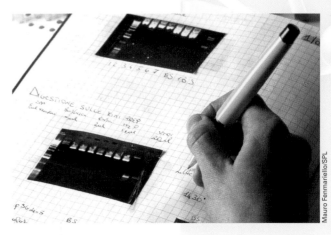

DNA fingerprints produced by gel electrophoresis of DNA fragments

The paper or gel acts as a kind of 'molecular sieve' with the result that larger particles move more slowly than smaller ones. In electrophoresis, the distance moved *relative to the dye* is the crucial measure that allows experimenters to determine the molecular mass of the substance.

Summary

Carbohydrates

- Carbohydrate molecules contain the elements carbon, hydrogen and oxygen only. The ratio of hydrogen atoms to oxygen atoms is 2:1.
- Monosaccharides are carbohydrates. The atoms are arranged in a single ring-like structure.
- The formula of α-glucose and β-glucose and all other hexose monosaccharides is $C_6H_{12}O_6$.
- The structures of α-glucose and β-glucose are:

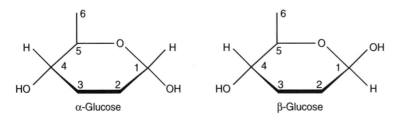

α-Glucose β-Glucose

- Two monosaccharides can be joined by condensation to form a disaccharide. In the formation of maltose, two α-glucose molecules are joined with the loss of a molecule of water (H_2O). The formula of maltose is $C_{12}H_{22}O_{11}$.
- The bond joining the two molecules of α-glucose is an α-1,4-glycosidic bond.
- Polysaccharides are formed when many monosaccharide molecules join by condensation. Starch contains two polymers of α-glucose — amylose and amylopectin. Glycogen is also a polymer of α-glucose. Cellulose is a polymer of β-glucose.

- Starch and glycogen are storage carbohydrates. They have compact molecules that enable much glucose to be stored in a small place. They are insoluble, which means that they have no osmotic effects within the cell and do not move from the cell.
- The unbranched cellulose molecules hydrogen bond with each other to form fibrils. These align to form the fibres that are the basis of plant cell walls.

Proteins

- Amino acids contain carbon, hydrogen, oxygen and nitrogen. They have the following general structure:

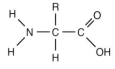

- Amino acids can be joined by condensation. The bond between two amino acids is a peptide bond. A large number of amino acids joined in this way form a polypeptide.
- Proteins are polymers of amino acids. They have several levels of structure:
  - the primary structure is the sequence of amino acids in a polypeptide chain
  - the secondary structure is the folding of the primary structure into either an α-helix or a β-pleated sheet; these structures are held in shape by hydrogen bonds
  - the tertiary structure is the further folding of the secondary structure into either a fibrous or globular shape; these structures are held in place by further hydrogen bonds, disulphide bridges and ionic bonds
  - some have a quaternary structure in which two or more polypeptide chains, each with a tertiary structure, are bonded together; a haemoglobin molecule consists of four polypeptide chains

Lipids

- Triglycerides are lipids; a triglyceride molecule is an ester of three fatty acid molecules and one glycerol molecule; the ester bonds are formed by condensation.

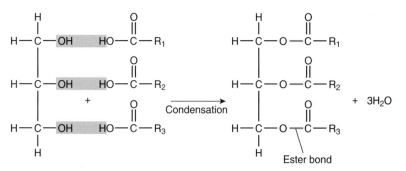

- Fatty acid molecules can be either saturated (all carbon–carbon bonds are single), monounsaturated (one carbon–carbon double bond) or polyunsaturated (more than one carbon–carbon double bond).
- A phospholipid molecule consists of two fatty acids and a phosphate group bonded to a molecule of glycerol. The phosphate group gives the molecule a hydrophilic 'head' and the fatty acids give the molecule hydrophobic 'tails'.
- Phospholipid bilayers are the basis of biological membranes.

Identifying biological molecules

- Reducing sugars react with Benedict's solution when heated to give a yellow/orange/red precipitate.
- Non-reducing sugars must first be hydrolysed by boiling with HCl and then neutralised before they will react with Benedict's solution.
- Proteins react with Biuret reagent to give a mauve/purple colour.
- The emulsion test for lipids produces a milky-white colour in water.
- Chromatography can be used to separate mixtures of soluble substances; the R_f value of each substance in a particular solvent is unique.
- Gel electrophoresis separates molecules in an electric field according to their molecular mass.

Questions

Multiple-choice

1 Hexoses are:
   A disaccharides with molecules that contain six carbon atoms
   B monosaccharides with molecules that contain six oxygen atoms
   C monosaccharides with molecules that contain six carbon atoms
   D disaccharides with molecules that contain six oxygen atoms
2 The main advantage of the high level of branching in a molecule of amylopectin is that:
   A the many 'ends' allow rapid hydrolysis
   B much can be stored in a small space
   C there are no osmotic effects
   D it is insoluble
3 Which of the following statements about cellulose is *not* true?
   A it is a polymer of β-glucose
   B the molecule is unbranched
   C the glucose molecules are joined by β-1,6 bonds
   D adjacent molecules form hydrogen bonds with each other
4 The secondary structure of a protein can be:
   A a globular or a fibrous structure
   B a specific sequence of amino acids
   C a dipeptide
   D an α-helix or a β-pleated sheet

5 Condensation involves:

   A the creation of new bonds with the addition of a molecule of water

   B the creation of new bonds with the loss of a molecule of water

   C the breaking of existing bonds with the addition of a molecule of water

   D the breaking of existing bonds with the loss of a molecule of water

6 In gel electrophoresis, large negatively charged particles move:

   A further than smaller molecules towards the positive electrode

   B further than smaller molecules towards the negative electrode

   C a shorter distance than smaller molecules towards the negative electrode

   D a shorter distance than smaller molecules towards the positive electrode

7 In a saturated fatty acid:

   A there are only single bonds between carbon atoms

   B there is one double bond between carbon atoms

   C there is one triple bond between carbon atoms

   D there is more than one double bond between carbon atoms

8 Phospholipids form bilayers in water because:

   A the hydrophilic head is repelled by the water and the hydrophobic tail is attracted by it

   B the hydrophilic head is attracted by the water and the hydrophobic tail is repelled by it

   C both the hydrophilic head and the hydrophobic tail are attracted by the water

   D both the hydrophilic head and the hydrophobic tail are repelled by the water

9 When heated with Benedict's solution, sucrose does not cause a colour change because it is:

   A a reducing sugar

   B a disaccharide

   C a non-reducing sugar

   D a compound sugar

10 A triglyceride molecule is an ester of:

   A three fatty acids and ethanol

   B two fatty acids and glycerol

   C two fatty acids and ethanol

   D three fatty acids and glycerol

Examination-style

1 The diagram shows two amino acids:

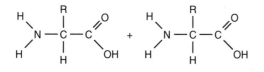

   (a)(i) Copy the diagram and indicate the amino group on each amino acid.

                                                   (1 mark)

(ii) Draw another diagram to show how these two amino acids could form a dipeptide. *(2 marks)*

(iii) Name both the process involved in the formation of the dipeptide and the type of bond formed. *(2 marks)*

(b) Describe how chromatography can be used to separate a mixture of amino acids. *(4 marks)*

Total: 9 marks

2 The diagram shows the arrangement of the atoms in a monounsaturated fatty acid:

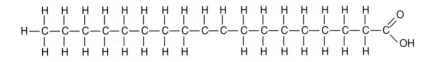

(a) Copy the diagram and add any double carbon–carbon bonds that may exist in this molecule. *(2 marks)*

(b) A molecule of this fatty acid contains more carbon atoms than a molecule of α-glucose.

(i) Give *three* other differences between the two molecules. *(3 marks)*

(ii) Give *one* similarity between the two molecules. *(1 mark)*

Total: 6 marks

3 Five solutions labelled P, Q, R, S and T are known to be:
- amylase (an enzyme that digests starch to maltose)
- albumen (a protein)
- starch
- sucrose
- glucose

The following tests are carried out:
- Each solution is tested with iodine solution. This allows identification of solution S.
- The remaining four solutions are tested with Benedict's solution. This allows identification of solution P.
- The remaining three solutions are tested with Biuret reagent. Solutions R and T both turn purple. Solution Q can now be identified.

(a) Identify, giving reasons, solutions P, Q and S. *(3 marks)*

(b) How could solutions R and T be distinguished? *(4 marks)*

Total: 7 marks

4 A molecule of lactose is formed by the condensation of a molecule of β-glucose and a molecule of galactose. Both β-glucose and galactose have the formula $C_6H_{12}O_6$.

(a) Draw a molecule of β-glucose. *(2 marks)*

(b) Explain how β-glucose and galactose can both have the formula $C_6H_{12}O_6$ and yet be different substances. *(1 mark)*

(c) How many oxygen atoms are there in a molecule of lactose? Explain your answer. *(2 marks)*

(d) Galactose is a reducing sugar. What does this mean? *(2 marks)*

Total: 7 marks

5 (a) Describe how you would test a solution to see if it contained a protein. *(2 marks)*

(b) The diagram shows the structure of a protein molecule.

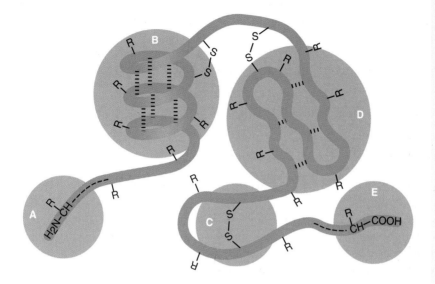

(i) Identify the region that represents:
  - an α-helix *(1 mark)*
  - a β-pleated sheet *(1 mark)*

(ii) Explain why the final shape of a protein molecule is determined by its primary structure. *(4 marks)*

Total: 8 marks

Chapter 3

Moving substances in and out of cells

This chapter covers:
- the structure of plasma membranes
- diffusion
  - simple diffusion
  - facilitated diffusion
- active transport
- osmosis
- exocytosis and endocytosis
- the factors affecting the rate at which substances move across membranes

A cell is a complex system in which many biochemical reactions take place continuously. The reactants may be formed within the cell or they may be imported from other cells. Similarly, the products of the reactions may be used within the cell or they may be exported from the cell. The way in which substances are moved into and out of cells depends on several factors, including the size of the particles of the substance, its solubility in water or lipid, and the relative concentrations inside and outside the cell. Every cell is surrounded by a plasma membrane and this regulates the transport of substances into and out of the cell. The cell walls that surround some cells are freely permeable to even the largest molecules.

◀ A system refers to a set of interacting particles. In this book, a system could be a cell, a solution or a suspension.

Box 3.1 Particles, atoms, ions and molecules

'Particle' is a generic term that covers atoms, ions and molecules.

An atom is an uncharged particle. It is the smallest particle of an element that can take part in a chemical reaction (e.g. an oxygen atom or an iron atom). An ion is a charged particle. It may be just one atom that has become charged (e.g. oxide, O^{2-} or iron(II), Fe^{2+}) or a group of atoms that is charged (e.g. hydrogencarbonate, HCO_3^-). A molecule is an uncharged particle made from several atoms, which may be the same (e.g. an oxygen molecule, O_2) or different (e.g. a copper sulphate molecule, $CuSO_4$).

Particles have a certain amount of **kinetic energy** that causes them to move in a random manner. Sometimes, movement across membranes is the direct result of random movement of particles. So why should molecules of glucose move into, or out of, a liver cell? How do cells lining the small intestine absorb sodium ions? These processes involve movement in a particular direction.

> When you are describing the motion of particles, be careful not to use phrases such as 'the particles *need* to move into …' or 'the cell *needs* the particles to move into it…'. Needing is an emotion or a desire. Cells and particles do not have emotions or desires!

Plasma membrane structure

Membranes within a cell have the same appearance, and the same structure, as the **plasma membrane** surrounding the cell. Each membrane appears in an electron micrograph as a three-layered structure — two darker outer layers with a paler layer between them. There have been several models proposed to explain this; the one that is now generally accepted is the **fluid mosaic model**.

A previous model suggested that the plasma membrane had a lipoprotein 'sandwich' structure. It proposed that the two outer layers were protein with a layer of lipid sandwiched between them.

Figure 3.1 The fluid mosaic model of the structure of a plasma membrane

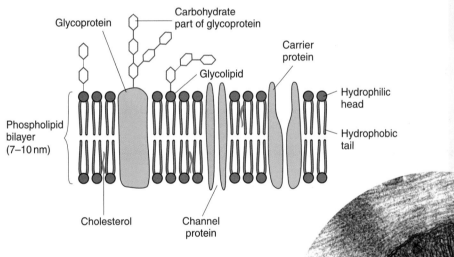

Glycoprotein

Carbohydrate part of glycoprotein

Carrier protein

Glycolipid

Hydrophilic head

Phospholipid bilayer (7–10 nm)

Hydrophobic tail

Cholesterol

Channel protein

False-colour transmission electron micrograph of mitochondria showing the membrane appearance

The fluid mosaic model is so named because it suggests that:
- the phospholipid molecules are not fixed absolutely in one position, but move (as do the particles in a fluid), although the movement is mainly lateral (not in all directions as in a fluid); the protein molecules move to a much lesser extent
- when either surface is viewed, there is a 'mosaic' pattern made from the protein molecules and the 'heads' of the phospholipids

Steve Gschmeissner/SPL

(× 42 500)

The different proteins in the plasma membrane have different functions. Many of the **integral (transmembrane) proteins** are involved in moving particles across the membrane. They can be:

- **ion pores** or channels — to allow the passage of ions across the membrane
- **transport proteins** — to carry molecules such as glucose and amino acids through the membrane
- **ATP-dependent pumps** — to move substances actively across the membrane

Peripheral proteins in the inner phospholipid layer may help to anchor other proteins in the membrane. Those in the outer phospholipid layer often have carbohydrate chains attached, i.e. they are glycoproteins. These are important in cell recognition and as receptors for molecules such as hormones. Some proteins in the membrane are enzymes and catalyse reactions at or near the cell surface.

e Be sure that you know the *functions* of the various components of the plasma membrane, as well as their names. You may be asked, for example, to 'identify the component that is responsible for cell recognition', rather than just to 'identify a peripheral protein'.

Diffusion

Simple diffusion

Simple diffusion is defined as 'the net movement of particles from an area of high concentration to an area of lower concentration'. This can only take place in a fluid (a liquid or a gas). In a solid, the particles are fixed in position and cannot move to allow diffusion to take place. Simple diffusion does not necessarily involve a membrane. When someone sprays air freshener in a room, the particles of the freshener diffuse from the point of spraying (the high concentration) to the rest of the room (the lower concentration).

◀ Diffuse means spread out.

Box 3.2 Diffusion of air freshener

Why do the particles of air freshener spread out? Later, why do they not become concentrated again in a small area? Without an input of energy, systems tend to move towards a lower energy state (a rock rolls down a hill, not up it) and to a more disorganised or random condition (the particles in an iced lolly do not remain in that organised state for long). The combination of these two factors determines the **free energy** of a system. A reaction or process will only occur spontaneously if the free energy decreases. This is what happens in diffusion. Random motion of the particles leads to a decrease in free energy, by making the system more random or disorganised. Therefore, the particles cannot return to a highly concentrated state — ever.

Diffusion *can* occur across a membrane, provided the particles are physically able to cross it. A plasma membrane contains a phospholipid bilayer and the 'tails' of the phospholipids are non-polar, i.e. they are not charged. This makes it difficult for ions (charged particles) to pass through. The phospholipids are tightly packed, which means that large molecules are unlikely to be able to pass through. Table 3.1 gives examples of some substances that can diffuse across the plasma membrane and others that cannot.

If the particles of a substance are lipid-soluble, even if the particles are quite large, they can diffuse across the plasma membrane. If the particles are not

If a substance is lipid-soluble, its particles can mix with those of a lipid. This allows such particles to pass between the molecules of phospholipid in the ◀ plasma membrane.

lipid-soluble, diffusion through the plasma membrane is only possible if they are small and non-polar (uncharged). Plasma membranes are **partially permeable** — they allow some particles to pass through but not others.

Substance	Type of particle	Is the particle charged?	Size of particle	Is the particle lipid-soluble?	Can the particle diffuse across the membrane?
Water	Molecule	No	Small	No	Yes
Glycerol	Molecule	No	Small	Yes	Yes
Fatty acids	Molecule	Slightly	Medium	Yes	Yes
Carbon dioxide	Molecule	No	Small	No	Yes
Oxygen	Molecule	No	Small	No	Yes
Glucose	Molecule	No	Medium	No	No
Sodium chloride	Ions (Na^+, Cl^-)	Yes	Small	No	No
Protein	Molecule	No	Large	No	No

Table 3.1 Types of particle that can diffuse across the plasma membrane

Factors that affect the rate of diffusion

Concentration gradient

For *net* diffusion to occur, there must be a concentration difference of substance on either side of a membrane. This difference in concentrations is called a **concentration gradient**. Particles cross the membrane in both directions because of random movement. However, more particles move from the higher concentration than from the lower concentration. Therefore, there is a *net* movement from the higher concentration to the lower concentration. This continues until the concentrations on each side of the membrane are equal, i.e. the concentration gradient is zero.

The greater the difference in the two concentrations, the faster the initial rate of net diffusion will be. The rate of net diffusion slows down as the two concentrations become closer to each other.

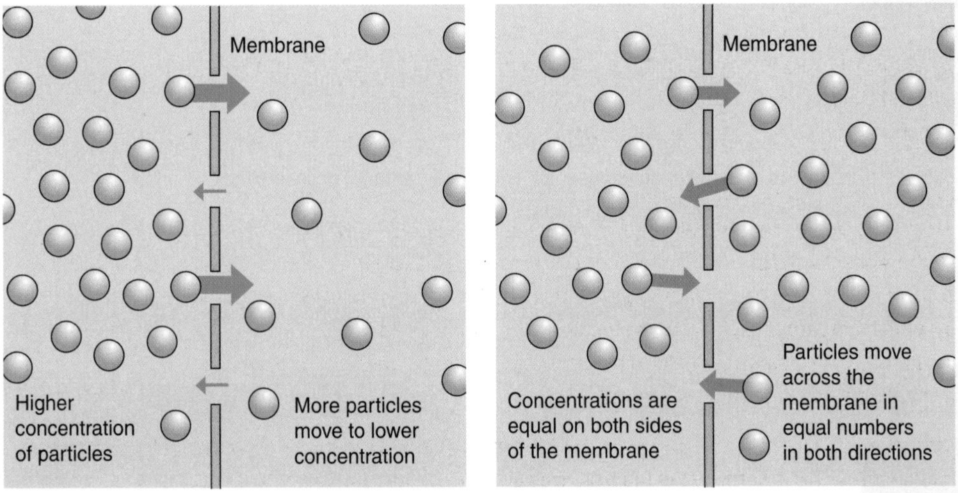

When a concentration gradient is present, diffusion occurs spontaneously as the system moves from a relatively ordered state to a random state.

In an examination, you need not use the word 'net'. The examiner will assume that you are describing the net movement of particles, unless you state otherwise.

Figure 3.2 The concentration gradient affects the rate of diffusion

Membrane

Higher concentration of particles

More particles move to lower concentration

Membrane

Concentrations are equal on both sides of the membrane

Particles move across the membrane in equal numbers in both directions

Diffusion also occurs through *layers* of cells called **exchange surfaces**. For example:

- oxygen and carbon dioxide diffuse through epithelial cells in the alveoli
- urea diffuses through epithelial cells in kidney tubules

> The rate of diffusion of a substance across a membrane (or exchange surface) is proportional to the difference in concentration across the membrane (or exchange surface).

> In an examination, you may be asked to describe the movement of particles in terms of a concentration gradient. Particles can move *down* a concentration gradient (from high concentration to low) or, sometimes, *against* a concentration gradient (from low concentration to high). Never say that particles move *along* a concentration gradient. This does not make clear in which direction the particles are moving.

Thickness of surface

The distance that particles have to travel affects how long it takes for them to cross the membrane and therefore the rate of diffusion. All plasma membranes are essentially the same thickness, but the layers of cells in different exchange surfaces are not. A thin exchange surface allows faster diffusion than a thick one does.

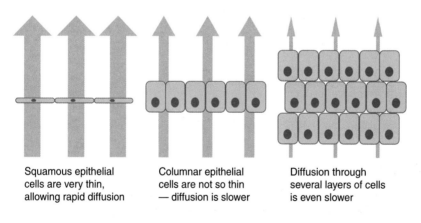

Squamous epithelial cells are very thin, allowing rapid diffusion

Columnar epithelial cells are not so thin — diffusion is slower

Diffusion through several layers of cells is even slower

Figure 3.3 The thickness of an exchange surface affects the rate of diffusion

> The rate of diffusion of a substance across an exchange surface is inversely proportional to the thickness of the exchange surface.

Surface area

Another factor that affects the rate of diffusion across a membrane or exchange surface is the surface area. A large surface area allows faster diffusion (more particles will cross per second) than a small surface area. Cells specialised for absorption frequently have a plasma membrane with microvilli to increase the surface area.

The rate of diffusion of a substance across a membrane (or exchange surface) is proportional to the surface area of the membrane (or exchange surface).

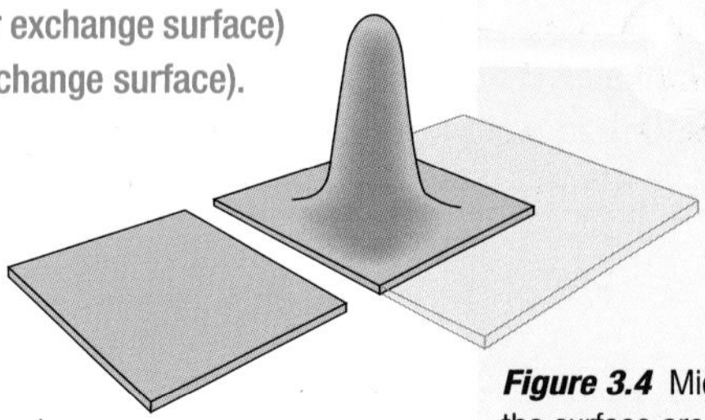

Figure 3.4 Microvilli increase the surface area of a plasma membrane

Fick's law

The effect of all these factors on diffusion is summarised in **Fick's law**:

$$\text{rate of diffusion} \propto \frac{\text{surface area} \times (C_2 - C_1)}{\text{thickness of exchange surface}}$$

where $(C_2 - C_1)$ = difference in concentration

> The symbol $\propto$ means 'is proportional to' and *not* 'is equal to'. So, if you are asked to write the formula for Fick's law, do *not* use the equals sign. Write out the equation in full. Do *not* write:
>
> $$\text{Fick's law} \propto \frac{\text{surface area} \times (C_2 - C_1)}{\text{thickness of exchange surface}}$$
>
> This does not mention 'rate of diffusion' and so is incorrect.
>
> A question may test your understanding of Fick's law by asking you to state which of the three factors must be large or small to achieve the maximum rate of diffusion. To achieve a high rate of diffusion, both the terms on the top line (surface area and concentration difference) must be large, while that on the bottom line (thickness of exchange surface) must be small.

In summary, simple diffusion describes the movement of particles across a membrane as a direct result of random motion. It is a passive process, requiring no extra energy in the form of ATP from respiration. The only energy involved is the kinetic energy of the molecules themselves.

Facilitated diffusion

Particles that cannot cross membranes by simple diffusion — for example, sodium ions, glucose and amino acid molecules — often enter or leave cells by **facilitated diffusion**. This process still relies on the presence of a concentration gradient across the membrane, down which the particles diffuse. However, the particles do not pass freely between the molecules of phospholipid. Movement is facilitated (made possible) by protein molecules that span the plasma membrane.

Channel proteins are made from several subunits and have a hole or pore running through the centre. They are responsible for the transport of ions into and out of cells and form **ion pores** or **ion channels**. Some are specific and only allow certain ions to pass through (e.g. sodium-ion channels, potassium-ion channels, calcium-ion channels); others are non-specific and allow several

A channel protein can be thought of as a tube that ◀ spans the membrane.

different ions to pass through. Some are open all the time whereas others have gates (**gated channels**) that are opened and closed by appropriate stimuli, such as pressure, or a change in voltage.

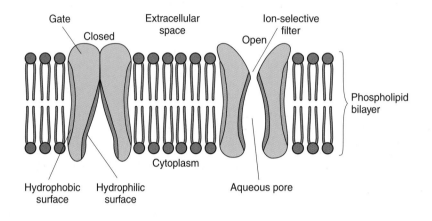

Figure 3.5 Different states of a gated ion channel

Carrier proteins transport medium-sized molecules into and out of cells. To facilitate the movement of the diffusing molecule, the carrier protein molecule usually has to undergo a conformational change. This means that it changes shape.

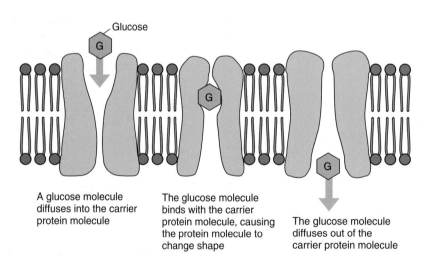

Figure 3.6 Facilitated transport of glucose across a plasma membrane

As with simple diffusion, there is net movement of particles across the membrane only when a concentration gradient is present.

Some carrier proteins function in **cotransport systems**. One of these is responsible for the uptake of sodium ions and glucose molecules in the small intestine and in the kidney. A similar system operates for the cotransport of sodium ions and amino acids.

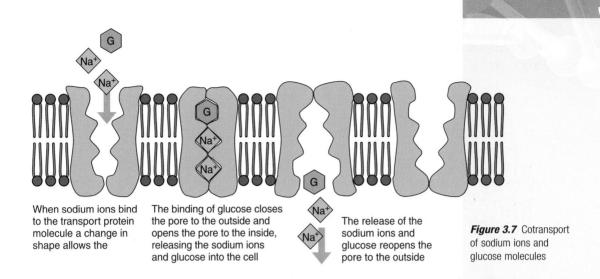

When sodium ions bind to the transport protein molecule a change in shape allows the

The binding of glucose closes the pore to the outside and opens the pore to the inside, releasing the sodium ions and glucose into the cell

The release of the sodium ions and glucose reopens the pore to the outside

Figure 3.7 Cotransport of sodium ions and glucose molecules

Box 3.3 Membrane proteins and the rate of diffusion

The presence of channel proteins and carrier proteins greatly affects the rate of diffusion of particles into and out of cells. For example, the rate of diffusion of chloride ions across the membrane of a red blood cell is increased by a factor of 10^7 and the permeability of most cells to glucose is increased by a factor of 50 000.

However, the presence of channel and carrier proteins does impose a finite limit on the rate of facilitated diffusion. Each protein can only transport a certain number of particles per second. Increasing the concentration gradient increases the rate of facilitated diffusion up to the point at which all the carrier proteins or ion channels are transporting at their maximum rate. Facilitated diffusion cannot then take place any faster. Any further increase in the concentration gradient has no effect. With simple diffusion, this is not the case. The initial rate is slower, but as the concentration gradient is increased, the rate of simple diffusion just keeps increasing.

The relationship between the rates of uptake of a solute by simple and facilitated diffusion and concentration gradient are shown in Figure 3.8.

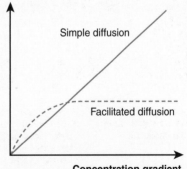

Figure 3.8 The change in rates of simple diffusion and facilitated diffusion as the concentration gradient increases

Fick's law has to be modified slightly for facilitated diffusion. Surface area in itself does not influence the rate of facilitated diffusion, but the number of transport or channel protein molecules does. The law must be rewritten as:

$$\text{rate of diffusion} \propto \frac{\text{number of transport protein molecules} \times (C_2 - C_1)}{\text{thickness of exchange surface}}$$

Since the exchange surface is always a plasma membrane, the rate is really only influenced by the number of transport proteins and the difference in concentration.

Active transport

Simple diffusion and facilitated diffusion move substances from a high concentration to a lower concentration — *down* a concentration gradient. Sometimes, substances must be moved *against* a concentration gradient — from a low concentration to a higher one. This cannot happen by diffusion, since it would tend to concentrate particles rather than spread them out. It can only happen if energy is put in to drive the process. In living organisms, this energy is released from the ATP produced in respiration. The proteins used to actively transport substances across plasma membranes are called **pumps**.

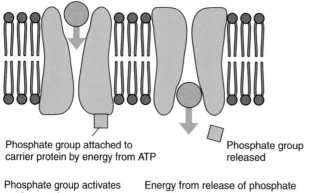

Figure 3.9 Role of ATP in active transport

Phosphate group attached to carrier protein by energy from ATP

Phosphate group released

Phosphate group activates carrier protein to accept particle to be transported

Energy from release of phosphate group used to change shape of carrier protein — transporting particle across membrane

There is a protein pump that transports sodium ions out of a cell at the same time as it transports potassium ions into a cell. This protein is known as the **sodium–potassium pump**. The configuration of the protein is such that three sodium ions are transported out of the cell while only two potassium ions are brought in.

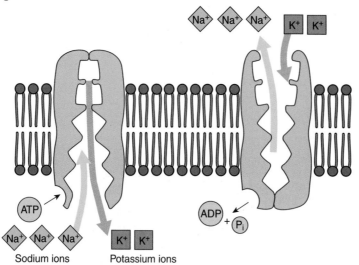

Figure 3.10 The sodium–potassium pump

Sodium ions   Potassium ions

Box 3.4 All three processes

Absorption of a substance can sometimes involve active transport, facilitated diffusion *and* simple diffusion. This diagram shows the mechanism of the absorption of glucose into capillaries through the epithelial cells of the small intestine.

The sodium–potassium pump actively transports sodium ions out of the cell. This reduces the concentration of sodium ions in the cell and creates a concentration gradient between the lumen of the small intestine and the cell, which allows more sodium ions to enter through the cotransport protein. However, for a sodium ion to enter, a molecule of glucose must also enter. These glucose molecules then pass, by facilitated diffusion, out of the cell down the concentration gradient. This gradient is maintained by the flow of blood. Without the active transport of sodium ions out of the epithelial cell, the uptake of glucose would be considerably reduced.

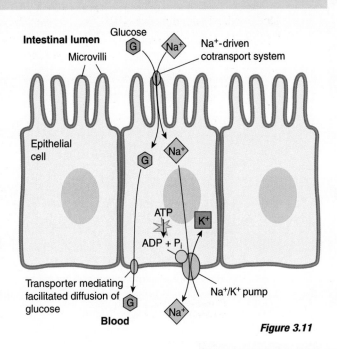

Figure 3.11

In examination questions, the full details of the cotransport of glucose are not always shown. You may be given a simplified version such as the one below:

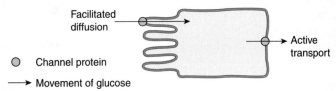

This version, although not completely correct, shows that an active process is involved in removing glucose from the cell and, therefore, maintaining a concentration gradient between the lumen and the cell, allowing glucose to enter the cell by facilitated diffusion.

Osmosis

Osmosis is the process by which water moves across a partially permeable membrane. It is, effectively, the diffusion of water. However, we do not refer to the concentration of water molecules, but to **water potential**. Water potential is a measure of the free energy of the water molecules in a system. Therefore, water moves, by osmosis, from a system with a high water potential to a system with a low water potential. The symbol for water potential is the Greek letter ψ (psi).

Water potential is measured in units of pressure — pascals (Pa), kilopascals (kPa), or megapascals (MPa). Pure, liquid water has a higher water potential than any other system. It is defined as zero:

ψ(pure water) = 0 Pa

All other systems (cells, solutions and suspensions) have a water potential that is lower than that of water. Therefore, their water potential values are negative.

Osmosis is the movement of water from a system with a high (less negative) water potential to one with a lower (more negative) water potential, across a partially permeable membrane.

Why water potential values are negative

The water potential of a system is due to the number of water molecules in that system. In pure water, there are only water molecules. When a solute is added, some of the water molecules form 'hydration shells' around the solute molecules. This reduces the number of (free) water molecules in the system and so the water potential is reduced. Since pure water is assigned a water potential of zero, the solution must have a negative water potential. A more concentrated solution will take more free water molecules out of the system and lower the water potential still further, making it more negative.

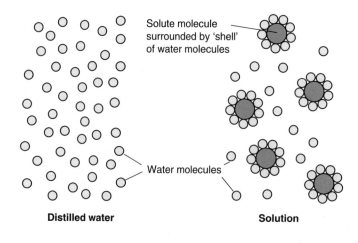

Distilled water   **Solution**

Figure 3.12 Adding a solute reduces the water potential of a system

Cells contain many molecules in an aqueous system. The sugars, ions and proteins present in a cell give it a negative water potential. Different concentrations of these substances result in cells with different water potentials. Water will move between them until the water potentials are all the same.

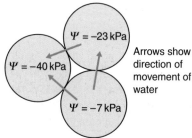

Arrows show direction of movement of water

Figure 3.13 Water movement between cells with different water potentials

Box 3.5 Osmosis in living systems

Treating dehydration

People with kidney failure can easily become dehydrated. Their dehydration is treated by putting them on a 'drip'. A solution containing ions and sugars is dripped into the blood plasma. Water cannot be used to rehydrate them, as this would dilute the plasma, increasing its water potential. This would create a water potential gradient between the plasma and the red blood cells. Water would enter the red blood cells, through the plasma membranes, by osmosis and would keep on entering. With only a thin plasma membrane surrounding each cell, the red blood cells would swell and burst.

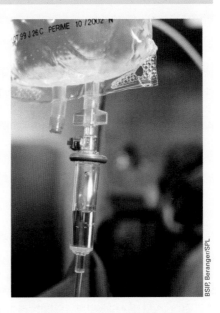

Watering plants

The reason for the changes in this coleus plant is related to the structure of plant cells. The cell wall surrounding each plant cell gives some support. When the cell takes in water by osmosis, the contents swell and put pressure on the cell wall, stretching it slightly. The cell is said to be **turgid**. Groups of turgid plant cells 'push' against each other. It is this pressure that keeps the stems of young seedlings upright. If a cell loses water, the contents shrink and no longer press against the cell wall. The cell is said to be **flaccid**. Flaccid cells do not press against other cells. The cells in this wilted coleus plant are flaccid.

Exocytosis and endocytosis

Large molecules, such as proteins, cannot pass through plasma membranes; they are too big. So how do they get into and out of cells?

Exocytosis: the removal of large molecules from a cell

Proteins are synthesised in the ribosomes and those that are to be exported from the cell are frequently modified in the Golgi apparatus. The modified protein leaves the Golgi apparatus in a vesicle — the protein is surrounded by a phospholipid bilayer. This means that the protein is isolated from the rest of the cell contents. The vesicle moves to the cell surface and the membrane of the vesicle fuses with the plasma membrane. As soon as this happens, the protein is outside the cell. This process is **exocytosis**. Cells that secrete enzymes and hormones do so by exocytosis.

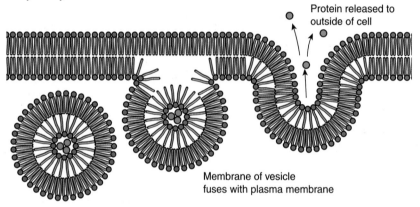

Protein released to outside of cell

Membrane of vesicle fuses with plasma membrane

Vesicle — membrane surrounding protein molecules

Figure 3.14 Exocytosis of protein molecules

Endocytosis: the uptake of large molecules by cells

In **endocytosis**, the molecules that are outside the cell are first drawn into a small 'pouch' or invagination of the plasma membrane. This then 'buds' off from the plasma membrane to form a vesicle containing the molecules. The molecules are released from the vesicle by the action of enzymes from lysosomes.

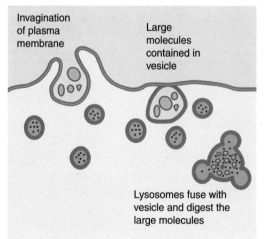

Invagination of plasma membrane

Large molecules contained in vesicle

Lysosomes fuse with vesicle and digest the large molecules

Figure 3.15 Stages in endocytosis

◀ Each time a cell secretes protein molecules by exocytosis, a little extra membrane is added to the plasma membrane. This extra membrane must eventually be returned to the interior. Each vesicle released to the interior of the cell during endocytosis removes a little of the plasma membrane. This must be recycled or the cell will shrink!

Transport processes compared

The transport processes that occur in living organisms are compared in Table 3.2.

Table 3.2

Process	Influence of concentration	Energy requirement	Type of particles moved across the plasma membrane	Transport proteins
Simple diffusion	Occurs down a concentration gradient — from high to low	Kinetic energy of the particles — passive process	Lipid-soluble, small, non-polar particles	None
Facilitated diffusion	Occurs down a concentration gradient — from high to low	Kinetic energy of the particles — passive processs	Ions and medium-sized particles that are insoluble in lipid (e.g. glucose)	Channel proteins or carrier proteins
Active transport	Occurs against a concentration gradient — from low to high	ATP from respiration in addition to kinetic energy of the particles — active process	Ions and medium-sized particles that are insoluble in lipid (e.g. glucose)	Pumps
Osmosis	Occurs down a water potential gradient — from high to low (less negative to more negative)	Kinetic energy of the particles — passive process	Water	None
Endocytosis or exocytosis	Concentration does not influence movement	Kinetic energy of the particles — passive process	Particles too large to be transported by other processes (e.g. proteins, cholesterol)	None

The kinetic energy of the particles is responsible for their movement. Therefore, the rates of all the processes will increase with rising temperature — as the particles gain more kinetic energy. However, increasing the temperature too much will denature transport proteins. This will reduce the rates of facilitated diffusion and active transport.

> In an examination, do not write that *energy* is not needed for diffusion to take place. *ATP* is not needed for diffusion to take place, but diffusion could not occur without the kinetic energy of the particles of the diffusing substance. The same is true of facilitated diffusion, osmosis, endocytosis and exocytosis.

Summary

Plasma membrane structure

- The fluid mosaic model of membrane structure suggests a fluid phospholipid bilayer with interspersed protein molecules, forming a mosaic pattern.
- The two main types of protein are integral (transmembrane) proteins that span the membrane and peripheral proteins that occur only on one surface of the phospholipid bilayer.

- Integral proteins are often involved in transport. There are ion channels/pores and transport proteins (both involved in facilitated diffusion) and pumps that are used in active transport.

Transport processes

- Substances are transported into and out of cells by simple diffusion, facilitated diffusion, active transport, osmosis, endocytosis and exocytosis. Transport through a *layer* of cells may involve more than one of these processes.
- Simple diffusion is the movement of particles down a concentration gradient (from a high concentration to a lower concentration). Transport proteins and ATP are not needed. Simple diffusion can occur across a membrane but often occurs in systems where no membrane is present.
- Facilitated diffusion is the movement of particles across a membrane through a channel protein or carrier protein. Movement is down a concentration gradient and ATP is not needed.
- Active transport is the movement of particles across a membrane through pumps (ATP-dependent transport proteins). Movement is against a concentration gradient and ATP is required.
- Osmosis is the movement of water across a partially permeable membrane from a high (less negative) water potential to a lower (more negative) water potential. Movement is, therefore, down a water potential gradient. Transport proteins and ATP are not needed.
  - Animal cells placed in a solution of higher water potential take in water by osmosis and burst because the plasma membranes cannot withstand the internal pressure.
  - Plant cells placed in a solution with a higher water potential take in water by osmosis but do not burst because the cell wall is able to withstand the internal pressure. The cells become turgid.
- Exocytosis is the movement of a membrane-bound vesicle containing large molecules (e.g. protein) to fuse with the plasma membrane and so release the molecules.
- Endocytosis is the formation of a membrane-bound vesicle containing large molecules (e.g. cholesterol) by invagination of the plasma membrane.

Factors affecting diffusion rate

- The rate of diffusion across an exchange surface (which may be a plasma membrane or a specialised exchange surface one or more cell layers thick) is described by Fick's law:

$$\text{rate of diffusion} \propto \frac{\text{surface area} \times (C_2 - C_1)}{\text{thickness of exchange surface}}$$

where $(C_2 - C_1)$ is the difference in concentration between the solutions on each side of the exchange surface.
- The rate of diffusion is increased by:
  - increasing the surface area
  - increasing the concentration gradient
  - decreasing the thickness of the exchange surface
  - increasing the temperature

Questions

Multiple-choice

1 The fluid mosaic model proposes that plasma membranes consist of:

  A a protein bilayer with phospholipids interspersed between the protein molecules

  B two layers of lipid with protein between them

  C two layers of protein with lipid between them

  D a phospholipid bilayer with protein molecules interspersed between the phospholipid molecules

2 Proteins in the plasma membrane may be involved in:

  A transport of ions in and out of cells through ion pores

  B cell recognition

  C the sodium–potassium ion pump

  D all of the above

3 Substances that prevent respiration from occurring also prevent active transport from taking place because:

  A there will be no oxygen available

  B there will be no ATP available

  C there will be too much carbon dioxide

  D all of the above

4 Diffusion always involves the movement of particles:

  A out of a cell

  B into a cell

  C down a concentration gradient

  D against a concentration gradient

5 Protein molecules are removed from a cell by:

  A facilitated diffusion

  B exocytosis

  C active transport

  D simple diffusion

6 Active transport always involves:

  A movement against a concentration gradient

  B a transport protein acting as a pump

  C the release of energy from ATP

  D all of the above

7 Ions cannot pass across a plasma membrane by simple diffusion because the particles are:

  A too large

  B non-polar

  C hydrophobic

  D charged

8 When placed in a solution that has a more negative water potential, animal cells:

  A lose water by osmosis and shrink

  B take in solutes from the solution and shrink

  C take in water by osmosis, swell and burst

  D lose solutes to the solution and swell

9 Facilitated diffusion always involves:
   A movement of ions
   B movement against a concentration gradient
   C ATP
   D transport proteins
10 Potato chips placed in water remain firm for a long time because:
   A the cells gain water by osmosis and become flaccid
   B the cells lose water by osmosis and become turgid
   C the cells lose water by osmosis and become flaccid
   D the cells gain water by osmosis and become turgid

Examination-style

1 The diagram below shows the structure of part of a plasma membrane as seen in section.

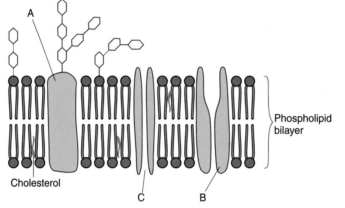

(a) Name the structures labelled A and B.   (2 marks)
(b) Describe the function of the structure labelled C.   (2 marks)
(c) Explain why phospholipid molecules in the membrane are
   orientated in the way shown in the diagram.   (3 marks)

Total: 7 marks

2 The graph below shows the change in the rate of uptake of two substances, A and B, by a cell as the external concentration of each changes. Initially, the internal concentration of both substances is the same. One of the substances is absorbed by simple diffusion, the other by facilitated diffusion.

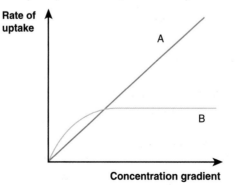

(a) Describe how the curves are:
  (i) similar (*1 mark*)
  (ii) different (*1 mark*)
(b) Which substance, A or B, is absorbed by facilitated diffusion?
  Explain how this can be deduced from the evidence in the graph. (*4 marks*)
(c) Describe how cells in the pancreas secrete the inactive
  enzyme trypsinogen. (*4 marks*)

Total: 10 marks

3 An investigation was carried out into the permeability of plasma membranes
of beetroot cells. These cells contain a purple-red pigment that, ordinarily, can
only pass through the plasma membranes to a very limited extent. The
procedure was as follows:

- Remove some cylinders of beetroot using a cork borer.
- Cut ten discs of beetroot, 5 mm thick.
- Wash the discs until no more colour escapes.
- Place the discs in a test tube containing 10 cm³ distilled water, which has
  been allowed to equilibrate in a water bath at 20°C for 10 min.
- Replace the test tube in the water bath for 20 min.
- Swirl the tube and pour some of the liquid into a cuvette.
- Measure the intensity of the colour of the water by placing the cuvette in
  a colorimeter, set to read absorbance.
- Repeat twice.
- Repeat the whole procedure at temperatures other than 20°C.

The results obtained are represented in the graph below.

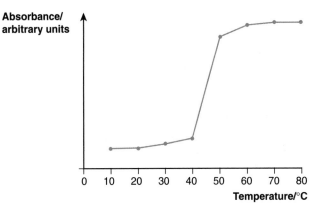

(a)(i) Suggest why there was some coloration of the water even
  at low temperatures. (*2 marks*)
  (ii) Explain why it was necessary to wash the beetroot discs. (*2 marks*)
(b)(i) Describe the change in absorbance as the temperature
  increases. (*2 marks*)
  (ii) Use the fluid mosaic model of membrane structure to
  explain the changes described in (b)(i). (*3 marks*)

Total: 9 marks

4 The diagram below represents the uptake of glucose, sodium ions and water by a cell in a kidney tubule.

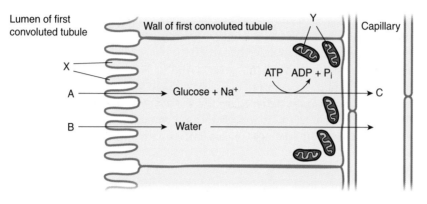

(a) Use Fick's law to explain how the structures labelled X help to maintain a high rate of absorption from the lumen of the kidney tubule. *(3 marks)*

(b) Explain how the presence of the organelles labelled Y is essential to the absorption of glucose. *(4 marks)*

(c) Copy and complete the table below by placing a tick or a cross in each box to indicate whether the feature does or does not apply to each process. *(3 marks)*

	Feature of process		
Process	Substance moves against concentration gradient	Process is passive	Process requires carrier proteins
A			
B			
C			

Total: **10 marks**

5 Plasma membranes consist of a phospholipid bilayer in which protein molecules are interspersed.

(a) The table below shows the percentage masses of protein, lipid and carbohydrate in four different plasma membranes.

	Percentage mass		
Membrane	Protein	Lipid	Carbohydrate
A	18	79	3
B	51	49	0
C	52	44	4
D	76	24	0

(i) Calculate the mean ratio of protein to lipid for the four plasma membranes. *(2 marks)*

(ii) Describe two functions of protein molecules in plasma membranes. *(2 marks)*

(iii) Describe one function of carbohydrates in plasma membranes. *(1 mark)*

(iv) Suggest why plasma membrane D has a much higher protein content than plasma membrane A. *(2 marks)*

(b) When phospholipid bilayers are heated, the phospholipid 'tails' become more mobile. At a critical transition temperature, they absorb a great deal of heat and become so mobile that they behave like a liquid. The graph below shows the effect of temperature on the heat absorption of a pure phospholipid bilayer and one to which 20% cholesterol has been added.

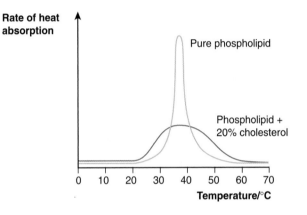

(i) How would the phospholipid tails behaving like a liquid affect the permeability of a plasma membrane? Explain your answer. *(3 marks)*

(ii) Over what range of temperatures does the pure phospholipid bilayer undergo the transition where the phospholipid tails become liquid? *(1 mark)*

(iii) How is this different for the bilayer with 20% cholesterol added? *(2 marks)*

(iv) Suggest a function for cholesterol molecules in plasma membranes. Explain your answer. *(2 marks)*

Total: 15 marks

Chapter 4

The nature and properties of enzymes

This chapter covers:
- enzymes as biological catalysts
- the way in which enzymes are able to catalyse reactions
- models of enzyme action:
  - the lock-and-key model
  - the induced-fit model
- factors affecting enzyme action:
  - temperature
  - pH
  - substrate concentration
  - enzyme concentration
  - inhibitors

Enzymes catalyse the many biochemical reactions that take place in cells. This ensures that the reactions take place efficiently when the enzyme is present and hardly at all when the enzyme is absent. Protein synthesis, and therefore enzyme synthesis, is controlled by DNA. Switching on and off the production of specific enzymes enables DNA to control the reactions that take place in a cell.

Enzymes and catalysis

A **catalyst** is a substance that speeds up a reaction. The nature of the reaction is unaltered; only the speed at which it takes place is affected. There is no overall change to:
- the nature of the products
- the energy change that takes place during the reaction
- the catalyst itself

This is true of all catalysts, including enzymes, which are **biological catalysts**. Catalysis enables biochemical reactions in a cell to take place quickly, at a temperature that will not damage the structure of the cell. To understand how this is possible, we must consider how chemical reactions take place.

Imagine a reaction in which substance A reacts with substance B to form substance AB. We can write an equation for this as:

$$A + B \rightarrow AB$$

However, this does not tell the whole story. The equation gives only the **reactants** (starting materials) and the **products** — it does not show *how* the reaction takes place. Before the final products are formed, the reactant molecules collide and enter a **transition state**, in which bonds in the molecules become strained. The molecules are said to be **activated**. There is more likelihood of strained bonds breaking and new bonds forming — in other words, that the reactant molecules will react to form the products. However, under normal conditions, few reactant molecules have sufficient kinetic energy to enter the transition state on collision, so the reaction proceeds slowly. A catalyst effectively lowers the energy required (the **activation energy, E_a**) for the molecules to enter the transition state by providing an alternative pathway for the reaction, which has lower activation energy. More reactant molecules have this lower energy requirement and so the reaction proceeds more quickly.

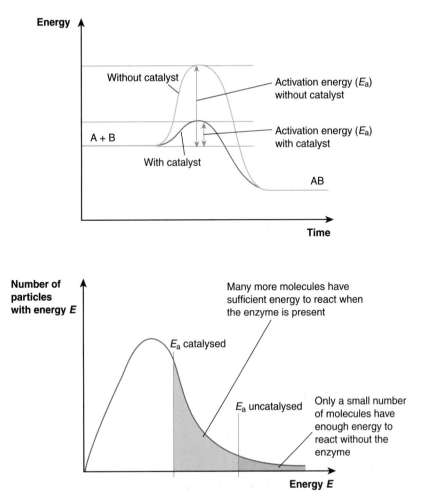

Figure 4.1 Effect of a catalyst on the activation energy of a reaction

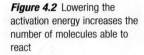

Figure 4.2 Lowering the activation energy increases the number of molecules able to react

When reactant molecules bind to a catalyst, the binding strains the bonds and allows them to enter the transition state with a much lower energy input (lower activation energy) than would normally be the case. In this way, catalysts are able to speed up chemical reactions.

 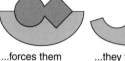

| Reactants about to bind | The orientation of the molecules and the strain on their bonds... | ...forces them into a transition state... | ...they then react, requiring little energy, and the product is released |

Figure 4.3 Binding to the active site of an enzyme strains the bonds of substrate molecules and allows them to enter the transition state

Most (but not all) biological catalysts are enzymes. Enzymes are globular proteins with a specific tertiary structure. The most significant part of this tertiary structure is the **active site**. This region of the enzyme molecule binds with **substrate** (reactant) molecules to form an **enzyme–substrate complex**. While bound to the active site, the reactants react and the product is released. The active site is shaped so that only certain substrate molecules are able to bind, and so each enzyme can catalyse only one reaction. The enzyme is said to be **specific**.

Recently, it has been shown that some RNA molecules can catalyse certain biological reactions.

Two models of enzyme action

The lock-and-key model

The **lock-and-key model** was first proposed in 1894 by a German biochemist named Fischer. The model proposes that the shapes of the substrate molecules are *complementary* to that of the active site, rather like the shape of a key is complementary to that of the lock it fits.

| Enzyme and substrate | A complex of enzyme and substrate allows reaction | Products are released and the enzyme is free to accept a new substrate molecule |

Figure 4.4 The lock-and-key model of enzyme action

This model can explain enzyme specificity but does not explain how the substrate molecules become strained in order to enter the transition state.

*In an examination, be careful not to write, 'The shape of the substrate is the *same* as the active site'. It is not — if it were, they would not be able to bind. One egg cannot sit inside another egg because they are the same shape. However, an egg can sit in an eggcup because the shapes are *complementary*.*

The induced-fit model

The induced-fit model was proposed by Koshland in 1958. It suggests that the binding of substrate molecules to the active site produces a conformational change (change in shape) in the active site and in other regions of the enzyme molecule. This conformational change puts the substrate molecules under tension, so they enter the transition state and are able to react.

Figure 4.5 The induced-fit model of enzyme action

As the enzyme and substrate bind, a change of shape occurs

The reaction proceeds as the enzyme and substrate bind

Products are released and the enzyme returns to its original shape

The induced-fit model is now generally accepted as offering a better explanation of enzyme action, but both models suggest that enzyme-controlled reactions proceed in two stages:

substrate + enzyme → enzyme–substrate complex

enzyme–substrate complex → enzyme + products

The rate of a chemical reaction is the rate at which reactants are converted into products. In the case of an enzyme-controlled reaction, this is determined by how many molecules of substrate bind with enzyme molecules to form enzyme–substrate complexes. The number of molecules of reactants that form enzyme– substrate complexes with each molecule of an enzyme, per second, is the **turnover rate** of the enzyme.

Box 4.1 Rate of reaction and turnover rate

Rate of reaction and turnover rate/enzyme activity are not the same. Rate of reaction describes the amount of substrate used or product formed irrespective of how many enzyme molecules catalyse the reaction. Enzyme activity is a measure of the fraction of maximum turnover at which each enzyme molecule is working. The rate of a reaction in which ten molecules of enzyme catalyse the reaction at maximum turnover will be slower than one in which 30 molecules of the same enzyme catalyse the same reaction at 70% maximum turnover. Suppose the turnover rate is 100 molecules per second. In the first example 1000 (100×10) molecules of substrate per second would form enzyme–substrate complexes. In the second example, 2100 (70×30) molecules of substrate per second would form enzyme–substrate complexes, increasing the rate of reaction even though the turnover rate/enzyme activity is lower.

Factors affecting enzyme activity

The turnover rate and, therefore, the activity of the enzyme is influenced by a number of external factors, including:

- temperature
- pH
- substrate concentration
- the presence of inhibitors

Temperature

When the temperature is raised, particles in a system are given more kinetic energy, which has two main effects.

- 'Free' particles move around more quickly. This increases the probability that a substrate particle will collide with an enzyme molecule.
- Particles within a molecule vibrate more energetically. This puts strain on the bonds that hold the atoms in place. Bonds begin to break and, in the case of an enzyme, the shape of the molecule and the active site, in particular, begin to change. The enzyme begins to **denature**.

The activity of an enzyme at a given temperature is a balance between these two effects. If the raised temperature results in little denaturation but a greatly increased number of collisions, the activity of the enzyme will increase. If the increased temperature causes significant denaturation, then despite the extra collisions, the activity of the enzyme will probably decrease. The temperature at which the two effects just balance each other is the **optimum temperature** for that enzyme. Any further increase in temperature will cause increased denaturation that will outweigh the effects of extra collisions.

A decrease in temperature means that fewer collisions will occur.

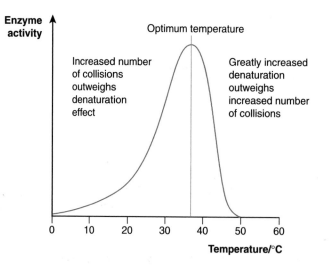

Figure 4.6 Effect of temperature on enzyme activity

Note that the graph is not symmetrical. Above the optimum temperature, the enzyme denatures very quickly to the point at which the shape of the active site has changed so much that an enzyme–substrate complex cannot form. At this point, the turnover rate, and therefore the reaction rate, is zero.

Box 4.2 Optimum temperature

Enzymes do not all have the same optimum temperature; they are adapted to work most efficiently within the organism in which they are found. For example, the optimum temperature for enzymes:

- in human beings is around 37°C (normal body temperature)
- in plants growing in the Arctic may be less than 5°C
- in bacteria that live in hot springs (thermophilic bacteria) may be over 90°C

pH

pH is a measure of the hydrogen ion concentration of a solution or other liquid system. The pH scale ranges from 0 to 14. Solutions with a pH of less than 7 are acidic, those with a pH of more than 7 are alkaline and a solution with a pH of exactly 7 is neutral.

The majority of enzymes in human beings function most efficiently within the pH range 6.0–8.0, although the optimum pH of pepsin (an enzyme found in the stomach) is between pH 1.0 and pH 3.0. Significant changes in pH can affect an enzyme molecule by:

- breaking ionic bonds that hold the tertiary structure in place, leading to denaturation of the enzyme molecule
- altering the charge on some of the amino acids that form the active site, making it more difficult for substrate molecules to bind

These effects occur if the pH becomes either more acidic or more alkaline.

◀ pH is an inverse logarithmic scale. Each pH unit represents a ten-fold change in hydrogen ion (H^+) concentration. pH 0 represents the highest H^+ concentration. A pH 1.0 solution has one-tenth (0.1) of this H^+ concentration; a pH 4 solution has one ten-thousandth (0.0001). pH 14 represents the lowest H^+ concentration.

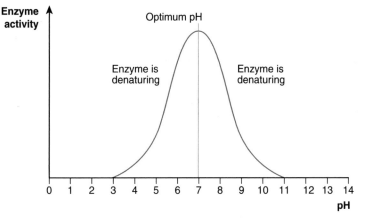

Figure 4.7 Effect of pH on enzyme activity

Substrate concentration

The activity of an enzyme depends on the number of substrate molecules per second that bind to form enzyme–substrate complexes. This is related to the number of substrate molecules present. A small number of substrate molecules results in few collisions and the formation of few enzyme–substrate complexes. Increasing the concentration of the substrate results in more collisions and the formation of more enzyme–substrate complexes — each enzyme molecule is active for more of the time. Since increasing the substrate concentration increases the activity of each enzyme molecule, the overall rate of reaction is increased. Eventually, a situation could be reached in which, because of the high substrate concentration, each enzyme molecule is working at maximum turnover — that is, each active site is binding with substrate molecules continually and there is no 'spare capacity' in the system. Increasing the substrate concentration beyond this point cannot increase the activity of the enzyme or the rate of reaction because all the active sites are occupied.

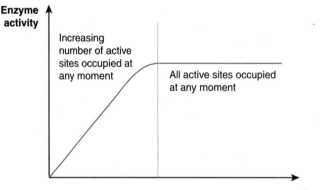

Figure 4.8 Effect of substrate concentration on enzyme activity when enzyme concentration is constant

Consider an enzyme-controlled reaction in which the concentration of enzyme is kept constant. As the reaction proceeds, the substrate concentration decreases — as each molecule of substrate is used, there will be fewer remaining. Since the concentration of enzyme molecules remains the same, fewer substrate molecules bind with each active site as time progresses. Eventually, none of the active sites will be occupied and no product will be formed.

The turnover rate of each enzyme molecule decreases with time. Therefore, the reaction rate also decreases.

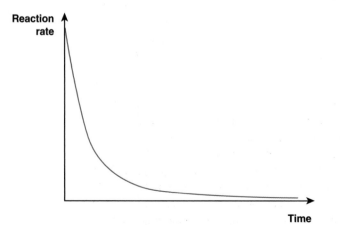

Figure 4.9 The change in reaction rate of an enzyme-controlled reaction over a period of time

Enzyme concentration

The rate of an enzyme-controlled reaction is influenced by the concentration of the enzyme. Assuming a constant large supply of substrate molecules, each enzyme molecule will work at maximum turnover. Therefore, the reaction rate will be directly proportional to the number of enzyme molecules, which is equivalent to the concentration of the enzyme.

However, increasing the concentration of the enzyme will *not* increase the *activity* of the enzyme. Each enzyme molecule will be working at maximum turnover, so the activity of the enzyme is likely to remain constant. It is possible to imagine a situation in which the enzyme concentration is so high that each enzyme molecule is no longer working at its maximum turnover. Increasing the enzyme concentration beyond this point would *decrease* the activity of the enzyme (although the rate of reaction would still increase).

Inhibitors

Inhibitors are substances that prevent enzymes from forming enzyme–substrate complexes and so stop, or slow down, the catalysis of the reaction.

Competitive inhibitors

Competitive inhibitors have molecules with shapes that are complementary to all, or part, of the active site of an enzyme. They are often similar in shape to the substrate molecules. They can bind with the active site and prevent substrate molecules from binding. The binding is only temporary and the competitive inhibitor is quickly released.

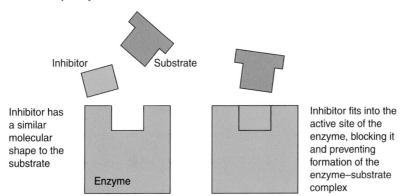

Figure 4.10 A competitive inhibitor blocks the active site so substrate molecules cannot bind

The overall effect on the rate of reaction depends on the relative concentrations of substrate and inhibitor molecules. Each molecule of competitive inhibitor can inhibit (temporarily) one enzyme molecule — but only if it can collide with the enzyme molecule and bind with the active site. To do this, it must *compete* with the substrate molecules for the active site — hence the name, competitive inhibitor. If there were 99 substrate molecules for every inhibitor molecule, then 99% of the collisions would be between enzyme and substrate and only 1% between enzyme and inhibitor. Therefore, at any one time, only 1% of the enzyme molecules would be inhibited and the reaction would proceed at 99%

of the maximum rate. If the ratio were 90 substrate molecules to ten inhibitor molecules, there would be 10% inhibition and the reaction rate would fall to 90% of maximum.

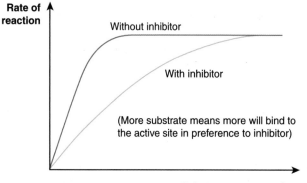

Figure 4.11 Effect of substrate concentration on inhibition by a competitive inhibitor

Non-competitive inhibitors

Non-competitive inhibitors do not compete for the active site. Instead, they bind to another part of the enzyme called the allosteric site. This produces a **conformational change** in the part of the enzyme molecule that includes the active site. As a result, the active site can no longer bind with the substrate and catalyse the reaction.

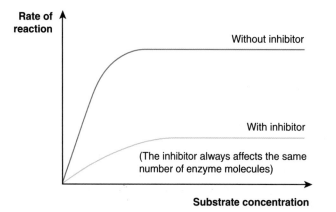

Figure 4.12 Effect of substrate concentration on inhibition by a non-competitive inhibitor

The effect of non-competitive inhibitors is independent of the concentration of substrate molecules. Suppose there are enough inhibitor molecules to bind with the allosteric sites of 80% of the enzyme molecules. These enzyme molecules will be inhibited irrespective of the number of substrate molecules, as the two are not competing for the same site.

Inhibitors and the regulation of cell metabolism

Many substances are produced in cells as a result of a series of reactions, which can be represented as:

$$A \xrightarrow{e_1} B \xrightarrow{e_2} C \xrightarrow{e_3} D$$

where e_1, e_2 and e_3 are enzymes catalysing the reactions.

All the reactions in this sequence are enzyme controlled. Therefore, inhibition of any of these enzymes will interrupt the process. However, the main function is to produce substance D for use by the cell. If the requirement for substance D decreases, or ceases altogether, then the concentration of D will increase within the cell. This is at least inefficient (producing something that is not being used) and may be potentially harmful because high concentrations could be toxic. Such reaction sequences are often controlled by **end-product inhibition**. The end product (D) inhibits the enzyme controlling the first stage of the reaction sequence, thus:

End-product inhibition

$$A \xrightarrow{e_1} B \xrightarrow{e_2} C \xrightarrow{e_3} D$$

Substance D normally acts as a non-competitive inhibitor, which prevents the enzyme e_1 from catalysing the reaction that converts A to B. As a result, the entire reaction sequence is halted. When the inhibition is removed, the reaction sequence can start again. Sometimes, a decrease in the concentration of D is sufficient to remove the inhibition. In other cases, the inhibitor must be removed by a substance known as an **activator**.

Enzymes are often kept in an inactive state in a cell by an inhibitor and are activated by a specific activator only when they are required.

Summary

Enzymes and catalysis

- A catalyst speeds up a chemical reaction with no effect on:
  - the products formed
  - the energy change
  - the nature of the catalyst itself
- A catalyst speeds up a reaction by lowering the activation energy required for reactants to enter the transition state.
- Nearly all biological catalysts are enzymes. They are globular proteins with a specific tertiary shape, part of which forms an active site.
- A substrate molecule binds with the active site to form an enzyme–substrate complex. This then forms the products. The products are released from the enzyme molecule, which is unaltered.
- The lock-and-key model of enzyme action suggests a rigid structure for the enzyme molecule, with the shape of the substrate and active site being complementary to each other. This model explains enzyme specificity but not how the transition state is achieved.
- The induced-fit model of enzyme action suggests that binding of the substrate induces a conformational change in enzyme structure, which puts the substrate molecule under tension, causing it to enter the transition state.
- The number of substrate molecules that bind to the active site of an enzyme molecule per second is the turnover rate.

Factors affecting enzyme activity

- Temperature — below the optimum temperature, the low level of kinetic energy limits the number of enzyme–substrate complexes formed; above the optimum temperature, denaturation of the enzyme prevents binding of the substrate.
- pH — above and below the optimum pH, changes occur in the tertiary structure of the enzyme molecule and in the charges on the amino acids making up the active site; both prevent binding of the substrate.
- Substrate concentration — if the concentration of enzyme remains constant, increasing the substrate concentration increases the number of enzyme–substrate complexes formed until, at any one time, all the active sites are occupied; the rate of reaction increases to its maximum.
- Enzyme concentration — if the substrate concentration is high and constant, increasing the enzyme concentration increases the rate of reaction.
- Inhibitors:
  - competitive inhibitors have molecules that are often similar in shape to the substrate molecules and that compete for the active site; the extent of the inhibition depends on the ratio of substrate molecules to inhibitor molecules
  - non-competitive inhibitors bind to a region away from the active site, producing a conformational change in the enzyme that prevents the substrate from binding; the extent of the inhibition is independent of the substrate concentration

Questions

Multiple-choice

1 A catalyst is a substance that:
   A speeds up a chemical reaction and alters the energy change and products formed
   B speeds up a chemical reaction and alters the energy change but not the products formed
   C speeds up a chemical reaction and alters the products formed but not the energy change
   D speeds up a chemical reaction and does not alter either the energy change or the products formed
2 Enzymes are specific because:
   A the molecule has a unique tertiary structure
   B each has a specific active site
   C the shape of the substrate molecule is complementary to that of the active site
   D all of the above
3 The induced-fit model of enzyme action proposes that:
   A there is a conformational change in the enzyme molecule and the substrate molecule binds unaltered

B there is no conformational change in the enzyme molecule and the substrate molecule binds unaltered

C there is no conformational change in the enzyme molecule and the substrate molecule is put under tension as it binds

D there is a conformational change in the enzyme molecule and the substrate molecule is put under tension as it binds

4 The turnover rate of an enzyme is:

A the overall rate at which the product of the enzyme-catalysed reaction is formed

B the number of enzyme–substrate complexes formed per enzyme molecule per second

C the total number of enzyme–substrate complexes formed

D the total amount of product formed

5 The optimum temperature of an enzyme is the temperature at which:

A most collisions between enzyme and substrate occur

B the maximum number of enzyme–substrate complexes are formed

C the enzyme is denatured

D all the active sites are occupied at any given moment

6 Solutions with an extreme pH can:

A alter the charge on amino acids in the active site

B reduce the number of enzyme–substrate complexes formed

C alter the tertiary structure of the enzyme

D all of the above

7 Non-competitive inhibitors can:

A bind with the active site to prevent substrate molecules from binding

B change the shape of the active site to prevent substrate molecules from binding

C alter the charge on amino acids in the active site to prevent substrate molecules from binding

D all of the above

8 In an enzyme-catalysed reaction at constant enzyme concentration, increasing the concentration of substrate molecules will:

A increase the rate of reaction to a maximum, then level off

B increase the rate of reaction indefinitely

C increase the rate of reaction to an optimum, then decrease the rate of reaction

D have no effect initially, then increase the rate of reaction

9 Which of the following graphs represents the effect of temperature on enzyme action?

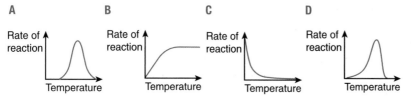

10 Inhibition by competitive inhibitors is:

   A caused by the inhibitor binding to a region of the enzyme other than the active site

   B dependent on the relative concentrations of substrate and inhibitor molecules

   C long lasting

   D responsible for end-product inhibition

Examination-style

1 (a) What is an enzyme?   (*3 marks*)

   (b) (i) Explain what is meant by enzyme specificity.   (*2 marks*)

       (ii) Describe the lock-and-key model of enzyme action.   (*3 marks*)

                                                              Total: 8 marks

2 The graph below shows the effect of substrate concentration on the rate of an enzyme-controlled reaction under three conditions:

   ● a competitive inhibitor present

   ● a non-competitive inhibitor present

   ● no inhibitor present

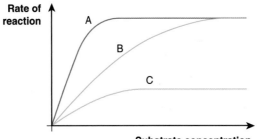

   (a) Which of the three curves represents the effect of a competitive inhibitor? Explain your answer.   (*3 marks*)

   (b) Explain how a non-competitive inhibitor produces its effect.   (*3 marks*)

                                                              Total: 6 marks

3 The rate of enzyme action depends on a number of factors, including the concentration of the substrate. The graph below shows the rate of reaction of an enzyme at 25°C at different substrate concentrations.

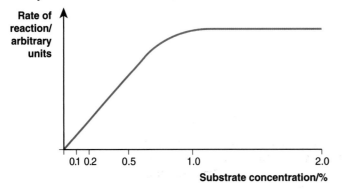

(a) Explain the shape of the graph in terms of kinetic theory and enzyme–substrate complex formation:
    (i) from substrate concentration 0.1% to 0.5%
    (ii) from substrate concentration 1.0% to 2.0%   (*4 marks*)
(b) Sketch, on the graph, the curve you would expect if the experiment had been carried out at 35°C rather than 25°C.   (*1 mark*)
(c) The graph below represents an energy level diagram of a reaction proceeding without an enzyme and the same reaction with an enzyme.

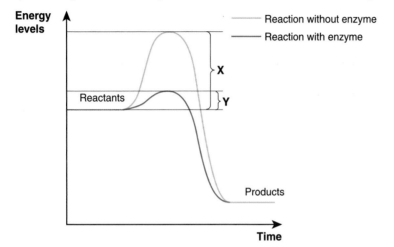

    (i) Describe two ways in which the energetics of the two reactions are similar.   (*2 marks*)
    (ii) Explain the differences between the regions marked X and Y on the diagram.   (1 mark)

Total: 8 marks

4 Hydrogen peroxide decomposes slowly to give water and oxygen. The reaction is catalysed in many cells by catalase. In an investigation into the effect of temperature on the rate of decomposition of hydrogen peroxide by catalase, the rate of reaction was measured by collecting the oxygen produced in a 10 minute period at different temperatures. All other factors were kept constant. The results are summarised in the graph below.

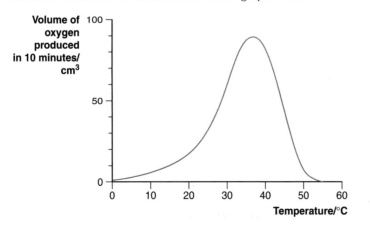

(a) (i) According to this graph, what is the optimum temperature of catalase? *(1 mark)*

(ii) Explain why this might not be an accurate estimate of the optimum temperature. *(2 marks)*

(b) In a control experiment (no enzyme present but all other factors the same as in the other experiments) carried out at 20°C, 0.5 cm³ of oxygen was collected. Assuming no experimental error, explain why this small amount of oxygen was produced. *(2 marks)*

(c) (i) Explain the difference in the volumes of oxygen collected at 20°C and at 30°C. *(2 marks)*

(ii) Explain the difference in the volumes of oxygen collected at 35°C and at 50°C. *(2 marks)*

Total: 9 marks

5 (a) The graph below shows the activity of three enzymes at different temperatures. Each enzyme comes from a different organism.

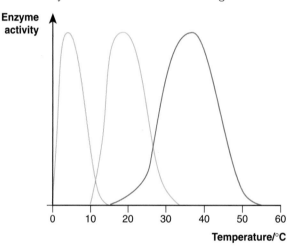

Suggest an explanation for the different activities of the enzymes. *(4 marks)*

(b) A metabolic pathway in which each stage is controlled by enzymes is represented as:

$$A \xrightarrow{e_1} B \xrightarrow{e_2} C \xrightarrow{e_3} D \xrightarrow{e_4} E$$

(i) Use this example to explain what is meant by end-product inhibition. *(3 marks)*

(ii) Explain what is meant by the induced-fit model of enzyme action. *(3 marks)*

Total: 10 marks

Chapter 5

Tissues, organs and systems

This chapter covers the levels of organisation that exist within a complex, multicellular organism, and why those levels of organisation have evolved. The topics are:

- surface area-to-volume ratios, supply and demand in different sized organisms
- how cells are organised into tissues
- some examples of animal and plant tissues
- how tissues are organised into organs
- some examples of animal and plant organs
- how organs are organised into organ systems
- some examples of animal and plant organ systems

The first organisms were unicellular (single-celled). They had no need for complex organs or systems. They obtained all the substances they needed by absorption across their plasma membranes by the processes described in Chapter 3. Their metabolic waste was also excreted across their plasma membranes. Over billions of years, the unicellular organisms evolved into complex multicellular organisms. In multicellular organisms, these simple ways of obtaining and removing substances no longer sufficed. Tissues, organs and organ systems evolved.

Surface area, volume, supply and demand

Very small organisms obtain oxygen by simple diffusion through their surface. The demand for oxygen is satisfied by the rate at which it can be supplied. However, in bigger organisms, simple diffusion cannot supply enough oxygen and so specialised organs have evolved.

Following on from Fick's law (Chapter 3), a key feature in determining the rate of diffusion of oxygen (the supply rate) is the surface area of the organism. The amount of oxygen needed (the demand) is influenced by a number of factors — for example, temperature, which affects the rate of metabolic reactions.

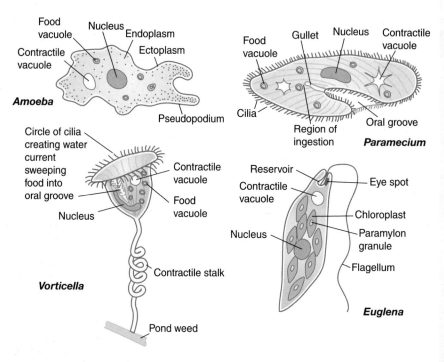

Amoeba

Food vacuole, Nucleus, Endoplasm, Ectoplasm, Contractile vacuole, Pseudopodium

Paramecium

Food vacuole, Gullet, Nucleus, Contractile vacuole, Cilia, Region of ingestion, Oral groove

Vorticella

Circle of cilia creating water current sweeping food into oral groove, Contractile vacuole, Food vacuole, Nucleus, Contractile stalk, Pond weed

Euglena

Reservoir, Contractile vacuole, Nucleus, Eye spot, Chloroplast, Paramylon granule, Flagellum

Figure 5.1 These small, single-celled organisms obtain oxygen through their plasma membranes by simple diffusion

However, at any given temperature, a large organism needs more oxygen than a small organism of the same type. The demand for oxygen is largely determined by the volume of the organism. As long as supply can keep pace with demand, diffusion through the body surface as a method of obtaining oxygen remains effective.

A measure of the efficiency of this process is the **surface area-to-volume ratio** of an organism. A large ratio indicates that the process is likely to be efficient; a small ratio, that it is not so efficient. We can show mathematically what happens to this ratio as organisms get bigger. For simplicity, imagine that the organism is a cube, and the length of each edge is 1 arbitrary unit (au):

- the area of each face is $1 \times 1 = 1$ au^2
- there are six faces to a cube, so the total surface area is 6 au^2
- the volume is $1 \times 1 \times 1 = 1$ au^3
- the ratio of surface area to volume $= 6/1 = 6$

Consider a cubic cell in which the length of each edge is 2 au. The total surface area is $6 \times 2 \times 2 = 24$ au^2 and the volume is $2 \times 2 \times 2 = 8$ au^3. The surface area-to-volume ratio is $24/8 = 3$ — lower than that of the smaller cube.

If you calculate the values for cubes of edge 4 au and 8 au, you will find that the surface area-to-volume ratios are 1.5 and 0.75 respectively.

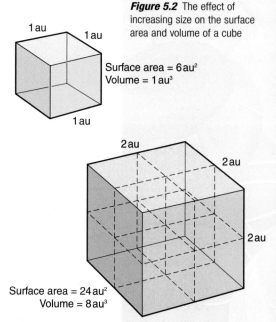

Figure 5.2 The effect of increasing size on the surface area and volume of a cube

1 au 1 au 1 au

Surface area = 6 au^2
Volume = 1 au^3

2 au 2 au 2 au

Surface area = 24 au^2
Volume = 8 au^3

Of course, living organisms are not cubic. However, the principle that as organisms become larger, the ratio of surface area to volume becomes smaller holds true.

As organisms increase in size, and their volumes increase to a greater extent than their surface areas, the demand for oxygen outstrips the ability to supply it through the body surface. At some point, uptake of oxygen through the body surface becomes too inefficient and more efficient organs for gaseous exchange are required. An important feature of all these specialised organs is that they have a large surface area. They restore the high surface area-to-volume ratio needed for the supply of oxygen to meet the demand. Examples of specialised gaseous exchange organs include:

- lungs — millions of alveoli provide the large surface area
- gills — the many gill lamellae provide the large surface area
- leaves — spongy mesophyll provides the large surface area

(a) Whales have lungs to obtain oxygen
(b) Fish have gills to obtain oxygen
(c) Trees need oxygen for respiration

> *e* You should be able to distinguish between a *gas-exchange organ* and a *gas-exchange surface*. Lungs are organs specialised for gas exchange, but the gas-exchange surface is provided by the alveoli. Similarly, gills are gas-exchange organs, but the gas-exchange surface is provided by the gill lamellae.

As well as specialised gas-exchange organs, organs specialised for feeding and digestion have evolved, together with organs for reproduction, excretion and movement. Once parts of the body become specialised for different functions, a transport system is necessary. Coordinating systems have also evolved to control body functions.

Cells and tissues

What allowed specialised organs to evolve was the development of **specialised cells** — for example, cells that could contract to produce a pulling force became muscle cells and cells that could transmit an impulse became nerve cells. In multicellular organisms, these specialised cells are found grouped together in **tissues**.

> A tissue is a group of similar cells that all perform the same function.

There are far too many different types of tissue to describe all of them in this book. However, some examples that you are likely to meet again in the course are described below.

Epithelia

An **epithelium** is a layer of cells that covers a body part of an animal. Usually it consists of a single layer of cells sitting on a thin, glycoprotein 'basement membrane'. However, some epithelia are several cells thick; these are called **stratified epithelia**. If the epithelium lines an organ, it may be referred to as an **endothelium**. Unlike many other types of cell, most epithelial cells retain the ability to divide. This is important because cells that line or cover structures are continuously worn away and have to be replaced.

◀ A layer of cells covering a plant organ is called an epidermis.

Cells of **squamous epithelium** are extremely thin. In the lungs, they form the walls of the alveoli and aid gas exchange by contributing to the short diffusion pathway. In the arteries, they provide a smooth inner lining to the wall of the artery, reducing resistance to the flow of blood. The **columnar epithelium** cells lining the small intestine have **microvilli** to increase the surface area for uptake of nutrients.

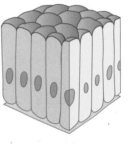

(a) **(b)**

Figure 5.5
(a) Squamous epithelium cells
(b) Columnar epithelium cells

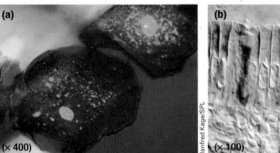

(a) (× 400) **(b)** (× 100)

(a) Squamous epithelial cells from the mouth
(b) Columnar epithelial cells in the small intestine

Connective tissue

Connective tissue consists of relatively few specialised cells in a non-cellular matrix that contains protein fibres. Bone and cartilage are typical examples of connective tissue. The non-cellular matrix of bone contains calcium salts that confer hardness. Different types of cartilage contain different proportions of protein fibres. This results in varying degrees of elasticity or rigidity.

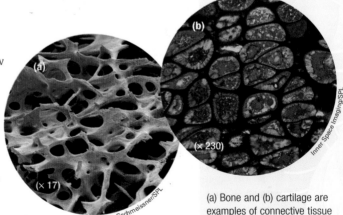

(a) (× 17) **(b)** (× 230)

(a) Bone and (b) cartilage are examples of connective tissue

Blood

Blood does not conform to the definition that a tissue is 'a group of similar cells all performing the same function'. Blood consists of several types of cell transported by a liquid — the plasma. Blood can be thought of as a kind of connective tissue in which the plasma is the non-cellular matrix and the blood cells are the specialised cells. Blood has more than one function, so there is more than one type of cell.

Red blood cells

Red blood cells are the most numerous cells in the blood — about 5 million mm^{-3}. That adds up to a lot of red blood cells in the 5 dm^3 of blood in an average adult! The structure of red blood cells is related to their function of transporting oxygen because:

- their biconcave disc shape gives a large surface area and short diffusion pathway for the exchange of oxygen and allows more haemoglobin to be packed in than a flat disc would
- they contain haemoglobin for the efficient transport of oxygen
- having no nucleus allows more haemoglobin to be packed into the cell

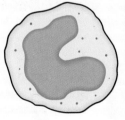

Red blood cells

White blood cells

There are many different types of white blood cell. Three important types are lymphocytes, monocytes and granulocytes.

Lymphocytes

There are two main types of **lymphocyte**:

- B-lymphocytes produce antibodies against specific antigens.
- T-lymphocytes kill foreign cells directly.

Lymphocytes are a little larger than red blood cells and have a large, round nucleus.

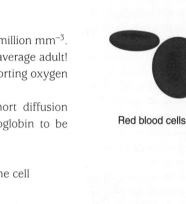

(× 6000)

Eye of Science/SPL

Lymphocytes are just a little larger than red blood cells

Lymphocyte

Monocytes

Monocytes have a diameter about twice that of red blood cells and have a C-shaped (horseshoe-shaped) nucleus.

Monocytes can squeeze out of capillaries to engulf pathogens by **phagocytosis** (a kind of endocytosis).

Monocyte

Granulocytes

Granulocytes are large white blood cells with a multi-lobed nucleus and granular cytoplasm.

Granulocytes are also involved in phagocytosis.

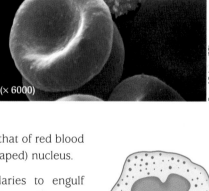

Granulocyte

Identifying white blood cells

The key below will help you to identify the types of white blood cell.

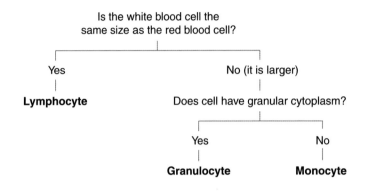

e The term phagocyte describes *any* cell that can carry out phagocytosis. It is *not* a type of white blood cell — several types of white blood cell can carry out phagocytosis. It may not even be a blood cell — for example, *Amoeba* is a phagocyte.

Tissues and organs

Organs are structures within an organism that are made of several types of tissue. Each tissue performs its own function and is essential to the overall functioning of the organ.

The heart is the organ that pumps blood around the body. To do this, it contains:

* **cardiac muscle** — to provide the force to pump the blood as the muscle contracts
* blood in blood vessels in the wall of the heart — to carry oxygen to the cardiac muscle cells so that aerobic respiration can take place to release the energy needed for their contraction
* specialised conducting tissue (**Purkyne tissue**) to carry impulses to the cardiac muscle and cause contraction

A muscle is an organ. It contains muscle tissue, together with arteries and veins (each made from epithelial, smooth muscle and connective tissue), blood and nervous tissue. A nerve contains mainly nervous tissue, but also contains blood vessels, blood and connective tissue.

In other words, the cardiac muscle contracts, the blood transporting oxygen and glucose allows the release of energy for the contractions and the Purkyne tissue 'tells' it when to contract.

Arteries and veins are also organs because they contain several types of tissue. However, capillaries contain only endothelial tissue and so cannot be classified as organs (see p. 94).

A leaf is an organ in photosynthetic plants. It contains several tissues:

* upper and lower **epidermis**, to protect the leaf from damage, infection and dehydration; the lower epidermis also allows gas exchange

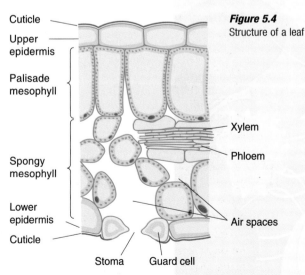

Figure 5.4
Structure of a leaf

Cuticle

Upper epidermis

Palisade mesophyll

Xylem

Phloem

Spongy mesophyll

Lower epidermis

Cuticle

Air spaces

Stoma   Guard cell

- **palisade mesophyll** — the main photosynthetic layer, with columnar cells (allowing tight packing), each containing many chloroplasts to ensure maximum light absorption
- **spongy mesophyll**, to allow diffusion of gases in both directions between the atmosphere (via the stomata) and the palisade layer
- veins containing:
  - **xylem** to transport water to the leaf
  - **phloem** to transport organic substances to and from the leaf

Organ systems

Major body processes are not usually performed by single organs but by groups of organs working together. If we consider the circulation of blood, the heart provides the force to move blood through a system of blood vessels, which carry the blood to all parts of the body. Together, the heart, arteries, veins and capillaries form the circulatory system. The breathing system comprises the lungs, trachea, larynx and nasal cavity, as well as the diaphragm and intercostal muscles that make breathing movements possible. Other organ systems include:

◀ See if you can work out which organs make up each system.

- the digestive system
- the nervous system
- the musculoskeletal system
- the reproductive system
- the excretory system

Although each organ system is responsible for a major body process, systems do not work in isolation. The circulatory system transports substances between the other systems; the nervous system controls the functioning of the other systems.

Summary

- Small organisms exchange materials with the environment across their body surfaces; the demand for these materials is influenced by the organism's volume.
- The surface area-to-volume ratio is an indicator of the potential efficiency of exchanging materials across a surface.
- As organisms increase in size, volume increases to a greater extent than surface area, reducing both the surface area-to-volume ratio and the efficiency of exchanging materials across the body surface.
- A group of similar cells all performing the same function is a tissue.
- Epithelia are tissues that line or cover organs in animals; they usually consist of a single layer of cells.
- Blood is an unusual connective tissue in which several types of cell are suspended in a liquid (the plasma).
- An organ is a structure that consists of several different tissues, each performing different functions that contribute to the overall functioning of the organ.
- An organ system consists of a number of organs that, together, carry out a major bodily process (e.g. transport by the circulatory system).

Questions

Multiple-choice

1 As organisms increase in size, the surface area-to-volume ratio:

   A increases

   B remains the same

   C decreases

   D increases to a maximum, then remains steady

2 Squamous epithelial cells in the lungs increase the efficiency of exchange of gases by diffusion because:

   A they have microvilli to increase their surface area

   B they rest on a glycoprotein basement membrane

   C they are extremely thin

   D their shape helps to maintain a concentration gradient

3 A tissue is:

   A a group of similar cells carrying out the same function

   B a group of similar cells carrying out different functions

   C a group of different cells carrying out the same function

   D a group of different cells carrying out different functions

4 The aorta contains smooth muscle, elastic tissue and endothelium. It is, therefore:

   A a tissue

   B an organ

   C an organ system

   D some other structure

5 It is true of organ systems that:

   A they consist of several organs working together

   B each system carries out a major body process

   C the breathing system, the circulatory system and the nervous system are examples

   D all of the above

Examination-style

1 Blood is a complex tissue comprising the plasma and, suspended in the plasma, the blood cells.

   (a) Human red blood cells are specialised cells. They are highly adapted to their function of transporting oxygen around the body.

   (i) Explain, in terms of Fick's law, two ways in which the shape of red blood cells makes them efficient at exchanging oxygen with their surroundings. *(3 marks)*

   (ii) How is the absence of a nucleus in red blood cells an adaptation to their function? *(2 marks)*

(b) Some red blood cells and two different types of white blood cell are shown in the diagram below.

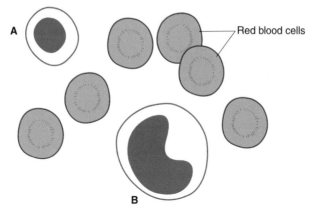

Identify, with reasons, the types of white blood cell labelled A and B.

(2 marks)

Total: 7 marks

2 The diagram below shows a cross-section through an artery, a vein and a capillary.

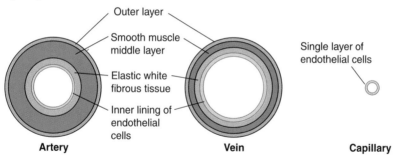

(a) Use information from the diagram to explain why arteries and veins are classified as organs, whereas a capillary is not. *(3 marks)*

(b) (i) What is an endothelium? *(2 marks)*

(ii) Explain the function of the endothelial lining of an artery and a vein. *(2 marks)*

Total: 7 marks

3 The biceps muscle is an organ. It contains several tissues, including muscle tissue, nervous tissue and blood (in blood vessels).

(a) What is a tissue? *(2 marks)*

(b) Suggest the function of each of the tissues named in the overall functioning of the biceps. *(3 marks)*

(c) Explain why the biceps muscle is classified as an organ but muscle is a tissue. *(2 marks)*

Total: 7 marks

Chapter 6

The circulatory system at rest and in exercise

This chapter covers:
- the nature of the mammalian circulatory system
- the structure of the heart and of the different types of blood vessel
- how the heart pumps blood through the circulatory system
- control of the heartbeat
- the formation of tissue fluid and the exchange of substances between capillaries and surrounding cells
- the effect of exercise on cardiac output and on the distribution of blood throughout the body

The circulatory system is one of the main organ systems found in a mammal. It links other organ systems by transporting substances between them. Contractions of the ventricles of the heart generate the force to pump blood through the blood vessels that comprise the circulatory system. In the capillaries, some of the substances in the plasma leave the blood as tissue fluid, which allows exchange of substances between the blood and the cells. Although the heartbeat is myogenic, it is influenced by both nerves and hormones.

> The heartbeat is said to be myogenic because it originates in the heart muscle itself. The prefix 'myo' always denotes muscle.

The structure of the mammalian circulatory system

Mammals have a **double circulation**. During a complete circulation of the body, the blood passes through the heart twice. It is pumped to the lungs to be oxygenated (the **pulmonary circulation**) and then returns to the heart to be pumped to other parts of the body that use the oxygen (the **systemic circulation**).

Two major advantages of a double circulatory system over a single circulatory system are that:
- blood passing to the tissues is always oxygenated (saturated with oxygen) because the pulmonary and systemic circulations are separate

- blood is delivered to the tissues at high pressure (producing a more efficient circulation) because it is pumped twice by the heart

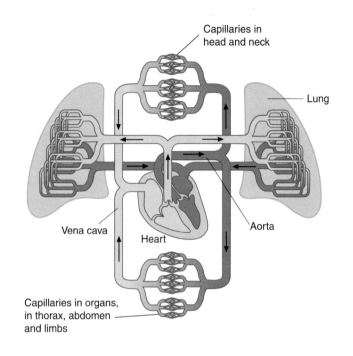

Capillaries in head and neck

Lung

Vena cava

Heart

Aorta

Capillaries in organs, in thorax, abdomen and limbs

Figure 6.1 The double circulatory system of a mammal

Patrick Fox

Patrick Fox

The circulatory system needs to respond to a change in activity level

The billions of cells that make up the human body all need a supply of oxygen and nutrients, and their metabolic waste products have to be removed. Arteries carry blood to all regions of the body and veins bring blood back. The main components of the circulatory system are shown in Figure 6.2.

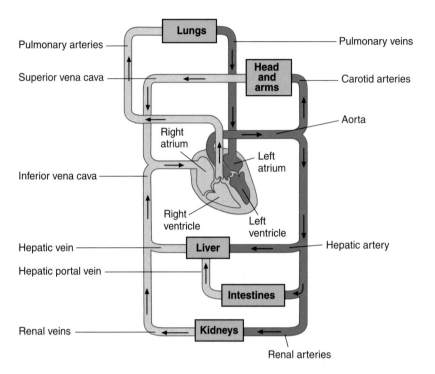

Figure 6.2 The main components of the circulatory system of a mammal

◀ Arteries *always* carry blood *away* from the heart; veins *always* carry blood towards the heart.

Within an organ, the blood is distributed by **arterioles** (small arteries). These branch into smaller and smaller arterioles that eventually carry blood to the **capillaries**. These microscopic blood vessels carry blood to individual cells. From here it passes into **venules** (small veins) and then into the vein that carries the blood from the organ.

The heart

At the centre of the circulatory system is a muscular pump — the heart. This organ supplies the force to pump blood to all parts of the body. It is made largely from cardiac muscle but also contains Purkyne tissue, blood vessels, blood and connective tissue.

Box 6.2 The heart's own blood supply

The cardiac muscle in the heart wall respires continuously to release the energy needed for contraction. To supply the oxygen and glucose needed, the cardiac muscle has its own blood supply — the coronary circulation. Two coronary arteries branch off the aorta just as it leaves the left ventricle. These carry blood into arterioles and the millions of capillaries that supply the cardiac muscle cells. The coronary arteries are narrower than many other arteries and can become blocked more easily. A build-up of atheroma (a mixture of fatty substances including cholesterol) in the coronary arteries narrows them still further. A dislodged blood clot can quite easily block a narrowed coronary artery, causing a coronary thrombosis.

Coronary arteries

Blockage in artery

The heart is divided into four chambers:

- right and left **atria**, to receive blood returning from the systemic and pulmonary circulations respectively
- right and left **ventricles** to force blood through the pulmonary and systemic circulations respectively

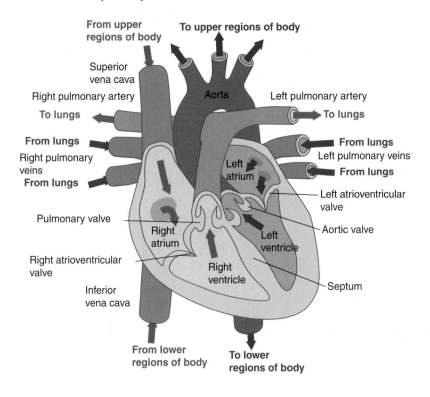

Figure 6.3 Structure of the mammalian heart

◀ The left atrioventricular valve is sometimes called the mitral valve, or the bicuspid valve. The right atrioventricular valve is sometimes called the tricuspid valve.

Box 6.3 Valves in the circulatory system

Four valves control the flow of blood in the mammalian heart; one between each atrium and ventricle and one at the base of each artery leading from the ventricles (Figure 6.3). There are also valves in veins. All the valves are one-way and work on essentially the same principle. Blood is a fluid; it flows from an area of high pressure to an area of low pressure. The valves in the circulatory system open when high pressure is forcing the blood in the 'correct' direction. If high pressure tries to force blood in the 'wrong' direction, the valves are forced shut.

Blood vessels

There are three basic types of blood vessels:

- **Arteries** carry blood under high pressure away from the heart to the organs.
- **Veins** carry blood under low pressure away from the organs towards the heart.
- **Capillaries** carry blood close to every cell within an organ.

The structure of each type of blood vessel is adapted to its function.

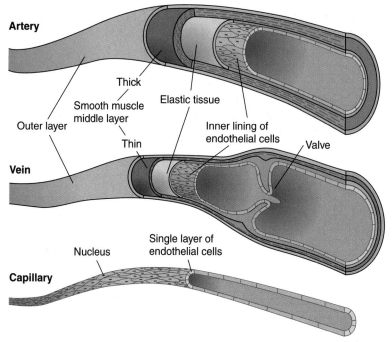

Figure 6.4 Structures of an
artery, a vein and a capillary

Arteries

As the ventricles contract, they put the blood under great pressure. As they relax, the pressure drops considerably. As a result, there is a continuous *flow* of blood through the arteries, but the *pressure* fluctuates greatly. We say that the pressure is **pulsatile**. The walls of arteries must not only be able to withstand the high pressures but must be able to compensate for the low pressures. They have a number of tissues in their walls that allow them to do this:

- The outer layer of connective tissue is protective and holds the artery 'open' when the pressure falls.
- The middle layer contains smooth muscle and elastic tissue. This is the thickest layer in the wall of an artery. It allows arterial walls to be stretched when the ventricles contract and cause an increase in blood pressure. It also allows arteries to return to their original diameter when the pressure falls (as the ventricles relax again) — this is called **elastic recoil**. Elastic recoil of the walls of major arteries acts as a secondary pump; as the artery constricts, the force exerted by the wall prevents the pressure of blood from falling too far. The smooth muscle in this layer is innervated. This allows the nervous system to control the diameter of arteries through contraction or relaxation of the smooth muscle in their walls.
- The inner **endothelial layer** creates a smooth surface offering minimal resistance to blood flow.

A risk factor in coronary heart disease is the build-up of atheroma in the inner linings of arteries. This makes the linings less smooth, which promotes the formation of blood clots.

Veins

The veins carry blood that has lost most of the pressure created by the ventricles. This is a result of the formation of **tissue fluid** in the capillaries. The walls of capillaries are 'leaky' and as fluid is forced out, the pressure of the remaining fluid drops.

- The wall of a vein contains the same tissues that are present in the wall of an artery, but there are less of them. This is because veins do not have to cope with surges of high pressure or to create elastic recoil.
- The lumen of a vein is larger than that of a similar-sized artery. This allows low-pressure blood to move through the vein with less resistance than there would be if the lumen were narrow.
- Most veins have one-way valves at intervals along their length, to prevent backflow of blood.

(× 35)

CNRI/SPL

Capillaries

Capillaries are microscopic blood vessels. Their walls consist of a single layer of squamous epithelium cells only.

The structure and function of arteries, arterioles, capillaries and veins are compared in Table 6.1.

Light micrograph of a section through an artery (left) and a vein (right)

Table 6.1

Feature	Artery	Arteriole	Capillary	Vein
Cross-section of vessel	Thick wall and narrow lumen	Thinner wall than artery, but relatively more muscle	Microscopic vessels; wall one cell thick	Valves, thin wall, little muscle, large lumen
Blood flow	To an organ, away from the heart	Within an organ, to capillaries in different parts of the organ	Around cells of the organ	Away from an organ, towards the heart
Type of blood	Oxygenated*	Oxygenated*	Blood becomes deoxygenated*	Deoxygenated*
Blood pressure	High and in pulses (pulsatile)	Not quite as high and less pulsatile	Pressure drops throughout capillary network	Low and non-pulsatile
Main functions of vessels	Transport of blood to an organ	Transport in an organ; redistribution of blood	Formation of tissue fluid to allow exchange between blood and cells of an organ	Transport of blood back to the heart
Adaptations to the main function	Large amount of elastic tissue in wall allows stretching due to pulses (surges in blood pressure) and recoil after pulses; endothelium forms a smooth layer to give least resistance	Large amount of smooth muscle under nervous control to allow redistribution of blood; constriction limits blood flow to an area; dilation increases blood flow; constriction of *all* arterioles increases resistance and blood pressure	Small size allows an extensive network close to all cells of an organ; thin, permeable ('leaky') wall allows formation of tissue fluid for exchange with surrounding cells	Large lumen and thin wall offer least resistance to flow as blood is under low pressure; valves prevent backflow of blood

* Except the pulmonary and umbilical blood vessels

How the circulatory system of a mammal functions

The cardiac cycle

The main events of the cardiac cycle

The four chambers of the heart are continually contracting and relaxing in a definite, repeating sequence called the cardiac cycle. When a chamber is contracting, we say it is in systole; when it is relaxing, we say it is in diastole. So, ventricular systole refers to contraction of the ventricles, whereas atrial diastole refers to relaxation of the atria. The two sides of the heart work together. As the left atrium contracts, so does the right atrium. As the right ventricle relaxes, so does the left ventricle.

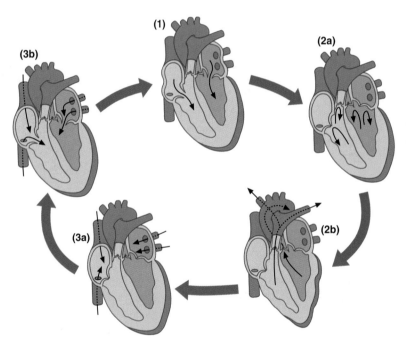

Figure 6.5 The cardiac cycle

Referring to Figure 6.5:
- **Stage 1: Atrial systole/ventricular diastole** The walls of the atria contract. This raises the pressure of the blood in the atria above that in the ventricles and forces open the atrioventricular valves. Blood passes through these valves into the ventricles.
- **Stage 2a: Ventricular systole/atrial diastole** The ventricles contract. This quickly raises the pressure of the blood in the ventricles above that in the atria, and so closes the atrioventricular valves. However, the pressure is still below that in the main arteries, which means that the aortic and pulmonary valves remain closed.
- **Stage 2b: Ventricular systole/atrial diastole** The ventricles continue to contract. When the pressure of the blood exceeds that in the main arteries, the

pulmonary and aortic valves are forced open. Blood is ejected into the pulmonary artery (carrying blood to the lungs) and aorta (carrying blood into arteries that serve all other parts of the body, including the heart itself).

- **Stage 3a : Ventricular diastole/atrial diastole** The ventricles begin to relax and the pressure of the blood quickly falls below that in the main arteries. The higher pressure in these arteries closes the aortic and pulmonary valves.
- **Stage 3b: Ventricular diastole/atrial diastole** As the ventricles continue to relax, the pressure in the ventricles falls below that in the atria. The higher pressure in the atria forces the atrioventricular valves open. Even though the atria are not contracting, blood flows through the open valves by passive ventricular filling.

Pressure changes during the cardiac cycle

The events of the cardiac cycle create pressure changes that are responsible for moving blood through the heart and into the pulmonary and systemic circulations. Figure 6.6 shows the pressure changes in the left atrium, left ventricle and aorta during one cardiac cycle.

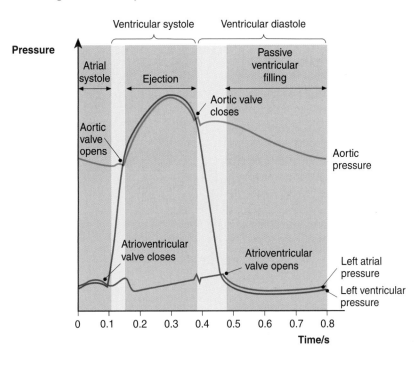

Figure 6.6 The pressure changes during the cardiac cycle

Notice that a valve opens and closes at times in the cycle when the balance of pressures on opposite sides of the valve changes. For example, at 0.1s, the pressure in the ventricle becomes greater than that in the atrium and so the atrioventricular valve is forced shut. At 0.15, the pressure in the ventricle exceeds that in the aorta and so the aortic valve is forced open.

A graph for the changes in the right atrium, right ventricle and pulmonary artery shows all the same features, but the pressures in the right ventricle and pulmonary artery are lower.

℮ You may be asked to explain the changes that occur at various points in the cardiac cycle from a graph such as that shown in Figure 6.6. Remember that:
- atrioventricular valves open as soon as the pressure in the atria becomes greater than that in the ventricles; they close as soon as the pressure in the ventricles becomes greater than that in the atria
- the aortic and pulmonary valves open as soon as the pressure in the ventricles becomes greater than that in the two arteries; they close as soon as the pressure in the two arteries becomes greater than that in the ventricles.
- blood flows from a high-pressure region to a low-pressure region.

Controlling the cardiac cycle

The events of the cardiac cycle must take place in the correct sequence, with the correct timing. A group of cells in the right atrium form the **sinoatrial node** (SA node), which acts as a natural **pacemaker**. The SA node initiates electrical impulses that spread through the heart, causing the cardiac muscle to contract. The impulses are carried not by nervous tissue but by specialised, conducting, cardiac muscle fibres called **Purkyne tissue**. This tissue conducts the impulse throughout the atria, stimulating contraction, to the **atrioventricular node** (AV node). This is the only location where the impulse can pass from atrium to ventricle; all other tissue dividing the two is non-conducting. The impulse is conducted slowly through the AV node. This allows time for the atria to complete their contractions. The impulse then passes along two bundles of Purkyne tissues in the ventricles (the bundles of His) and the cardiac muscle in the ventricles is stimulated to contract. These events are summarised in Table 6.2.

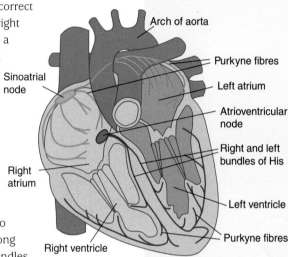

Figure 6.7 The electrical conducting system of the heart

Arch of aorta
Purkyne fibres
Left atrium
Atrioventricular node
Right and left bundles of His
Left ventricle
Purkyne fibres
Right ventricle
Right atrium
Sinoatrial node

Table 6.2

Event in electrical conducting system	Event in cardiac cycle	Stage of cardiac cycle
The SA node generates an impulse; the impulse spreads along Purkyne fibres to all parts of the atria	Cardiac muscle in atria contracts, cardiac muscle in ventricles is relaxed — blood is forced through AV valves from atria to ventricles	Atrial systole/ ventricular diastole
The impulse is held up at the AV node	Cardiac muscle in atria contracts, cardiac muscle in ventricles is relaxed — blood continues to be forced through AV valves	Atrial systole/ ventricular diastole
The impulse is conducted along the bundles of His through the ventricle walls	Cardiac muscle in atria is relaxed, cardiac muscle in ventricles contracts; AV valves closed; then aortic/pulmonary valves opened — blood ejected into main arteries	Atrial diastole/ ventricular systole
No impulse	Cardiac muscle in atria and ventricles is relaxed — passive ventricular filling	Atrial and ventricular diastole

Venous pumps

The cardiac cycle pumps blood through the heart and into the arteries. What force brings blood back to the heart in the veins? As blood flows through capillaries, the pressure falls dramatically because of:

- the formation of tissue fluid
- the increase in total cross-sectional area

Box 6.4 Capillaries and cross-sectional area

Each individual capillary has a minute cross-sectional area. However, in any one organ there are millions of capillaries. When all the organs are considered, the total cross-sectional area of the capillaries is thousands of times greater than that of the aorta. It is the equivalent of one huge blood vessel with a diameter about 70 times that of the aorta. The same force from the heart pumping blood into that area could only generate a fraction of the pressure that is found in the aorta.

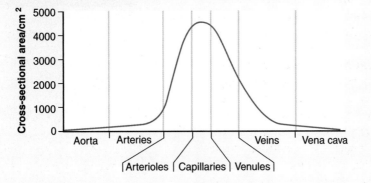

The relationship between the rate of flow of blood and blood pressure in the various types of blood vessel is shown in Figure 6.8.

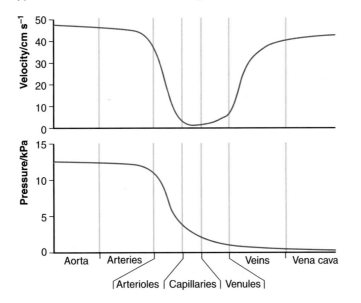

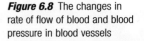
Figure 6.8 The changes in rate of flow of blood and blood pressure in blood vessels

The pressure falls in the capillaries and, therefore, so does the rate of flow of the blood. The slower flow rate allows more time for exchange of materials with the surrounding cells. When the blood flows back into the veins, the rate of flow recovers but the pressure remains low. So, how *does* blood return from the big toe to the heart?

There are several forces acting on blood in veins:
- **Following blood** — as more blood enters veins from the capillaries, it pushes blood already in the veins further along.
- The **respiratory pump** — on inhaling and exhaling, the pressure in the thorax changes (Chapter 7). Inhaling reduces the pressure in the thorax, which means that there is less pressure acting on the veins in that region. This allows the veins to dilate and draw blood into the area. Exhalation increases the pressure and therefore increases the pressure on the veins. The one-way semilunar valves in veins prevent the blood from flowing backwards. It is 'squeezed' into the right atrium.

A giraffe's heart generates enough force to pump blood up to its brain; the venous pumps return blood from its feet to its heart

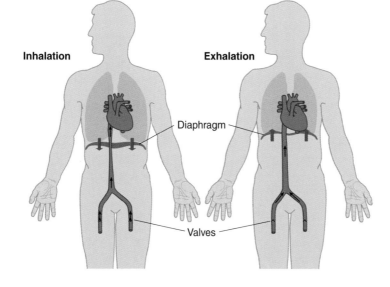

Figure 6.9
The respiratory pump

- The action of **skeletal muscles** — many veins are embedded in skeletal muscles or lie between muscle blocks. In order to maintain body posture, skeletal muscles are continually contracting slightly and then relaxing. This repeatedly puts pressure on veins and then removes that pressure. As the muscles contract, the pressure on the veins forces blood towards the heart. The one-way semilunar valves ensure that there is no backflow of blood.

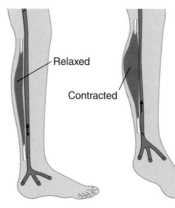

Figure 6.10 Contraction and relaxation of the skeletal muscles helps return venous blood to the heart

Cardiac output

Cardiac output is a measure of how hard the heart is working. It is the output from *each* ventricle per minute.

Each time the ventricles contract, they eject blood into the main arteries. The amount of blood ejected from the ventricle is called the **stroke volume** and, at any one time, it is the same for both ventricles. However, this is only one aspect of what determines cardiac output. The other is the **heart rate** — the number of beats per minute. Cardiac output (volume pumped per minute) is the product of the stroke volume (volume per beat) and the heart rate (number of beats per minute).

cardiac output = stroke volume × heart rate

e You may be given data about the volume of blood flowing per minute to various organs and asked to calculate the cardiac output. If the data include the volume flowing to the lungs, you need do no more work. The volume flowing to the lungs per minute represents the cardiac output of the right ventricle, which is identical to that of the left ventricle.

An increase in stroke volume or heart rate (or both) increases cardiac output. During exercise, the cardiac output increases to deliver more blood, carrying oxygen and glucose, to the skeletal muscles. During sleep, cardiac output decreases from the normal resting level because the metabolic activity of the body is low and less oxygen is needed by almost all organs.

How tissue fluid is formed

Blood flows close to every cell of the body in the capillary networks in all organs. However, it is **tissue fluid**, not blood, which carries glucose and oxygen to the cells. Tissue fluid is formed from blood in every capillary network. It flows around the cells, bathing them in a fluid that provides a constant environment. The constant pH and temperature of the tissue fluid help to provide optimum conditions for enzyme activity.

Tissue fluid forms because the capillary walls are permeable to most molecules and the pressure of the blood entering the capillaries is high enough to force materials across the capillary walls. However, the **plasma protein** molecules are too large to escape and so are not found in tissue fluid. Otherwise, tissue fluid has essentially the same composition as blood plasma.

As the tissue fluid leaves the blood, it carries with it dissolved oxygen and nutrients. These enter the cells from the tissue fluid by either passive or facilitated diffusion. Most of the tissue fluid that bathes the cells is returned to the blood in the capillary networks, taking with it dissolved carbon dioxide and other metabolic waste products. The remainder drains into the **lymphatic system**. The lymphatic vessels carry lymph towards the heart. Lymph is returned to the blood where veins from the head and neck join with those from the arm.

◀ A cardiac output of 6.5 dm³ means that the right ventricle is pumping 6.5 dm³ into the pulmonary circulation per minute and the left ventricle is pumping 6.5 dm³ into the systemic circulation per minute.

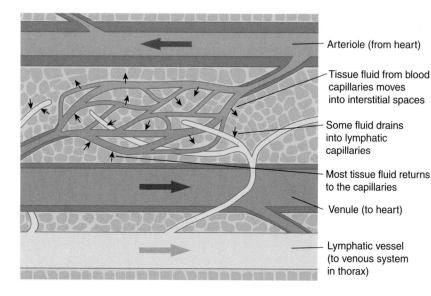

Figure 6.11 The circulation of tissue fluid and the formation of lymph

Arteriole (from heart)

Tissue fluid from blood capillaries moves into interstitial spaces

Some fluid drains into lymphatic capillaries

Most tissue fluid returns to the capillaries

Venule (to heart)

Lymphatic vessel (to venous system in thorax)

Fluids only flow because a force makes them do so. What are the forces that drive the formation and reabsorption of tissue fluid? The pressure of the blood resulting from the contraction of the ventricles is one factor — it creates a **hydrostatic pressure** in the blood. This acts in all directions, including outwards on the wall of any vessel carrying the blood. If the wall is permeable, liquid is forced out of the vessel.

The right ventricle produces the force for the formation of tissue fluid in the lungs; the left ventricle produces the force for the formation of tissue fluid in all other organs.

The other factor is the **water potential** of blood plasma. The plasma contains many dissolved substances. Therefore, it has quite a low water potential and this tends to draw water into the plasma by osmosis. The walls of the capillaries are permeable, so substances can leave and enter. At the arterial end of a capillary network, the hydrostatic effect outweighs the effect of the water potential and tissue fluid is forced out of the capillaries. The loss of fluid reduces the hydrostatic pressure of the blood, while the water potential remains more or less unchanged. At the venous end of the capillary network, the effect of the water potential outweighs that of the hydrostatic pressure and water is drawn back into the capillaries by osmosis. Other substances (such as carbon dioxide) diffuse into the blood down concentration gradients.

Figure 6.12 The forces involved in the formation and reabsorption of tissue fluid

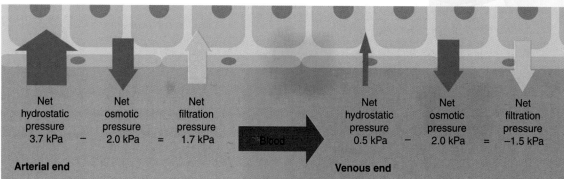

| Net hydrostatic pressure 3.7 kPa | − | Net osmotic pressure 2.0 kPa | = | Net filtration pressure 1.7 kPa | Blood → | Net hydrostatic pressure 0.5 kPa | − | Net osmotic pressure 2.0 kPa | = | Net filtration pressure −1.5 kPa |

Arterial end   **Venous end**

Worked example

You could be asked to calculate filtration pressures. Suppose the pressures at the arterial end of a capillary network are:

hydrostatic pressure = 4.3 kPa

water potential = –3.3 kPa (remember water potential is always a negative value)

Answer

To calculate the net filtration pressure, add the two pressures:

4.3 + (–3.3) = 1.0 kPa

This is a positive value, so the net filtration pressure is an *outward* force. At the venous end of the capillary network, the pressures might be:

hydrostatic pressure = 1.6 kPa

water potential = –3.3 kPa

Adding the two figures gives a value of –1.7 kPa. This is a negative value and so represents an *inward* force.

The effect of exercise on the functioning of the circulatory system

Skeletal muscles are more active during exercise. They respire faster to produce more ATP to release the extra energy needed for the increased activity. The increased rate of aerobic respiration demands increased supply of oxygen and glucose, both of which are transported to the muscles by the blood. Increased **pulmonary ventilation** (Chapter 7, pp. 121–122) brings air into the lungs more rapidly; increased hydrolysis of glycogen in the liver and in the muscles themselves makes more glucose available. It follows, therefore, that there must be an increase in cardiac output to transport the extra oxygen and glucose to the muscles.

Increasing cardiac output

Although the heartbeat is myogenic, the *rate* at which the SA node originates impulses is influenced by nerves and by hormones.

Nervous control

There is a region in the medulla oblongata of the brain (the region at the base of the brain where it joins with the spinal cord) called the **cardiovascular centre**. This is the area of the brain that regulates cardiac output. The neurones (nerve cells) involved in controlling cardiac output are part of the **autonomic nervous system**. Two nerves connect the cardiovascular centre to the SA node:

- the **cardiac nerve** — part of the sympathetic division of the autonomic nervous system
- the **vagus nerve** — part of the parasympathetic division of the autonomic nervous system

Box 6.5 Autonomic means 'independent'

The autonomic nervous system regulates many internal processes. It has two divisions that act antagonistically:
- increased activity of the sympathetic division produces responses that allow the body to be *more* active
- increased activity of the parasympathetic division produces responses that allow the body to be *less* active

The autonomic nervous system functions largely independently of the somatic nervous system, which integrates information from the senses to produce responses in skeletal muscle.

During exercise, the concentration of carbon dioxide in the plasma rises because of the increased respiration rate. This decreases the pH of the plasma. The change in pH is detected by **chemoreceptors** in the aortic arch, carotid artery and the medulla oblongata and impulses are sent to the cardiovascular centre. In response, the cardiovascular centre sends more impulses per second along neurones in the cardiac nerve (sympathetic). At their junction with the SA node, these neurones release **noradrenaline**, which increases the rate of discharge of the SA node, raising the heart rate. The stroke volume also increases, because the contractions are more forceful. At the end of a period of exercise, the carbon dioxide concentration falls and more impulses per second are sent along neurones in the vagus nerve (parasympathetic). At their junction with the SA node, **acetylcholine** is released, which reduces the rate of discharge of the SA node, lowering the heart rate.

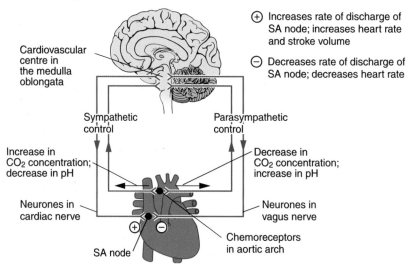

Figure 6.13 Nervous regulation of cardiac output

$\oplus$ Increases rate of discharge of SA node; increases heart rate and stroke volume

$\ominus$ Decreases rate of discharge of SA node; decreases heart rate

Cardiovascular centre in the medulla oblongata

Sympathetic control

Parasympathetic control

Increase in CO_2 concentration; decrease in pH

Decrease in CO_2 concentration; increase in pH

Neurones in cardiac nerve

Neurones in vagus nerve

Chemoreceptors in aortic arch

SA node

Hormonal control

Hormones also influence cardiac output. When we begin to exercise, the adrenal gland increases the secretion of adrenaline and noradrenaline. These two hormones travel in the bloodstream to the heart where they bind with:

- receptors in the SA node, increasing its rate of discharge
- receptors in the walls of the ventricles, increasing the force of the contractions

Redistribution of the flow of blood

At rest, 15–20% of the cardiac output passes to the skeletal muscles. During exercise, this can increase to 80–85%. As the cardiac output itself may have increased four- or five-fold, the muscles could be receiving about 20 times as much blood as at rest. This redistribution of blood is achieved by constriction of arterioles in some organs and dilation of arterioles in other organs. The arterioles leading to the skin, kidneys, brain, gut and liver all constrict; those leading to the skeletal and cardiac muscles dilate. This allows a larger proportion of an increased cardiac output to reach the cardiac and skeletal muscles.

During exercise, increased cardiac output, together with the redistribution of blood between the organs, allows a greatly increased volume of oxygenated blood to reach the skeletal muscles.

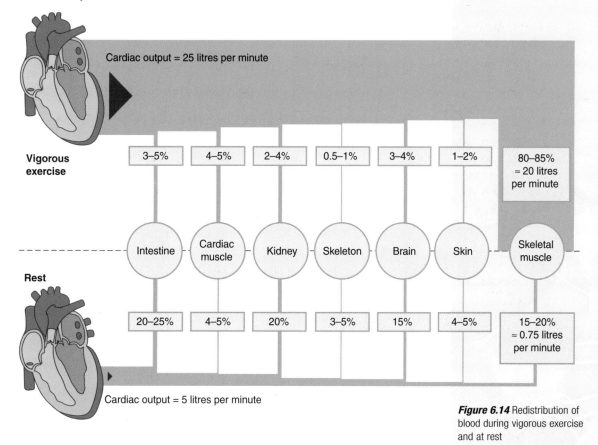

Figure 6.14 Redistribution of blood during vigorous exercise and at rest

The brain must receive the same *amount* of blood in order to continue to function normally. To receive the same amount, it needs a smaller *proportion* of the increased cardiac output. The same is true of the kidneys.

Blood flow can also be diverted away from capillary networks by the contraction of **precapillary sphincters** — small 'rings' of smooth muscle cells that surround the capillaries at the point where they branch off arterioles. When these contract, they constrict that region of the capillary and further reduce the blood flow into the capillary network.

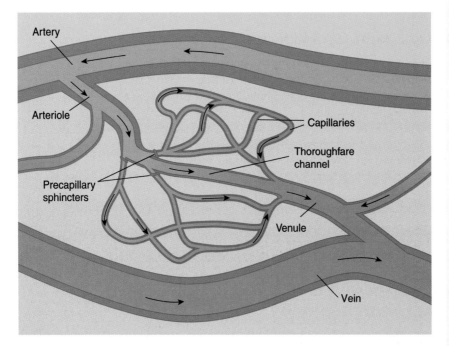

Figure 6.15 How precapillary sphincters can restrict the flow of blood through a capillary network

Summary

Structure of the mammalian circulatory system

- Mammals have a double circulatory system. The pulmonary circulation is through the lungs; the systemic circulation is through all other parts of the body.
- The heart is made from cardiac muscle and supplies the force to pump blood through the two circulations.
- The heart comprises four chambers:
  - left atrium, which receives oxygenated blood from the pulmonary circulation in the pulmonary veins
  - left ventricle, which pumps oxygenated blood into the systemic circulation via the aorta
  - right atrium, which receives deoxygenated blood from the systemic circulation in the vena cava
  - right ventricle, which pumps deoxygenated blood into the pulmonary circulation via the pulmonary arteries
- Arteries always carry blood away from the heart. An artery has a relatively small lumen and a thick wall that contains a lot of smooth muscle and elastic tissue. This allows the wall to be stretched under pressure and also allows elastic recoil.

- Veins carry blood towards the heart. A vein has a larger lumen than a similar-sized artery and a thinner wall. The larger lumen offers less resistance to the flow of blood under low pressure. Veins have valves to prevent the backflow of blood.
- Capillaries have walls consisting only of squamous epithelium, which allows exchange of materials between the blood and cells

How the circulatory system of a mammal functions

- In the cardiac cycle:
  - atrial systole forces blood through the atrioventricular valves into the ventricles
  - ventricular systole raises the pressure of blood in the ventricles, which first closes the atrioventricular valves and then opens the pulmonary and aortic valves as blood is ejected into the main arteries
  - atrial and ventricular diastole allow passive ventricular filling
- The heart is myogenic; the SA node generates impulses that are:
  - conducted rapidly along fibres of Purkyne tissue through the atria, stimulating their contraction
  - held up at the AV node, which conducts impulses only slowly
  - conducted rapidly through the ventricles along the bundles of His (also Purkyne tissue), stimulating their contraction
- The movement of blood back to the heart in veins is aided by:
  - following blood
  - pressure changes in the thorax caused by inhalation and exhalation
  - contraction and relaxation of skeletal muscle
- Cardiac output is the amount of blood pumped per ventricle per minute:
  cardiac output = stroke volume × heart rate
- Tissue fluid leaves blood at the arterial end of a capillary network because the effect of the hydrostatic pressure of the blood is greater than the effect of its water potential. Water returns to the blood at the venous end of a capillary network because the effect of the blood's water potential is greater than that of its hydrostatic pressure. Other substances diffuse back into the blood at the venous end.

The effect of exercise on the functioning of the circulatory system

- At rest and during exercise, the cardiovascular centre in the medulla oblongata regulates cardiac output; sympathetic neurones in the cardiac nerve and parasympathetic neurones in the vagus nerve link the cardiovascular centre to the SA node.
- Increasing the number of impulses per second along sympathetic neurones increases heart rate and stroke volume; increasing the number of impulses per second along parasympathetic neurones decreases heart rate.
- The hormones adrenaline and noradrenaline increase the heart rate and stroke volume.
- Arterioles leading to the gut and skin constrict, while those leading to skeletal muscles dilate. This allows a greater proportion of the cardiac output to reach skeletal muscles.

Questions

Multiple-choice

1 The double circulatory system of a mammal comprises:
   A arterial and venous circulations
   B pulmonary and systemic circulations
   C arterial and capillary circulations
   D venous and capillary circulations

2 When the left atrium contracts, it pumps blood:
   A through an atrioventricular valve into the aorta
   B through the aortic valve into the aorta
   C through the aortic valve into the left ventricle
   D through an atrioventricular valve into the left ventricle

3 The smooth muscle in the wall of a vein allows the wall to:
   A be stretched under high pressure
   B show elastic recoil
   C both of the above
   D neither of the above

4 If the pressure in the left ventricle is higher than that in the atrium, but lower than that in the aorta:
   A the atrioventricular valve is closed and the aortic valve is open
   B the atrioventricular valve is closed and the aortic valve is closed
   C the atrioventricular valve is open and the aortic valve is closed
   D the atrioventricular valve is open and the aortic valve is open

5 The ratio of the cardiac output of the left ventricle to that of the right ventricle is:
   A 2:1
   B 1:2
   C 1:1
   D none of the above

6 When the cardiovascular centre fires an increased number of impulses per minute along the vagus nerve:
   A the SA node increases its rate of discharge and the heart rate increases
   B the SA node decreases its rate of discharge and the heart rate decreases
   C the AV node decreases its rate of discharge and the heart rate decreases
   D the AV node increases its rate of discharge and the heart rate increases

7 Constriction of arterioles leading to organ A and dilation of those leading to organ B will:
   A increase the rate of blood flow to A and decrease the rate of flow to B
   B increase the rate of blood flow both organs
   C decrease the rate of blood flow to both organs
   D decrease the rate of blood flow to A and increase the rate of flow to B

8 At the arterial end of a capillary network, the hydrostatic pressure of the blood is 4.5 kPa and its water potential is −1.3 kPa. The net filtration pressure is:
   A 3.2 kPa
   B −3.2 kPa
   C 5.8 kPa
   D −5.8 kPa

9 Impulses from the SA node are held up at the AV node. This is important because:

  A it allows atrial systole to be completed before ventricular systole commences

  B it allows ventricular systole to be completed before atrial systole commences

  C both ventricles do not enter systole at the same time

  D both atria do not enter diastole at the same time

10 During exercise, the brain receives per minute:

  A the same proportion of the cardiac output but a smaller amount of blood

  B a smaller proportion of the cardiac output but a larger amount of blood

  C a larger proportion of the cardiac output but the same amount of blood

  D a smaller proportion of the cardiac output but the same amount of blood

Examination-style

1 The diagram shows how some substances are exchanged between a capillary and some surrounding cells.

  (a) Describe how tissue fluid is formed. *(3 marks)*

  (b) Explain one role of tissue fluid, other than the exchange of substances between blood and cells. *(2 marks)*

  (c) Explain why a capillary cannot be considered to be an organ, whereas an artery can. *(3 marks)*

  Total: 8 marks

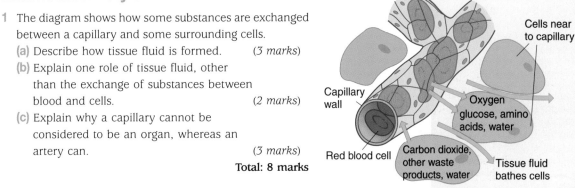

2 The graph shows the pressure changes in the left atrium, left ventricle and aorta during one cardiac cycle.

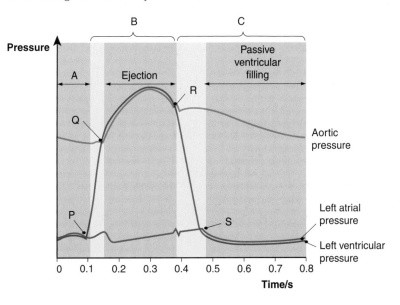

(a) Name the period of the cardiac cycle labelled B. Give reasons from the graph for your choice. *(2 marks)*

(b) What happens at the points in the cycle labelled:

   (i) P

   (ii) Q

   Explain your answers. *(4 marks)*

(c) Sketch a line on the graph that represents the changes in pressure in the *right* ventricle. *(1 mark)*

Total: 7 marks

3 The diagram shows a transverse section through an artery and a vein.

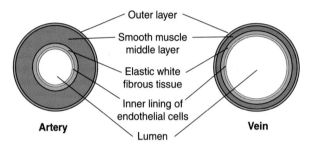

(a) Explain how each of the following features is an adaptation to the functioning of the vessel:

   (i) the amount of smooth muscle and elastic tissue in the wall of an artery *(2 marks)*

   (ii) the size of the lumen of a vein. *(2 marks)*

(b) Some aeroplane flights can last over 11 hours. During such flights, because of the long period of inactivity, passengers might experience 'pooling' of the blood in the veins of their legs.

   (i) Explain why the long period of inactivity may lead to pooling of the blood. *(3 marks)*

   (ii) Explain how normal breathing helps to return blood in veins to the heart. *(3 marks)*

Total: 10 marks

4 The graph shows the changes in volume of the left ventricle of a resting person over a period of time.

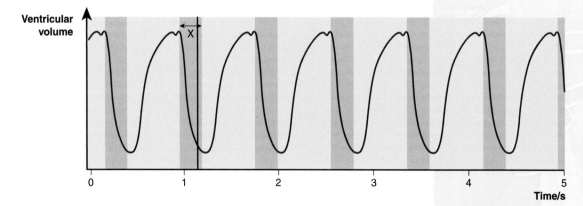

(a) (i) Describe and explain the main events of the cardiac cycle that occur during the period marked X. (3 marks)

(ii) Use the graph to calculate the heart rate of the person at rest. Show how you arrived at your answer. (2 marks)

(b) (i) Sketch a graph to show the changes in the volume of the left ventricle during a period of vigorous exercise. (2 marks)

(ii) Describe how the cardiovascular centre brings about an increase in cardiac output during exercise. (3 marks)

Total: 10 marks

5 Read the following passage.

One of the main challenges to maintaining the steady state of the body during vigorous exercise is the increased demand by the muscles for oxygen. This may be 15–20 times greater than at rest. In order to meet the increased oxygen demand, two major adjustments to blood flow must be made. There must be an increased cardiac output and a redistribution of the blood to the various organs. At the same time, the amount of blood flowing to important organs such as the kidneys and brain must be maintained.

The increased cardiac output is brought about by changes in the heart beat. The redistribution of blood to the various organs is possible because of the structure of the wall of the arterioles. At the same time, breathing becomes faster and deeper to supply the blood with the extra oxygen and remove the extra carbon dioxide that is being generated by the active muscles.

(a) Explain, as fully as you can, how the cardiac output can be increased. (4 marks)

(b) At rest, 15% of the cardiac output passes through the brain. What percentage would you expect to pass through the brain during exercise if the cardiac output increased by a factor of five? Explain your answer. (3 marks)

(c) Explain how the structure of the wall of arterioles allows the redistribution of blood to the various organs. (3 marks)

(d) The gas exchange system and the circulatory system are sometimes called a 'coupled unit'. Suggest what this means with reference to the response of both systems to increased oxygen demand of the muscles. (3 marks)

(e) Suggest why the amount of blood flowing to the kidney must remain constant. (2 marks)

Total: 15 marks

Chapter 7

The breathing system at rest and in exercise

This chapter covers:
- the structure of the breathing system
- the mechanisms of inhalation and exhalation
- gas exchange in the alveoli
  - the concept of partial pressure
  - the difference in composition of atmospheric and exhaled air
- the ways in which breathing is controlled
  - the distinction between breathing and respiration
  - the effect of exercise on breathing rate and depth of breathing

On inhalation, atmospheric air (a mixture of gases) flows into the alveoli in the lungs. Here, gas exchange takes place and a different mixture of gases is exhaled. The main differences in composition between inhaled and exhaled air are due to the exchange of oxygen and carbon dioxide in the alveoli. The oxygen absorbed into the red blood cells is transported to all living cells to allow energy release in aerobic respiration. The carbon dioxide produced by this process is carried in the blood plasma to the lungs. The rate of energy release by aerobic respiration is increased greatly during aerobic exercise. This necessitates an increase in the amount of oxygen transported to the cells; the rate and depth of breathing increase to achieve this.

The structure of the breathing system

All mammals breathe air and have specially adapted lungs to exchange gases with the atmosphere. Marine mammals, such as whales and dolphins, must return to the surface to breathe.

The structure of the human breathing system is shown in Figure 7.1.

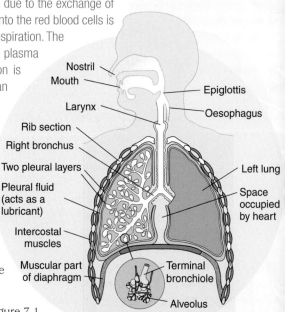

Figure 7.1 Structure of the human breathing system

Labels: Nostril, Mouth, Larynx, Rib section, Right bronchus, Two pleural layers, Pleural fluid (acts as a lubricant), Intercostal muscles, Muscular part of diaphragm, Epiglottis, Oesophagus, Left lung, Space occupied by heart, Terminal bronchiole, Alveolus

Box 7.1 'There she blows!'

When a whale returns to the surface after a dive, the first thing it does is to breathe out — with a lot of force — through a 'blowhole' in the top of its head.

In this violent exhalation, pressurised warm air from the whale's lungs together with oil droplets from the trachea and water from around the blowhole form a cloud of vapour called the 'blow'. In the nineteenth and twentieth centuries, 'there she blows!' was a cry from a whale-hunter to tell other members of the whaling ship crew that a whale had been sighted. Today, the same cry may come from enthusiastic whale watchers.

The first sign of a whale returning to the surface is a 'blow'

The breathing movements of a whale change according to its pattern of swimming. If the whale is swimming on the surface, then it can obtain all the oxygen it needs by breathing regularly. When it dives, however, it must take a supply of oxygen with it — but not in its lungs, as many people think. Before diving, the whale will have been breathing more rapidly to saturate its muscle store of myoglobin (similar to haemoglobin) with oxygen. Different whales have different patterns of diving and surfacing. However, they are all doing essentially the same thing — saturating myoglobin prior to the dive.

Some patterns of breathing in different whales are shown in the diagram.

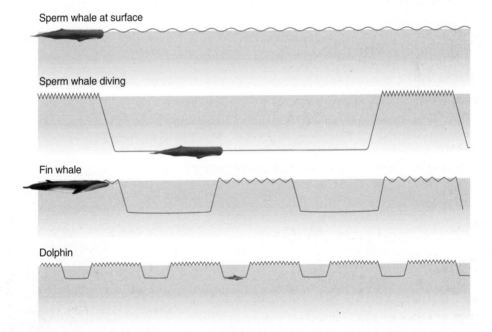

Sperm whale at surface

Sperm whale diving

Fin whale

Dolphin

Each peak represents a breathing movement by a whale at the surface. There is no scale on the vertical axis to show the depth to which the whale dives. Some dive to depths of over 3500 m (approximately 2 miles).

The mechanism of breathing

The breathing system moves air through the various passages into the alveoli, where gas exchange takes place. Air is a mixture of gases and, like any fluid (liquid or gas), it moves because of pressure differences. Fluids move from a region of high pressure to a region of low pressure.

To bring air into the lungs (**inhalation**), the pressure must be lower in the lungs than in the atmosphere. To move air out again (**exhalation**), the pressure must be higher in the lungs than in the atmosphere. Breathing movements create these pressure differences.

The lungs are located in the **thorax**. This region of the body is separated from the **abdomen** by the **diaphragm**. Viewed from above (or below), the diaphragm is seen to have two main regions:

- an external muscular region, the outer edge of which is attached to the body wall
- a central fibrous region, made from tough connective tissue, which cannot contract or relax, be stretched or be compressed

Contraction of the muscular region of the diaphragm pulls the fibrous region downwards from its normal dome-shaped position. This flattens the diaphragm and enlarges the thoracic cavity.

The lungs are protected by the ribcage. There are two sets of muscles between each pair of ribs — the **external intercostal muscles** and the **internal intercostal muscles**. These muscles are attached in different ways. Therefore, their contractions produce different effects. Contraction of the external intercostal muscles lifts the ribs upwards and outwards; contraction of the internal intercostals muscles pull the ribs downwards and inwards.

Inhalation

The mechanism of inhalation is shown in the flowchart below.

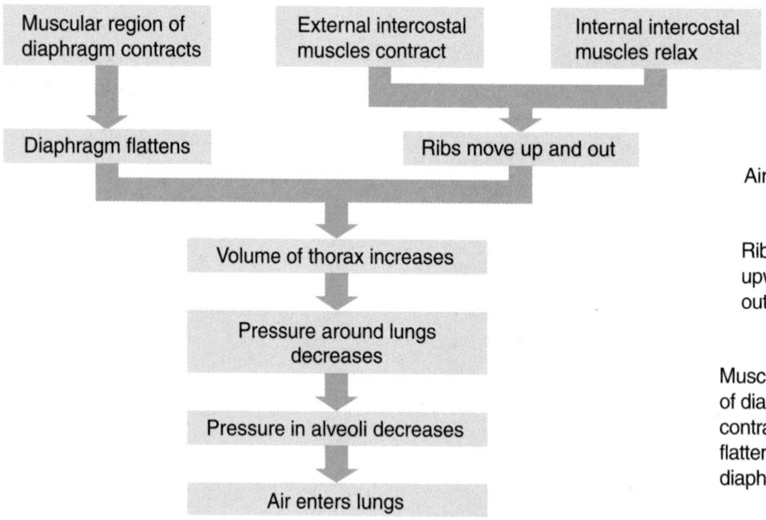

When you turn on a gas tap to light a Bunsen burner, gas flows from the region of high pressure in the gas pipe to the lower pressure area in the Bunsen tubing. ◀

Breathing movements alter the pressure between the ◀ pleural layers that surround the lungs and the lungs. When this pressure decreases, it allows the alveoli to inflate, decreasing the pressure in the alveoli.

In humans, the internal intercostal muscles play little part in breathing movements at rest. We stand upright on two legs, so once the external intercostal muscles stop contracting, ◀ the ribs fall back downwards and inwards under gravity. In four-legged mammals both sets of muscles are equally important because gravity neither assists nor hinders breathing movements.

Figure 7.2 Inhalation

Flowchart:

Muscular region of diaphragm contracts → Diaphragm flattens

External intercostal muscles contract / Internal intercostal muscles relax → Ribs move up and out

→ Volume of thorax increases → Pressure around lungs decreases → Pressure in alveoli decreases → Air enters lungs

Labels on figure: Air taken in; Ribcage moves upwards and outwards; Muscular part of diaphragm contracts and flattens the diaphragm; Lung

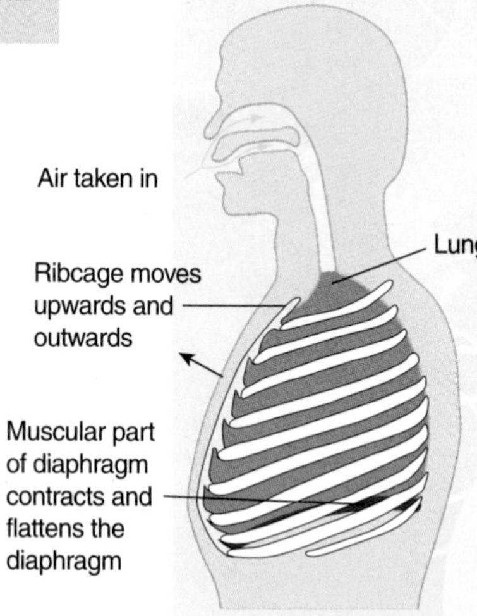

Exhalation

The mechanism of exhalation is shown in the flowchart below.

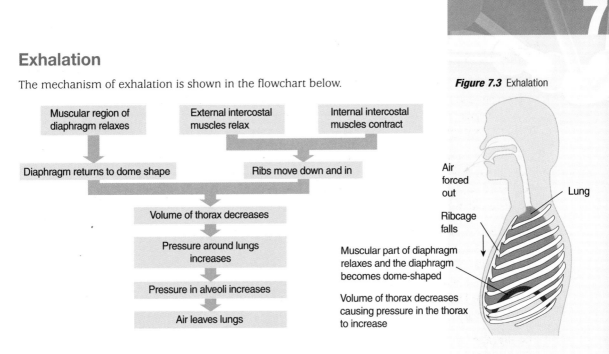

Figure 7.3 Exhalation

Gas exchange in the alveoli

Moving air into the alveoli

Breathing movements move air in and out of the lungs through the airways that eventually lead to the alveoli. Air is drawn into the nose and/or mouth, through the pharynx (throat), down the trachea and along a bronchus into each lung. From here it passes along ever-finer bronchi and bronchioles until it reaches a **terminal bronchiole**, which leads to several alveoli via alveolar ducts.

The function of the airways is to allow the passage of air into and out of the alveoli, where gas exchange, the main function of the lungs, takes place.

The relationship between the terminal bronchiole, alveoli and capillaries is illustrated in Figure 7.4.

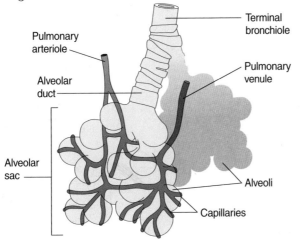

Figure 7.4 Alveoli are found at the end of terminal bronchioles

The rate and depth of breathing movements can be monitored using a spirometer. The way that a spirometer works is shown in the diagram below.

When the subject breathes, pressure changes in the air in the spirometer produce movements of a recording pen. This produces a trace on a drum revolving at constant speed. The trace that is produced is called a spirogram. It shows both the depth and the rate of breathing movements. The spirogram below shows the breathing movements of a person initially at rest and then becoming more active.

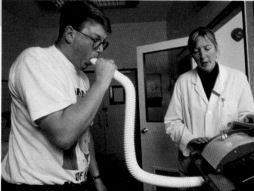

Photograph 7.2 A simple spirometer linked to a computerised recording system

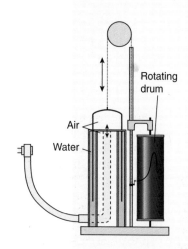

At rest, we inhale around 500 cm³ of air with each breath and exhale the same amount. This is known as the tidal volume. We could inhale more — we can all *choose* to inhale deeply. This extra potential to inhale is called the inspiratory reserve volume — about 3000 cm³ in an average adult. Similarly, without inhaling any more deeply, we can decide to exhale more forcefully. This extra exhalation is the expiratory reserve volume — about 1000 cm³ in an average adult. So, over and above the tidal volume, there is room for another 3000 cm³ air and an extra 1000 cm³ can be forced out. Therefore, the total amount of air that can be brought in and out of the lungs when breathing as forcefully as possible is about 4500 cm³. This is the vital capacity. However, we can never completely empty our lungs of air. The air left after the most forceful exhalation is the residual volume — about 1200 cm³.

total lung capacity = vital capacity + residual volume = 5700 cm³

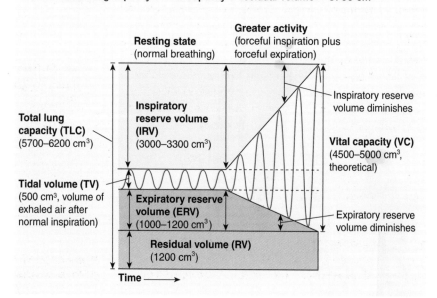

As a consequence of being surrounded by blood, alveoli are lined with fluid. This fluid contains a surfactant that is produced and secreted by specialised epithelial cells in the wall of each alveolus (Figure 7.5). The surfactant reduces the surface tension of the fluid, which prevents the walls of the alveoli from collapsing and sticking shut during breathing.

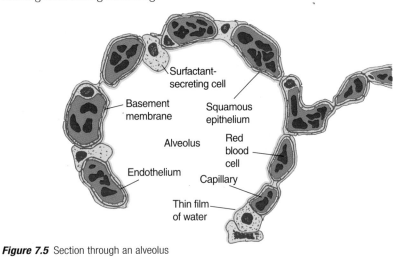

Figure 7.5 Section through an alveolus

Partial pressure and gas exchange

The pressure exerted by the air is caused by molecules of the gases that make up the air colliding with, and exerting a force on, the surface of an object. The molecules of the various gases produce an almost identical force when they collide with the surface. So the total atmospheric pressure is the sum of the pressures caused by the molecules of all the different gases that make up the air. As 78% of the molecules in the air are nitrogen molecules, they account for 78% of the total pressure — this is the **partial pressure** of nitrogen. Twenty-one per cent of the air is oxygen, so oxygen accounts for 21% of the total pressure. Other gases (including carbon dioxide and water vapour) account for the remaining 1%. We denote the partial pressure of a gas by the letter p, followed by the formula of the gas. For example, the partial pressure of oxygen is written as pO_2 and that of carbon dioxide is written as pCO_2. At sea level, atmospheric pressure (the sum of the partial pressures of all the gases in the atmosphere) is almost exactly 100 kPa. Therefore, the partial pressure of oxygen is 21 kPa (21% of 100 kPa).

$$\text{total atmospheric pressure} = pN_2 + pO_2 + pCO_2 + p\text{others}$$

$$100\,\text{kPa} = 78\,\text{kPa} + 21\,\text{kPa} + 0.03\,\text{kPa} + 0.97\,\text{kPa}$$

$$(100\%) \quad (78\%) \quad (21\%) \quad (0.03\%) \quad (0.97\%)$$

When a gas dissolves in a liquid, its molecules continue to exert a pressure and contribute to the total pressure of the liquid. The amount of a gas that can dissolve in a liquid is dependent on the partial pressure of the gas in the air around the liquid. Molecules of the gas diffuse into (or out of) the liquid until the two partial pressures are the same.

When you open a fizzy drink, it comes into contact with air that has a much lower partial pressure of carbon dioxide than that in the liquid. Carbon dioxide diffuses from the high partial pressure to the low partial pressure — quickly! The drink fizzes as carbon dioxide is lost.

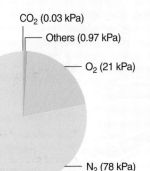

Figure 7.6 Partial pressures of atmospheric gases

Table 7.1 shows the partial pressures of oxygen and carbon dioxide in the atmosphere, in air in the alveoli and in blood plasma (in the pulmonary artery and in the pulmonary vein). Diffusion takes place until the partial pressures of the gases are the same in the alveolar air and the blood plasma.

Table 7.1

	Atmosphere/kPa	Alveolar air/kPa	Blood plasma in pulmonary artery/kPa	Blood plasma in pulmonary vein/kPa
Oxygen	21.00	11.20	5.30	11.20
Carbon dioxide	0.03	5.30	6.10	5.30

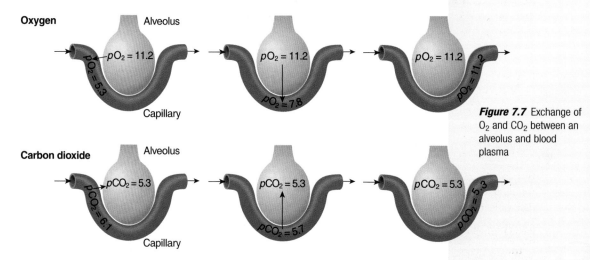

Figure 7.7 Exchange of O_2 and CO_2 between an alveolus and blood plasma

Partial pressure determines only how much oxygen and carbon dioxide are transported in simple solution in the blood plasma. However, most oxygen is transported combined with haemoglobin in the red blood cells. Only $0.3\,cm^3$ of oxygen is dissolved in $100\,cm^3$ plasma; the haemoglobin in the same volume of plasma carries $20\,cm^3$ oxygen. Gas exchange in the lungs saturates the plasma *and* the haemoglobin with oxygen. Most carbon dioxide is transported as hydrogencarbonate ions, quite independently of that transported in simple solution in the plasma.

Fick's law and gas exchange

Gas exchange in the alveoli occurs by passive diffusion. Therefore, the factors of Fick's law affect the overall efficiency of the process:

$$\text{rate of diffusion} \propto \frac{\text{surface area of exchange} \times \text{difference in concentration}}{\text{thickness of exchange surface}}$$

For efficient gas exchange, there must be a fast diffusion rate. This requires:
- a large surface area
- a large difference in concentration
- a short diffusion distance

The large surface area is provided, in part, by the 700 million alveoli present in the lungs of a human. Collectively, the alveoli have the area of a tennis court. However, it is the area over which exchange can actually take place that is important. This is represented by the total area of alveolar wall in contact with capillaries. So, the vast number of capillaries is also important in providing a large exchange surface.

The difference in concentration is maintained by constant ventilation of the lungs and circulation of the blood. Ventilation continually replaces air in the alveoli with atmospheric air that has a high partial pressure of oxygen and a low partial pressure of carbon dioxide. Circulation removes newly oxygenated blood from the capillaries next to the alveoli and replaces it with deoxygenated blood. The partial pressure of oxygen in this blood is lower than that of the alveolar air; the partial pressure of carbon dioxide in this blood is higher than that of alveolar air.

If you look back to Table 7.1, you will see that the concentration gradient between the pulmonary artery and alveolar air is greater for oxygen than it is for carbon dioxide. Despite this, the volumes of the two gases exchanged are almost identical. How can this be? This is a consequence of the moisture lining the alveoli. Carbon dioxide is much more soluble in water than oxygen is and it dissolves quickly in the water that lines the alveoli. This allows a more rapid transfer across the alveolar walls. If the concentration difference were the same for oxygen as for carbon dioxide, diffusion of oxygen would be much slower because of its lower solubility.

The short diffusion distance is a consequence of:
- the extreme thinness of the alveolar wall and the capillary wall — both comprise only squamous epithelial tissue
- alveoli and capillaries being pressed closely together — the interstitial space is very small
- the shape of the red blood cell — most of the oxygen diffuses from the air and combines with haemoglobin in red blood cells, the flattened shape of which means that all the haemoglobin is close to the plasma membrane

As a result of the diffusion of gases in the alveoli, the composition of air that is inhaled is different from that which is exhaled and from that which is present in the alveoli (Table 7.2).

◀ Two balloons the size of our lungs would have a surface area equivalent to that of a desktop.

Table 7.2

	Inhaled air/%	Alveolar air/%	Exhaled air/%
Oxygen	21.00	11.20	16.00
Carbon dioxide	0.03	5.30	3.00

As you might expect, alveolar air and exhaled air both contain less oxygen and more carbon dioxide than inhaled air. The composition of alveolar air and exhaled air is different because exhaled air is a mixture of air from the alveoli and air from the bronchial tree that did not reach the alveoli. This air has not been involved in gas exchange and, therefore, still has the same composition as atmospheric (inhaled) air. As a result, exhaled air has concentrations of oxygen and carbon dioxide that are intermediate between those of alveolar air and inhaled air.

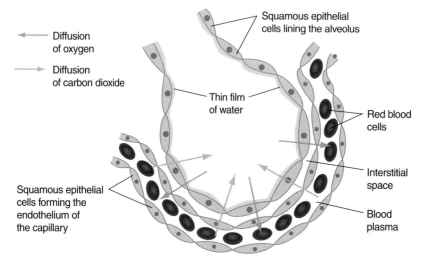

← Diffusion of oxygen

→ Diffusion of carbon dioxide

Squamous epithelial cells lining the alveolus

Thin film of water

Red blood cells

Interstitial space

Blood plasma

Squamous epithelial cells forming the endothelium of the capillary

Figure 7.8 The diffusion pathway between a capillary and an alveolus

The control of breathing

At rest, there is a basic rhythm of breathing that supplies the oxygen needed for aerobic respiration to release sufficient energy for the needs of the body. At the same time, it removes the carbon dioxide produced. On exercising, the energy requirement increases. Therefore, more oxygen is needed to allow a higher rate of aerobic respiration to meet the increased demand. The body adapts by breathing faster and more deeply. There are control mechanisms that allow these changes to take place. Any control system must have several components:

- sensors to detect changes in the system
- an integrator to respond to these changes and trigger corrective responses
- effectors to bring about the responses triggered by the integrator
- a means of communication between the components

There are two types of sensor:

- **stretch receptors**, which are located in the wall of the thorax
- **chemoreceptors,** which are sensitive to the concentration of carbon dioxide in the blood plasma and which are located in the aorta, the carotid artery and the brain

The integrator is the **respiratory centre** in the **medulla** of the brainstem. It comprises an **inspiratory centre** (triggering inhalation) and an **expiratory centre** (triggering exhalation). The effectors are the intercostal muscles and the

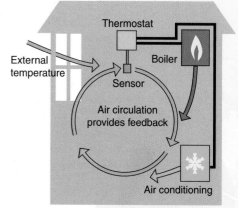

Thermostat

External temperature

Boiler

Sensor

Air circulation provides feedback

Air conditioning

Figure 7.9 An electronic control system has comparable components to a biological control system

diaphragm muscles. Nerves connect the sensors to the respiratory centre and the respiratory centre to the muscles. The basic rhythm of breathing is set using only information from the stretch receptors in the wall of the thorax. The flowchart below illustrates how this system operates.

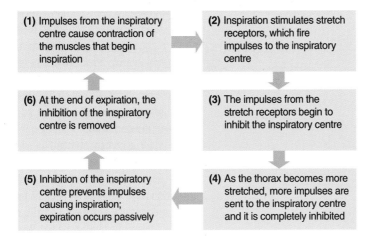

(1) Impulses from the inspiratory centre cause contraction of the muscles that begin inspiration

(2) Inspiration stimulates stretch receptors, which fire impulses to the inspiratory centre

(6) At the end of expiration, the inhibition of the inspiratory centre is removed

(3) The impulses from the stretch receptors begin to inhibit the inspiratory centre

(5) Inhibition of the inspiratory centre prevents impulses causing inspiration; expiration occurs passively

(4) As the thorax becomes more stretched, more impulses are sent to the inspiratory centre and it is completely inhibited

◄ Impulses pass to the diaphragm along the phrenic nerve and along the thoracic nerves to the intercostal muscles.

This system produces a breathing rate of about 15 breathing movements (inhalations and exhalations) per minute and a tidal volume of around 500 cm³ (0.5 dm³). This means that a total of 7.5 dm³ is breathed in per minute. This is called the minute volume or the **pulmonary ventilation rate**.

pulmonary ventilation rate = tidal volume × rate of breathing

However, on exercising, an increased pulmonary ventilation rate is needed to supply the extra oxygen. Other systems operate to bring this about. These are shown in the flowchart below.

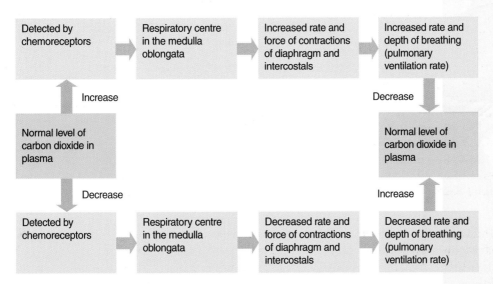

Detected by chemoreceptors

Respiratory centre in the medulla oblongata

Increased rate and force of contractions of diaphragm and intercostals

Increased rate and depth of breathing (pulmonary ventilation rate)

Increase

Decrease

Normal level of carbon dioxide in plasma

Normal level of carbon dioxide in plasma

Decrease

Increase

Detected by chemoreceptors

Respiratory centre in the medulla oblongata

Decreased rate and force of contractions of diaphragm and intercostals

Decreased rate and depth of breathing (pulmonary ventilation rate)

The sudden increase in plasma carbon dioxide caused by the onset of exercise quickly brings about the reflex responses shown; rate and depth of breathing both increase. However, this does not bring about an immediate decrease in the level of plasma carbon dioxide. This is because, throughout the exercise, the muscles continue to produce more carbon dioxide than normal. The high levels of plasma carbon dioxide continue to stimulate the chemoreceptors with the result that the pulmonary ventilation rate remains high. Only when exercise ceases, and the rate of carbon dioxide production returns to normal, does the increased pulmonary ventilation rate bring plasma carbon dioxide levels down to normal again. The pulmonary ventilation rate also then returns to normal.

Following exercise, the pulmonary ventilation rate is affected by high levels of lactate that accumulate in muscles as a result of anaerobic respiration. After exercise, lactate is removed by a process that needs oxygen. A separate control mechanism ensures that the pulmonary ventilation rate remains above normal until this has been achieved.

Summary

Structure

- The human breathing system comprises:
  - the airways in the lungs (bronchi, bronchioles, alveoli) and those outside the lungs (trachea, pharynx, nasal and mouth cavities)
  - the structures that surround the lungs and assist in the mechanisms of breathing movements (ribs, intercostal muscles and diaphragm)

Mechanism

- Inhalation and exhalation occur because breathing movements create pressure differences between the atmosphere and the air in the lungs.
- Inhalation is brought about because the contraction of the external intercostal muscles and contraction of the diaphragm muscle increase the volume of the thorax, which reduces pressure.
- Exhalation is brought about because the contraction of the internal intercostal muscles and the relaxation of the diaphragm muscle decrease the volume of the thorax and this increases pressure in the thorax.
- Inhalation draws air though the nasal cavity and pharynx, along the trachea, bronchi and bronchioles, and into the alveoli, where gas exchange takes place. Exhalation forces air from the alveoli back along the same route.

Gas exchange

- In the alveoli, oxygen diffuses from the alveolar air into the red blood cells (where it combines with haemoglobin) and carbon dioxide diffuses from the blood plasma into the alveolar air.
- Diffusion in the alveoli is efficient (in terms of Fick's law) because:
  - the many alveoli provide a large surface area

- continuous ventilation and circulation maintain a high concentration difference between alveolar air and the blood
  - the extremely thin walls of the alveoli and capillaries (consisting only of squamous epithelium on a basement membrane) provide a short diffusion distance
- Gas exchange is also more efficient because the alveoli are moist; this aids the diffusion of carbon dioxide in particular.
- The partial pressure of a gas is the contribution made by that gas to the total pressure of a system. It is a useful way of comparing concentrations of gases between a gaseous medium and a liquid medium.
- The volume of air moved in and out of the lungs with each breath is the tidal volume.
- At rest, the tidal volume is about 500 cm^3, but the inspiratory reserve volume and the expiratory reserve volume can increase this to about 4500 cm^3.
- There is about 1200 cm^3 air that is never exhaled, which forms the residual volume.

Control

- pulmonary ventilation rate = rate of breathing × tidal volume
- The pulmonary ventilation rate is controlled by the respiratory centre in the medulla of the brain.
- Stretch receptors in the walls of the thorax monitor the expansion and contraction of the thorax. Information from these receptors allows the respiratory centre to set a normal breathing pattern (around 15 breaths per minute and a tidal volume of 500 cm^3) at rest.
- Chemoreceptors in the aorta, carotid artery and in the medulla itself monitor the level of plasma carbon dioxide. Information from these is used by the respiratory centre to adjust the pulmonary ventilation rate during exercise.

Questions

Multiple-choice

1 Pulmonary ventilation rate is equal to:
   A breathing rate × residual volume
   B breathing rate × tidal volume
   C tidal volume ÷ breathing rate
   D residual volume ÷ breathing rate
2 Diffusion of oxygen and carbon dioxide in the alveoli is rapid because there is:
   A a large surface area, a low concentration difference and a short diffusion pathway
   B a small surface area, a high concentration difference and a short diffusion pathway
   C a large surface area, a high concentration difference and a long diffusion pathway
   D a large surface area, a high concentration difference and a short diffusion pathway

3 To bring about inhalation:
   A external intercostal muscles contract, internal intercostal muscles relax, diaphragm muscle contracts
   B external intercostal muscles contract, internal intercostal muscles contract, diaphragm muscle relaxes
   C external intercostal muscles relax, internal intercostal muscles relax, diaphragm muscle contracts
   D external intercostal muscles relax, internal intercostal muscles contract, diaphragm muscle relaxes

4 The pattern of normal (resting) inhalation and exhalation is set in response to information from:
   A chemoreceptors in the aorta and carotid artery
   B stretch receptors in the aorta and carotid artery
   C chemoreceptors in the intercostal muscles
   D stretch receptors in the intercostal muscles

5 The tidal volume is:
   A the total volume of air in the lungs
   B the volume inhaled added to the volume exhaled in one breath
   C the volume of air inhaled and then exhaled in one breath
   D the maximum volume of air that can be inhaled in one breath

6 The partial pressure of a gas is:
   A the proportion by volume of a gas in a mixture of gases
   B the part of the total pressure that a gas exerts due to its molecules colliding with each other
   C the part of the overall pressure of a mixture of gases that is due to that gas
   D the pressure of a gas when only some of its molecules exert a force

7 When air is exhaled, it:
   A diffuses out down a concentration gradient
   B is drawn out because of the higher pressure in the atmosphere
   C is forced out because of the higher pressure in the lungs
   D is drawn in because of the lower pressure in the lungs

8 During exercise, the pulmonary ventilation rate increases because chemo-receptors detect:
   A a decrease in the concentration of oxygen in the blood
   B an increase in the concentration of lactate (lactic acid) in the blood
   C an increase in the pH of the blood
   D an increase in the concentration of carbon dioxide in the blood

9 Ventilating the lungs means:
   A inhaling
   B exhaling
   C inhaling and exhaling
   D exchanging gases

10 When compared with inhaled air, exhaled air:
   A has a higher concentration of oxygen, a lower concentration of carbon dioxide and is more moist
   B has a higher concentration of oxygen, a lower concentration of carbon dioxide and is drier

C has a lower concentration of oxygen, a higher concentration of carbon dioxide and is more moist

D has a lower concentration of oxygen, a higher concentration of carbon dioxide and is drier

Examination-style

1 (a) The diagram below shows the main components of the human breathing system.

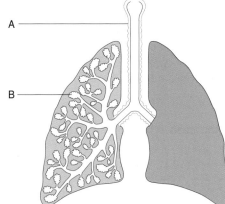

    (i) Name the structures labelled A and B. *(2 marks)*

    (ii) Explain why contraction of the external intercostal muscles and contraction of the diaphragm muscle cause air to be drawn into the lungs. *(3 marks)*

  (b) Use Fick's law to explain why gas exchange in the alveoli is efficient. *(4 marks)*

Total: 9 marks

2 The diagram shows two spirometer traces taken from the same person at different times.

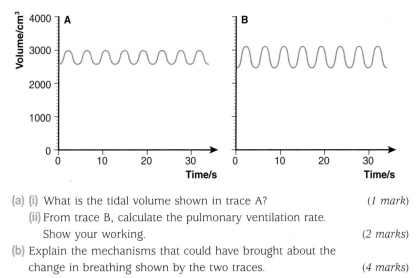

(a) (i) What is the tidal volume shown in trace A? *(1 mark)*

    (ii) From trace B, calculate the pulmonary ventilation rate. Show your working. *(2 marks)*

(b) Explain the mechanisms that could have brought about the change in breathing shown by the two traces. *(4 marks)*

Total: 7 marks

3 (a) Explain what is meant by the terms:
  (i) tidal volume
  (ii) inspiratory reserve volume
  (iii) vital capacity   (3 marks)
  (b) When a person suffers a serious chest wound, a condition known as pneumothorax can result. In this condition, air rushes into the space between the two pleural layers surrounding one of the lungs.
  (i) What effect will the wound have on the pressure of the air between the two pleural layers? Explain your answer.   (2 marks)
  (ii) Explain why the lung affected by pneumothorax can no longer be ventilated.   (3 marks)

Total: 8 marks

4 The diagram shows two spirometer traces. Trace A shows a normal breathing pattern of a person at rest. Trace B shows an abnormal pattern of breathing at rest.

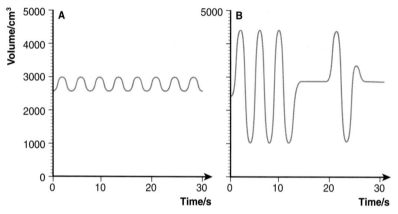

(a) Calculate the pulmonary ventilation rate shown by trace A.   (2 marks)
(b) Describe two ways in which the pattern of breathing shown by trace B differs from that shown in trace A.   (2 marks)
(c) The pattern of breathing shown in trace B is sometimes found in brain-damaged patients. Suggest how brain damage might produce an abnormal pattern of breathing.   (3 marks)

Total: 7 marks

5 The graph below shows the atmospheric pressure at different altitudes.

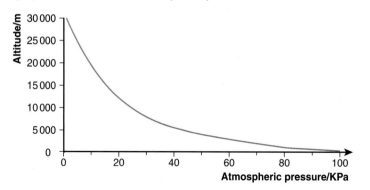

(a) Describe the change in atmospheric pressure between sea level and 1000 m. *(2 marks)*

(b) Assuming that oxygen makes up 21% of the atmosphere at all altitudes, calculate the partial pressure of oxygen at:

(i) sea level *(1 mark)*

(ii) an altitude of 5000 m *(1 mark)*

(c) Gas exchange takes place in the alveoli. Most of the oxygen absorbed diffuses into red blood cells and combines with haemoglobin to form oxyhaemoglobin.

(i) Explain why oxygen combining with haemoglobin does not affect the concentration gradient of oxygen between the alveolar air and the blood. *(2 marks)*

(ii) Suggest why people who live at high altitudes have more red blood cells per cm^3 blood than people who live at sea level. *(3 marks)*

(iii) Use Fick's law to explain the benefit, to a person who has just reached a high altitude, of breathing more quickly. *(3 marks)*

(d) Explain why, to a person not adapted to living at such altitudes, exercise is more difficult at higher altitudes. *(3 marks)*

Total: 15 marks

Chapter 8

Use of microbial enzymes in biotechnology

This chapter covers:

- the different types of microbial enzyme
- how microorganisms are selected and cultured
- how microbial enzymes are isolated
- how microbial enzymes are immobilised and the advantages of immobilisation
- some examples of the use of microbial enzymes; in particular, their use in biosensors

The use of microorganisms in biotechnology is not new. Yeast has been used to make bread and wine for thousands of years. However, most recent research has focused on the use of specific enzymes produced by microorganisms, rather than the use of whole organisms. This has led to more refined techniques for culturing microorganisms and for isolating the enzymes they produce. Microbial enzymes are used in a number of applications, including industrial processes, stain removers and biosensors.

Traditional biotechnology has been around for thousands of years

Ingram

Microbial enzymes

Like the enzymes from any organism, those from microorganisms have a number of important properties. Enzyme properties are discussed in Chapter 4 and summarised in Table 8.1, which also gives some of the consequences of these properties for biotechnology.

Table 8.1

Property of enzyme	Explanation	Consequence for biotechnology
Specific	An enzyme molecule has a unique tertiary structure and a unique active site	Enzyme only catalyses one reaction, leading to the formation of a specific product(s); purification is less complex than if many products were formed
Permanent inactivation by high temperatures	Enzymes are proteins; heat breaks the bonds that hold the tertiary structure in place	Effectiveness of the catalyst decreases rapidly above the optimum temperature and the rate of reaction also decreases; this determines the temperature of the reaction vessel
Inactivation by pH change	A change in pH affects the charge on the active site and weakens bonds in the tertiary structure	Catalysis decreases in conditions that are too acidic or too alkaline, so rate of reaction decreases
Maximum turnover rate related to substrate concentration	Each active site can bind with a limited number of substrate molecules per second	Increasing the substrate concentration above that which the active sites can turn over will not increase the rate of reaction
Effect of inhibitors	Inhibitors either block the active site (competitive inhibitors) or alter the shape of the active site (non-competitive inhibitors)	Impurities in the reaction vessel may act as inhibitors and reduce the rate of catalysis — and therefore the rate of reaction and the amount of product formed

Microorganisms do not produce enzymes for the benefit of enzyme technologists! The enzymes they produce catalyse metabolic reactions. Most of these reactions take place within the cells of the microorganisms and are catalysed by **intracellular enzymes**. However, some enzymes are secreted from the microbial cells to catalyse reactions outside the microorganism; these are **extracellular enzymes**. It is easier to isolate an enzyme that has been secreted by a microorganism than it is to isolate an enzyme retained inside the microbial cell.

◀ Human digestive enzymes hydrolyse food molecules in the lumen of the gut, not inside cells. They are, therefore, extracellular enzymes.

Selecting and culturing microorganisms

Selecting the microorganism

Once the need for a particular enzyme has been identified, the hunt is on for a suitable source. Bacteria are the most commonly used organisms as a source of enzymes because:

- they have a short life cycle (20 minutes under ideal conditions) and so multiply rapidly

- they are easily cultured because they have relatively simple nutritional requirements
- they are easy to genetically engineer
- they produce a large amount of enzyme in proportion to their biomass

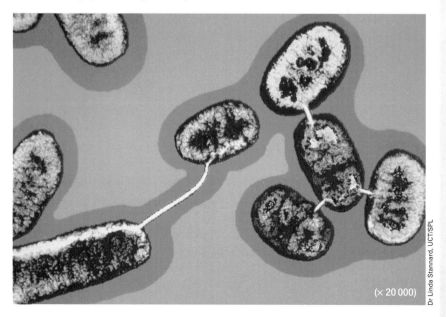

(e) Bacteria multiply by binary fission. In this process, the bacterial DNA replicates itself and then the whole cell divides into two. Each half receives one copy of the DNA and approximately half the organelles. Under ideal conditions, the process can be completed in 20 minutes.

Do not confuse binary fission with mitosis (pp. 171–176). There are similarities — one cell divides to produce two cells. There are also important differences. Strictly, mitosis is a division of the nucleus (not the whole cell). A bacterial cell does not have a nucleus, so it cannot divide by mitosis. Mitosis involves movement of chromosomes. Bacteria do not have chromosomes — another reason why they cannot divide by mitosis. So be careful — confusing the two processes will cost you marks in an examination.

(× 17 500)

CNRI/SPL

Bacteria reproduce by binary fission

Once a bacterium that produces the required enzyme has been found, it may need to be modified for a number of reasons. For example:
- it might not produce sufficient enzyme
- it might be pathogenic (cause disease)
- it might not reproduce quickly enough
- it might not be resilient enough to be cultured on a large scale

Modification used to be achieved by encouraging the exchange of genetic material between bacteria that produced the enzyme and different bacteria with some of the desired characteristics. Today, the modification is more likely to be carried out by genetic engineering.

Conjugation is a process in which bacteria exchange genetic material

(× 20 000)

Dr Linda Stannard, UCT/SPL

Culturing the microorganism

Establishing the conditions needed for culture

Once a bacterium has been identified and modified, the conditions needed to culture it must be established. Research is carried out to find:

- the optimum temperature
- the optimum pH
- the optimum oxygen concentration
- the ideal balance of nutrients
- other specific requirements

At this stage, the researchers try to establish methods of switching on and off the gene that controls enzyme production. Often, chemical 'promoters' must be present to switch on the gene. Identifying the nature of these promoters gives enzyme technologists a means of controlling production.

Box 8.1 Controlling production of an enzyme

When bacteria are cultured under favourable conditions, the number of live bacterial cells follows a predictable pattern. This is called the **bacterial growth curve**. It is divided into a number of phases, as shown in the figure below.

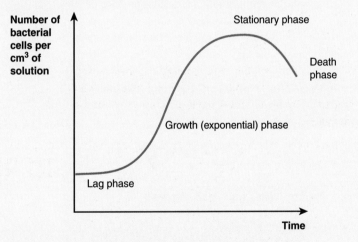

- Lag phase — the bacteria increase in size but do not divide.
- Rapid growth phase (exponential phase) — the bacteria multiply rapidly under the ideal conditions.
- Stationary phase — bacterial cells are dying at the same rate as they are being produced.
- Death phase — more bacterial cells are dying than are being produced.

The time at which production of the required enzyme is 'switched on' depends on a number of factors. It is most efficient to have the greatest number of bacteria producing the enzyme for the longest time. This may mean delaying production until the bacterial population has entered the stationary phase. At this point, the promoters can be added and enzyme production initiated.

The initial research to establish the optimum conditions needed by the bacterium is carried out in small laboratory fermenters.

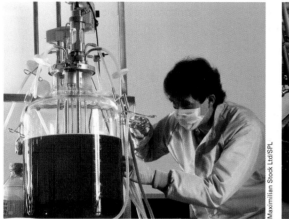

A small-scale fermenter

Research using a large-scale pilot plant

Although the vessels are called fermenters, there is usually very little fermentation occurring. Fermentation is a type of anaerobic respiration. In laboratory and industrial fermenters, oxygen levels are kept high to encourage aerobic respiration

However, conditions in a small-scale laboratory fermenter are not the same as those in an industrial fermenter, which may have a capacity of 500 000 dm^3.

A fermenter of capacity 500 000 dm^3 holds the equivalent of the contents of just over 1 million milk bottles!

Before scaling-up to this capacity, with all the costs entailed, a large-scale pilot plant is set up. Large-scale pilot fermenters have a capacity of up to 250 dm^3 and give a more realistic idea of the likely performance of the bacterium in an industrial fermenter. Often, conditions that were thought to be ideal in the laboratory prove to be far from ideal in larger fermenters. Sometimes a particular bacterium proves to be too inefficient at producing the required enzyme in the conditions in larger fermenters. In such cases, the bacterium must either be abandoned and a new one sought, or it must be modified to suit the conditions.

The stages involved in developing a commercial enzyme-manufacturing process using bacteria are summarised in the flowchart below.

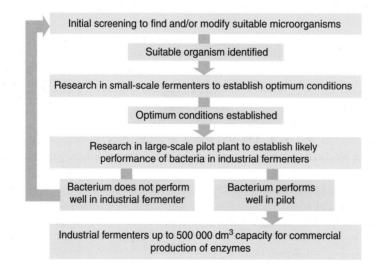

To establish a culture in an industrial fermenter, it is not appropriate simply to add a few cm³ of a bacterial culture. It would take too long for the population of bacteria to reach the size required for production of the enzyme to be 'switched on'. Having the fermenter fully operational all this time would not be economically viable. Instead, a 'fermenter train' is established, which allows a large inoculum of bacteria to be added to the fermenter. These bacteria reproduce rapidly to give a sufficiently large number for production of the enzyme to commence.

Figure 8.1 A large-scale fermenter

Box 8.2 A fermenter train

A fermenter train involves a series of culture vessels of increasing capacity. A typical train might include fermenters of 20 cm³, 200 cm³ and 20 dm³. The bacterial culture is first grown in the 20 cm³ vessel. When a viable population has been established, this is transferred to the 200 cm³ vessel (and another 20 cm³ culture established). When the population in the 200 cm³ vessel has reached its maximum, it is transferred to the 20 dm³ vessel. When the population is properly established, this provides the inoculum for the industrial fermenter.

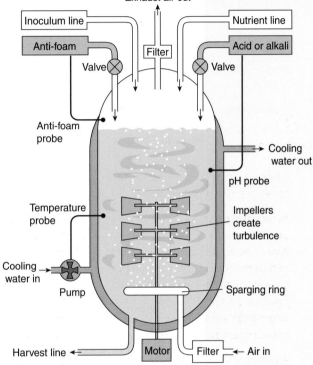

Maintaining conditions in the fermenter

It is important that the following conditions are maintained during culture of the bacteria:

- **Asepsis** — the culture must not be contaminated by other microorganisms. This is because they would compete with the cultured bacterium for nutrients and oxygen and they might produce toxic waste products that could inhibit its growth. Fermenters are usually steam-cleaned before introducing the pre-sterilised culture medium and the bacteria.
- **Suitable temperature** — if the temperature is too low, then the maximum rate of production of the enzyme will not be achieved because the biochemical reactions of protein synthesis will proceed only slowly. If the temperature is too high, the yield will be reduced because:
  - enzymes controlling reactions in the bacteria are denatured
  - the product enzyme is denatured

The metabolic activity of billions of bacteria generates a great deal of heat, so cooling is necessary. The temperature is monitored by thermistors and the rate of flow of coolant is adjusted accordingly (see Figure 8.1).

◀ The selection of culture medium can help in maintaining asepsis. Broad-spectrum media allow a range of microorganisms to grow; minimal media provide the nutritional requirements of just one type of bacterium. The more precisely tailored the medium is to the enzyme-producing bacterium, the less likely it is that other microorganisms will be able to grow.

- **Suitable pH** — conditions that are too alkaline or too acidic will alter the charge on the active site of the product enzyme and on those of enzymes inside the bacteria. pH probes monitor the pH and deviations from the optimum are corrected by the addition of acid or alkali.
- **Oxygenation** — the bacteria are aerobes and therefore need oxygen to respire aerobically. Probes monitor oxygen levels and the rate of oxygenation through the sparging ring is adjusted to meet the requirements.

In addition, the culture medium should supply all the nutrients that are needed by the bacterium. These include:
- carbohydrates — to act as a respiratory substrate
- amino acids — from which to synthesise proteins
- mineral ions, vitamins and nitrogenous bases (used in the synthesis of nucleic acids)

Under these conditions, bacterial growth will be rapid and production of the enzyme will be optimal.

Types of fermentation

So far, we have considered a type of culture in which a large fermenter is filled with culture medium and then 'seeded' with an inoculum of bacteria. The bacteria multiply and, when numbers are sufficient, promoters are added to 'switch on' the genes that control production of the enzyme. Production continues until conditions become unfavourable; the nutrient supply becomes exhausted and waste products accumulate. The bacterial population enters the death phase (phase of decline) and production is halted. The fermenter is emptied, cleaned and sterilised ready for a new batch of culture medium and bacteria. This is called **batch fermentation**. The enzyme is extracted from the contents of the fermenter.

Advantages of batch fermentation are that:
- the fermenter is relatively easy to set up and temperature, pH and oxygenation are easily controlled
- the fermenter can be used for more than one production process, allowing the manufacturer to respond quickly to market demands

Disadvantages of batch fermentation are that:
- continual emptying, cleaning, sterilising and refilling of the fermenter is inefficient and costly
- nutrient levels become depleted quickly, reducing productivity

In **continuous fermentation,** there is a constant flow of materials through the fermenter. The culture medium is added at a constant rate to match the rate at which the product is formed and removed from the fermenter.

Advantages of continuous fermentation are that:
- the process is more productive, as nutrients are constantly being replaced
- smaller, less costly, fermenters can be used because of the increased productivity

- the fermentation can run for weeks before the fermenter must be shut down and cleaned, again reducing costs

Disadvantages of continuous fermentation are that:
- it is difficult to monitor and maintain all the environmental factors and the system can therefore become unbalanced
- the development and setting up of the fermenter is costly

Isolating the enzymes

What comes out of the fermenter is a mixture of living and dead bacterial cells, unused nutrients, waste products of bacterial metabolism, the extracellular enzyme product and, probably, other extracellular enzymes. The processes involved in isolating pure enzyme from this mixture are collectively known as **downstream processing**.

The level of purity required depends on how the enzyme will be used. Enzymes for use in medicine and research must be of the highest purity. Enzymes used in washing powders can be less pure.

The main stages in downstream processing of an extracellular enzyme are shown in the flowchart below.

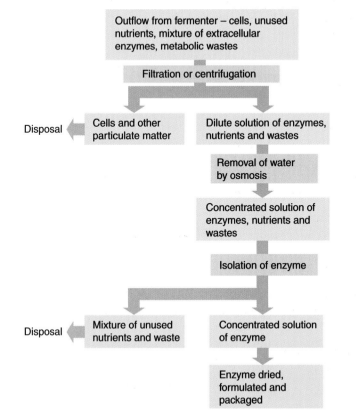

◀ Heat cannot be used to concentrate the dilute solution because this would denature the enzyme.

If the product is an intracellular enzyme, then the bacterial cells must first be disrupted to release the enzyme before downstream processing can proceed.

◀ Downstream processing is expensive. Imagine having to filter or centrifuge and concentrate 500 000 dm^3 (one million milk bottles) of liquid and then purify the concentrate. It is a huge operation.

Preparing enzymes for use

Some enzymes are used in much the same way as you might use enzymes in an experiment. They are simply mixed with the substrate and allowed to produce the product. Of course, the scale is very different.

This method of using enzymes has considerable problems. These include:
● recovering the enzyme so that it does not contaminate the product and so that it can be reused (enzymes are expensive to produce)
● purifying the recovered enzyme to a level at which it can be reused
● purifying the product, which is mixed with unused reactants

As a result of these problems, the technique of **enzyme immobilisation** was developed. Processes using immobilised enzymes are increasingly replacing those using free enzymes. There are a number of ways in which immobilisation is achieved, but the goal is the same in all cases — to fix enzymes in or on some inert medium (Figure 8.2).

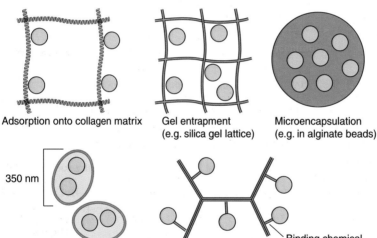

Figure 8.2 Some methods of immobilising enzymes

Adsorption onto collagen matrix Gel entrapment (e.g. silica gel lattice) Microencapsulation (e.g. in alginate beads)

350 nm

Semi-permeable membrane polymer microspheres Cellulose fibres form an insoluble matrix Binding chemical (e.g. glutaraldehyde)

Advantages and disadvantages of immobilised enzymes

Immobilised enzymes are held in place in or on an inert medium. This increases their stability at high temperatures and extremes of pH. **Thermostability**, in particular, has important implications for productivity. Increasing temperature has two effects on an enzyme-controlled reaction:
● More kinetic energy increases collisions between molecules, raising the reaction rate.

- More kinetic energy increases the tendency of the enzyme molecule to denature.

As temperature rises:
- molecules have more energy
- molecules move faster
- molecules collide more frequently
- the rate of reaction increases

Above the optimum temperature:
- bonds holding the tertiary structure break
- the enzyme is denatured
- the shape of the active site changes
- enzyme–substrate complexes cannot form

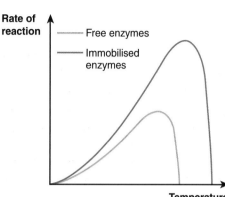

◀ The factor by which the reaction rate increases with each 10°C rise in temperature is called the Q_{10} factor for the reaction. An increase in temperature of 10°C may double the reaction rate. So for these reactions, $Q_{10} = 2$.

Figure 8.3 Effect of temperature on the rate of an enzyme-controlled reaction. Immobilised enzymes have an increased optimum temperature because of their thermostability

Immobilised enzymes do not denature so easily when the temperature increases. Therefore, the optimum temperature increases — it is shifted to the right, as shown in Figure 8.3.

Being able to run the reaction at an increased temperature, with no further denaturation, increases productivity. A 10°C rise could double the rate of reaction and so double the amount of product formed in a fixed time. A 20°C rise with no further denaturation could quadruple the rate of reaction. Set against this would be the increased cost of running the plant at these higher temperatures.

Other advantages of immobilising enzymes include the following:
- The enzyme can be recovered easily from the reaction vessel and reused many times. This is important because enzymes are expensive to isolate.
- The product is not contaminated by enzyme. This reduces the cost of downstream processing of the product.
- Immobilised enzymes can be controlled more effectively than free enzymes.
- Immobilised enzymes are suited to continuous production processes.

A disadvantage of immobilised enzymes is that their activity is reduced. This is because they are less accessible to the substrate molecules, particularly if they are encapsulated (Figure 8.4).

Immobilised enzymes and continuous processes

Immobilised enzymes are particularly suited to continuous production processes, such as that involved in the production of fructose syrup from glucose syrup (Figure 8.5). Fructose is used as a sweetener. It is used in preference to glucose because it is much sweeter and so less is needed to produce the same effect, thus reducing cost. Lactose-free milk is produced by the action of immobilised lactase in a similar continuous production process.

In such processes, the flow rate is crucial. This is because it influences the rate at which enzyme–substrate complexes form, which affects the activity of the enzyme:

Free enzyme

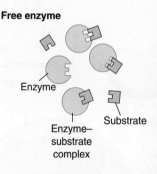

Enzyme

Substrate

Enzyme–substrate complex

Entrapped (immobilised) enzyme

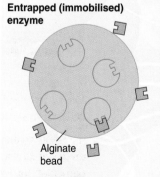

Alginate bead

Figure 8.4 Immobilisation can reduce the activity of an enzyme

- Too low a flow rate will result in a conversion that is not cost effective.
- Too high a flow rate will result in the product being contaminated with substrate.

The use of immobilised enzymes in continuous production means that the process can continue for long periods before the plant needs emptying and cleaning.

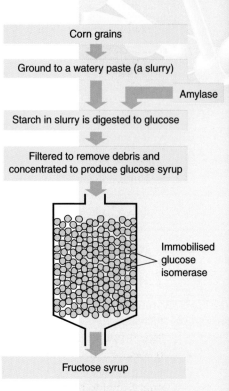

Figure 8.5 The continuous production process used in the manufacture of fructose syrup

> ### Box 8.3 An older continuous process
>
> The use of immobilised enzymes in continuous production processes may represent the cutting edge of design of biotechnological processes, but the principle of continuous production is not new. The percolating filter method of sewage treatment has been in operation for over 100 years. In this process, liquid sewage effluent drips continuously through a 'clinker' bed. Microorganisms held on the clinker absorb and respire the organic matter in the sewage. Treated sewage (the product) flows continuously out of the base of each filter bed.

Uses of microbial enzymes

Enzymes are now replacing inorganic catalysts in some industrial processes. Two advantages of using enzymes, rather than inorganic catalysts, are that:
- enzymes catalyse reactions at moderate temperatures (inorganic catalysts often require very high temperatures and pressures), thereby saving money
- enzymes are more specific than inorganic catalysts

Traditional biotechnology made use of whole microorganisms and there are some processes where this is still necessary. However, the progress made in isolating and purifying microbial enzymes has meant that many industrial processes now use single enzymes rather than whole microorganisms. The advantages of using specific enzymes rather than whole microorganisms include the following:
- None of the substrate is converted into microbial biomass (it is not used for growth of the microorganism).
- Only one reaction needs to be considered and the conditions for only that reaction need be optimised.
- Since there is only one enzyme active, there will be no (or very few) other products formed.
- It is easier to purify the product, particularly if immobilised enzymes are used.

However, in multi-stage processes, such as the fermentation of sugars in brewing, several enzymes are necessary. In this case it is easier to optimise conditions for one microorganism (yeast) that produces all the enzymes than to try to optimise conditions for individual enzymes from different sources.

Some examples of the uses of microbial enzymes are given in Table 8.2.

Industry	Microbial enzyme	Use
Dairy	Rennin Lipase	Cheese manufacture; forming 'curds' from milk protein Ripening of cheese
Brewing	Protease Amyloglucosidase	Breaking down yeast to improve clarity of beer Breaking down glucose to produce low-calorie beer
Washing powders	Proteases	Digesting biological stains (e.g. blood)
Confectionery	Amylase Glucose isomerase	Production of glucose syrup Production of fructose syrup
Leather	Trypsin	Removal of hair and excess tissue from hides to make leather more pliable
Medical	Trypsin Assorted enzymes	Dissolving blood clots and cleaning wounds Used in biosensors for diagnoses and assays

Table 8.2

Biosensors

The development of enzyme-based **biosensors** has increased our ability to monitor the concentrations of a range of substances easily and extremely accurately, without the need for chemical reagents. Two properties of enzymes are crucial in biosensors:

- They are specific and therefore respond to only one substance. For example, a glucose biosensor only responds to the presence of glucose, whereas chemical tests (such as Benedict's test) detect all reducing sugars.
- They are extremely sensitive, detecting very small amounts of the substance.

Some biosensors contain enzymes linked to colourless dyes. The reaction with the substrate produces a range of colours that correspond to different concentrations of the substance. Other biosensors produce an output voltage that is equivalent to a specific concentration of the substance. These biosensors give a more precise indication of concentration.

Clinistix® strips: a colour-change biosensor

Clinistix® strips are biosensors that detect the presence of glucose in liquids. They can be used to test samples of urine or blood for glucose to help diagnose diabetes. Each strip is embedded with two enzymes — glucose oxidase and peroxidase — and a colourless dye (reduced chromagen). When the strip is dipped in a liquid containing glucose, the following reactions take place:

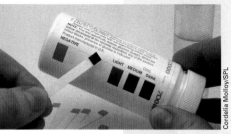

The Clinistix® biosensor is simple to use; it gives a one-off indication of glucose concentration

- Glucose oxidase catalyses the reaction between glucose and oxygen to produce gluconic acid and hydrogen peroxide.
- Peroxidase catalyses the reaction between hydrogen peroxide and reduced chromagen to form water and oxidised chromagen, which is coloured.

The degree of coloration produced gives an indication of the concentration of glucose in the liquid.

Voltage-output biosensors

Biosensors such as Clinistix® strips are ideal for obtaining a one-off indication of the concentration of a substance. However, they cannot provide continuous monitoring of changes in concentration over a period of time. For this purpose, voltage-output biosensors are required (Figure 8.6).

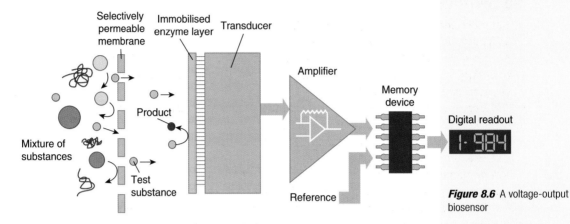

Figure 8.6 A voltage-output biosensor

- The selectively permeable membrane allows the test substance to pass through, but excludes most others.
- The test substance binds with the enzyme, reacts and forms a product.
- The transducer layer is specially formulated to be sensitive to only this product. As the product binds, it causes a change that results in a minute change in voltage.
- The change in voltage is amplified and passed to a memory device for storage and comparison.
- The memory device compares the voltage change with previous voltages that have been related to specific concentrations of the test substance.
- The memory device calculates the concentration of the substance and produces a digital readout.

◀ The amount of product formed depends on the concentration of the test substance in the liquid — enzyme concentration, pH and temperature are constant. The concentration of the product determines the extent of binding with the transducer and therefore the size of the voltage change produced.

> *e* You may have to list and explain advantages of enzyme-based biosensors over conventional biochemical tests for substances. You would need to explain properties such as the specificity of enzymes in terms of their unique tertiary structure and individually shaped active sites.

There are biosensors for many substances, including glucose, urea and cholesterol. New ones are being developed all the time.

Summary

Bacterial enzymes

- Bacteria are an ideal source of enzymes because they:
  - have simple nutritional requirements and are therefore easily cultured
  - produce a large amount of enzyme in relation to their biomass

- are easy to genetically engineer
- reproduce quickly
- Extracellular enzymes are secreted by bacterial cells into the culture medium; intracellular enzymes are retained within the cells.

Fermentation

- Optimum conditions of temperature, pH, oxygen level and nutrient balance are determined using small-scale fermenters.
- A large-scale pilot plant is used to investigate the likely performance of the bacterium in the production fermenter and may reveal that conditions need to be modified to optimise yield.
- A bacterial growth curve has four phases: lag phase, rapid growth phase (exponential phase), stationary phase and death phase.
- Bacteria may be grown by batch culture (batch fermentation) or in continuous culture (continuous fermentation).
  - A fermenter used for batch culture is relatively easy to set up and maintain, but must be emptied, cleaned and sterilised after each batch.
  - A fermenter used for continuous culture can remain in operation for weeks at a time and the process is more productive. However, conditions are difficult to maintain and set-up is costly.

Downstream processing

- Downstream processing of extracellular enzymes involves:
  - removal of cells and cell debris by filtration or centrifugation
  - concentration of the dilute solution by reverse osmosis
  - isolation of the enzyme from solution by precipitation or solvent extraction
  - drying, formulation and packaging of the purified enzyme
- To release intracellular enzymes, cells must be disrupted before the rest of the downstream processing can continue.

Immobilised enzymes and their uses

- Immobilisation of enzymes makes them more thermostable and more resistant to changes in pH.
- Immobilised enzymes can be recovered and reused easily and do not contaminate the product.
- Immobilised enzymes are used in continuous production processes, such as the production of fructose syrup, and in biosensors.
- Many biosensors make use of enzymes because they are specific and sensitive (detect small amounts of a substance).
- In voltage-output biosensors:
  - The substance diffuses through a selectively permeable membrane covering the biosensor and binds with the immobilised enzyme in the sensor.
  - The product formed by the reaction binds with a transducer, which produces a change in voltage.
  - The change in voltage is amplified and converted into a digital readout of the concentration of the substance.

Questions

Multiple-choice

1 Extracellular enzymes:
   A are retained in the bacterial cell
   B require more downstream processing than intracellular enzymes
   C both of the above
   D neither of the above

2 Which of the following best describes the stationary phase of a bacterial growth curve:
   A the number of bacteria is constant
   B the same number of bacteria are dying as are being produced
   C there are no bacteria being produced; reproduction has ceased
   D the rate of reproduction of the bacteria is constant

3 When compared with batch culture, in continuous culture of bacteria:
   A it is easier to set up the fermenter and maintain the conditions
   B it is easier to set up the fermenter but more difficult to maintain the conditions
   C it is more difficult to set up the fermenter but easier to maintain the conditions
   D it is more difficult to set up the fermenter and more difficult to maintain the conditions

4 Asepsis is important in the culture of bacteria because:
   A other bacteria may be pathogenic
   B other bacteria may compete with the cultured bacteria for nutrients
   C other bacteria may compete with the cultured bacteria for oxygen
   D all of the above

5 Immobilised enzymes:
   A can be recovered less easily than free enzymes
   B are more active than free enzymes
   C both of the above
   D neither of the above

6 Enzyme-based biosensors are more reliable than many biochemical tests because:
   A the enzymes hydrolyse the test substance
   B the enzymes only react with a single substance
   C the enzyme-based reactions do not require heat
   D all of the above

7 Downstream processing includes:
   A the preparation of the fermenter for production
   B the introduction of an inoculum of bacteria into the fermenter
   C the isolation of the enzyme from the other substances in the fermenter
   D the isolation and formulation of the enzyme

8 In a continuous production process involving immobilised enzymes, the flow rate of the substrate through the reaction column is important because:
   A too high a flow rate will remove some of the enzymes

B too low a flow rate will leave some product in the reaction column

C too high a flow rate will result in substrate contaminating the product

D too low a flow rate will result in some of the enzyme molecules becoming inactivated

9 Which of the following is *not* true of the Clinistix® glucose biosensor:

A glucose converts a colourless dye into a coloured form

B hydrogen peroxide oxidises chromagen

C the enzymes glucose oxidase and peroxidase catalyse a two-step process

D gluconic acid is formed during the process

10 The advantages of using specific enzymes, rather than whole microorganisms, in industrial processes are:

A multi-step processes can be controlled more easily

B downstream processing is more cost-effective as more products are formed

C both of the above

D neither of the above

Examination-style

1 (a) High-fructose corn syrup is used as a sweetener. It is produced from corn starch. The starch grains are ground to a slurry and then enzymes are added, which produce glucose syrup. This is concentrated and decolorised before it is passed through a column of immobilised glucose isomerase. Here, much of the glucose is converted to fructose, which is collected and purified. Fructose has the same energy content as glucose but it is much sweeter.

(i) Complete the flowchart. *(1 mark)*

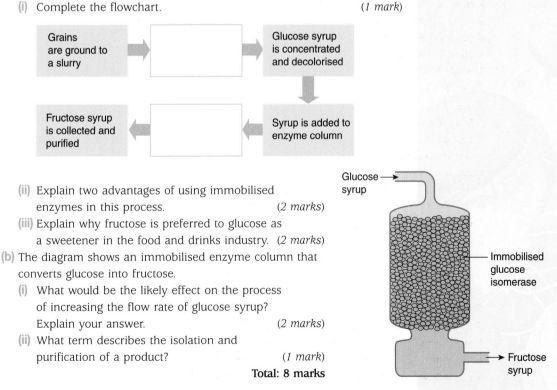

(ii) Explain two advantages of using immobilised enzymes in this process. *(2 marks)*

(iii) Explain why fructose is preferred to glucose as a sweetener in the food and drinks industry. *(2 marks)*

(b) The diagram shows an immobilised enzyme column that converts glucose into fructose.

(i) What would be the likely effect on the process of increasing the flow rate of glucose syrup? Explain your answer. *(2 marks)*

(ii) What term describes the isolation and purification of a product? *(1 mark)*

Total: 8 marks

2 (a) The diagram shows a section through an industrial fermenter.

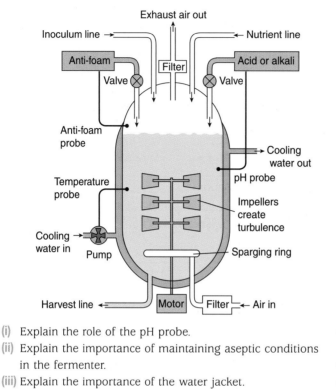

(i) Explain the role of the pH probe. *(3 marks)*

(ii) Explain the importance of maintaining aseptic conditions in the fermenter. *(3 marks)*

(iii) Explain the importance of the water jacket. *(2 marks)*

(iv) What type of fermentation (batch or continuous) is taking place in this fermenter? Explain your answer. *(2 marks)*

Total: 10 marks

3 Lactose-free milk is produced by passing milk through a reactor containing immobilised lactase. The lactose is converted into glucose and galactose.

(a) Give *two* methods of immobilising enzymes. *(1 mark)*

(b) (i) Give *two* advantages of using immobilised lactase, rather than free lactase. *(2 marks)*

(ii) Give *one* disadvantage of using immobilised lactase rather than free lactase. *(1 mark)*

(c) The graph shows the effect of flow rate of milk on the yield of glucose.

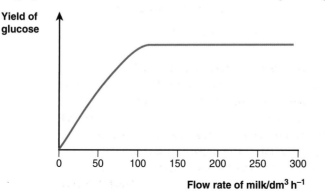

(i) Explain why using a flow rate of 250 dm³ h⁻¹ would not be commercially viable. *(2 marks)*

(ii) Copy the graph and sketch on it the curve you would expect if the process were carried out at 20°C rather than at 15°C. Explain why you have chosen to draw the curve that you have drawn. *(4 marks)*

Total: 10 marks

4 The diagram shows the main components of a voltage-output biosensor.

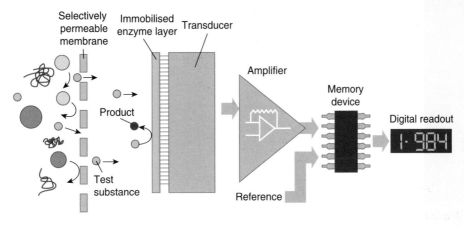

(a) What properties of enzymes make them suitable for use in biosensors? *(2 marks)*

(b) Explain the role of the transducer layer. *(3 marks)*

(c) Explain why the voltage change is proportional to the concentration of the test substance. *(3 marks)*

Total: 8 marks

5 The flowchart shows the main stages in the production of alcohol.

(a) Bacterial amylase is an extracellular enzyme. Explain why it would be easier to isolate than an intracellular enzyme. *(2 marks)*

(b) Explain the advantage of using yeast, rather than individual enzymes, for the stages labelled **X**. *(3 marks)*

(c) Beer is sometimes treated with bacterial amyloglucosidase to reduce the glucose content and produce low-calorie beer. Explain why the isolated enzyme is used rather than the bacterium itself. *(2 marks)*

Total: 7 marks

Chapter 9

Nucleic acids and protein synthesis

This chapter covers:
- the research leading to the discovery of the structure of DNA
- the structure of DNA
- how the DNA molecule replicates itself
- how DNA controls protein synthesis
- the genetic code

The unravelling of the structure of DNA in 1953 in Cambridge by two young research biochemists, James Watson and Francis Crick, was one of the most significant research events of all time. Biologists were finally able to understand how chromosomes duplicate themselves prior to cell division and how DNA controls protein synthesis.

A. Barrington Brown/SPL

Watson and Crick with their original model of the structure of DNA

The discovery of the structure of DNA

Sir Isaac Newton, the renowned physicist who discovered the laws of gravity, said: 'If I have seen further than other men, it is because I have stood on the shoulders of giants'. What he meant by this was that he was able to carry out groundbreaking research and formulate universal laws only because he could build on the work of others who had preceded him. Everyone associates Watson and Crick with the double-helix model of the structure of DNA. However, their molecular modelling was only possible because of the research findings of others who had gone before them. Some of the key events are outlined below.

◄ James Watson, Francis Crick and Maurice Wilkins received Nobel prizes for their contributions to unravelling the structure of DNA. Rosalind Franklin died before the prizes were awarded. Nobel prizes are never awarded posthumously.

Timeline for the discovery of DNA

1665 Robert Hooke observed and made drawings of cells of cork.

1831 Robert Brown described the nucleus of cells.

1836 Hugo von Mohl observed cell division (but not the involvement of chromosomes).

1865 Gregor Mendel published work on breeding in pea plants and identified the basic laws of inheritance. However, his work was largely ignored.

1869 Johann Miescher, through chemical analysis, identified nucleic acids in cells, but not their location.

1875 Eduard Strasburger described chromosomes and their location in the nucleus of a cell.

1885 Albrecht Kossel followed up the research of Miescher and identified the sugar and organic bases in nucleic acids.

Early 1900s Hugo de Vries 'rediscovered' Mendel's work and the principles of genetics were finally accepted.

1908 Archibald Garrod, despite not knowing the nature of genes, made the link between genes and enzymes. He proposed that people with the genetic condition alkaptonuria (inherited in a simple Mendelian fashion) lack a single oxidative enzyme as a result of a defective gene; later work, in the 1920s, proved him correct.

Early 1940s George Beadle and Edward Tatum showed that each gene controls only one biochemical reaction because the gene is responsible for the synthesis of one particular enzyme. This is the 'one gene, one enzyme' hypothesis.

1944 Avery and Macleod showed that DNA can transform (change the features of) a virus and so must be the genetic material. However, many people remained unconvinced.

1948–50 Erwin Chargaff showed that the amount of adenine in DNA always equals the amount of thymine and the amount of cytosine always equals the amount of guanine.

1952 Alfred Hershey and Martha Chase demonstrated that only the DNA of a virus is necessary to make a cell produce new viruses. DNA must be the material of inheritance.

1953 Rosalind Franklin provided X-ray diffraction photographs of DNA. Maurice Wilkins suggested a spiral structure for the molecule. Using the idea of a spiral, the fact that the amounts of adenine and thymine are equal, as are the amounts of cytosine and guanine, and Rosalind Franklin's evidence from X-ray crystallography, Watson and Crick constructed the double-helix model of DNA.

SPL

X-ray diffraction pattern of DNA, similar to that obtained by Rosalind Franklin

Box 9.1 The Hershey–Chase experiment

Hershey and Chase worked with bacteriophages (literally 'bacteria eaters'). Bacterio-phages are viruses that infect bacteria. They consist of a DNA 'core' surrounded by a protein coat. When a bacteriophage infects a bacterium, the DNA core is injected into the bacterial cell but the protein coat remains outside. Inside the cell, the viral DNA replicates itself and 'directs' the synthesis of more viral protein. The protein and DNA are assembled into new virus particles.

Hershey and Chase carried out the following experiment:

- Bacteriophages were labelled with radioactive sulphur and radioactive phosphorus. Sulphur is found in proteins but not in DNA; phosphorus is found in DNA but not in proteins. Therefore, the viruses contained DNA labelled with radioactive phosphorus and proteins labelled with radioactive sulphur.
- These bacteriophages were used to infect bacteria.
- The mixture was agitated in a blender in order to remove the viral coats.
- On filtering the mixture they found:
  - protein containing radioactive sulphur but no bacterial cells in the liquid
  - live bacterial cells containing radioactive phosphorus in the sediment

  This meant that only the DNA had entered the bacterial cells.
- On re-culturing the bacteria, the bacteriophages replicated themselves as normal.
- When the bacteriophages emerged from the bacterial cells, they contained DNA labelled with radioactive phosphorus.

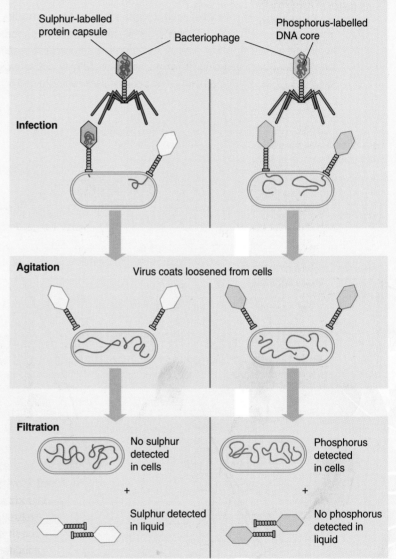

This experiment showed that replication of the viruses could occur without the protein coat. The viral DNA could replicate itself, instruct the host cell to synthesise viral DNA and protein, *and* organise the DNA and viral protein into new virus particles. It provided strong evidence that DNA is the hereditary material.

The structure of DNA

DNA molecules are huge. Each molecule consists of two strands twisted into a double helix. Each strand is made from millions of subunits called **nucleotides** (Figure 9.1) and is, therefore, a polynucleotide. Each nucleotide has three components:

- an **organic base** — either adenine, thymine, cytosine or guanine
- the pentose sugar **deoxyribose**
- a **phosphate** group

There are four different bases, each containing nitrogen, so there are four different types of nucleotide in a DNA molecule.

Two nucleotides can react to form a dincleotide in a similar way to two monosaccharides reacting to form a disaccharide (Figure 9.2).

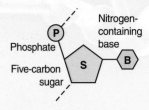

Figure 9.1 Structure of a nucleotide

◀ An organic base is a base because each nitrogen atom has a lone pair of electrons that can attract a hydrogen ion. Overall, the molecule of DNA (deoxyribonucleic *acid*) is acidic because of the many phosphate groups it contains. Each –OH in a phosphate group can release a hydrogen ion, making the surrounding medium more acidic.

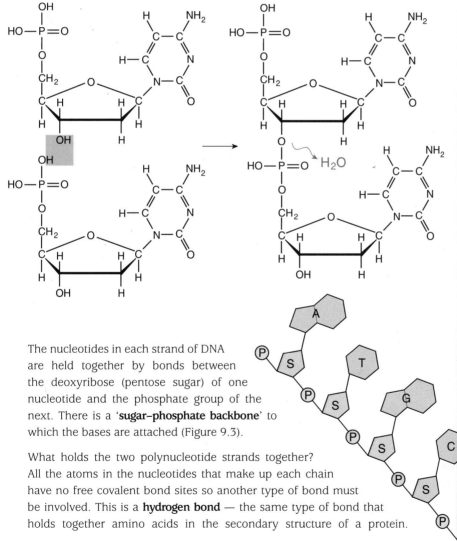

Figure 9.2 Two nucleotides reacting to form a dinucleotide; this is a condensation reaction

ℯ Be quite clear in your mind about the distinction between a *molecule* of DNA and a *strand* of DNA. There are *two* strands in *each* molecule.

The nucleotides in each strand of DNA are held together by bonds between the deoxyribose (pentose sugar) of one nucleotide and the phosphate group of the next. There is a '**sugar–phosphate backbone**' to which the bases are attached (Figure 9.3).

Figure 9.3 Part of one strand of a DNA molecule

What holds the two polynucleotide strands together? All the atoms in the nucleotides that make up each chain have no free covalent bond sites so another type of bond must be involved. This is a **hydrogen bond** — the same type of bond that holds together amino acids in the secondary structure of a protein.

Hydrogen bonds form between the organic bases of each polynucleotide strand (Figure 9.4).

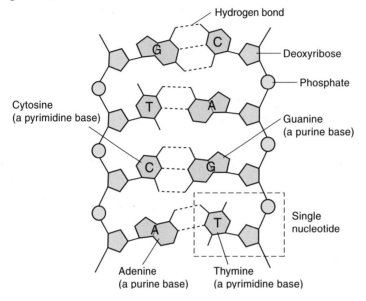

Hydrogen bond

Deoxyribose

Phosphate

Cytosine
(a pyrimidine base)

Guanine
(a purine base)

Single
nucleotide

Adenine
(a purine base)

Thymine
(a pyrimidine base)

Figure 9.4 The two strands that make up a DNA molecule are held together by hydrogen bonds

◀ Adenine (A) always bonds with thymine (T) and guanine (G) always bonds with cytosine (C)

There are two other important features concerning the way in which the two strands of DNA are held together:

- A nucleotide containing the base adenine on one of the strands is *always* paired with one containing thymine on the other strand. A nucleotide containing the base cytosine is *always* paired with one containing guanine. This is the **base-pairing rule**. It explains why, in 1950, Chargaff always found equal amounts of adenine and thymine in a molecule of DNA (whatever its origin), together with equal amounts of cytosine and guanine. Adenine and thymine are said to be **complementary bases**, as are cytosine and guanine.
- The strands are oriented opposite to each other. The 'start' or 'top' of one strand is paired with the 'end' or 'bottom' of the other. The two strands are said to be **anti-parallel**.

ℓ The percentage of adenine in a molecule of DNA is always equal to that of thymine and the percentage of cytosine is always equal to that of guanine. So, if just one of these figures is known, all the others can be calculated.

Suppose the percentage of cytosine in a molecule of DNA is 34%. By the base-pairing rule, the percentage of guanine must also be 34%. Cytosine and guanine together account for 68% of the bases in the molecule of DNA. Adenine and thymine must therefore account for 32% of the DNA. The amounts of adenine and thymine are equal, so each must account for 16%.

Box 9.2 Size and stability of DNA

DNA is a huge molecule, but its size varies from species to species. Describing this variation in size by using the difference in molecular mass gives some extremely large and rather unhelpful numbers. Instead, biologists use the idea that DNA is made from nucleotides containing bases — bigger molecules of DNA will contain more nucleotides and more bases. The size of a DNA molecule is expressed in terms of how many base pairs it contains. Because there are so many, these units are often kilobase pairs (thousands of base pairs) or megabase pairs (millions of base pairs).

DNA is a very stable molecule. If it were not, and were constantly changing, mutations would occur frequently. If it broke down easily, it would not be able to replicate effectively and the DNA passed on would not be identical to that in the original cell.

DNA replication

When cells divide, it is important that the daughter cells formed (apart from the sex cells) contain the same genetic information as the parent cell that produced them. To achieve this, DNA must be able to replicate itself exactly.

DNA molecules exist within chromosomes in the nucleus and are surrounded by a 'soup' of free DNA nucleotides. On replication, it is these nucleotides that are used to build the new strands of DNA. Although they did not know the details, Watson and Crick proposed that DNA replication would be **semi-conservative**. This means that the DNA molecule replicates in such a way that:

- each new DNA molecule formed contains one strand from the original DNA
- both new DNA molecules formed are identical to each other and to the original molecule

The process involves several enzymes and proteins, but the key stages are as follows:

- Molecules of DNA helicase break hydrogen bonds and 'unwind' part of the helix of the DNA molecule, revealing two single-stranded regions.
- Molecules of DNA polymerase follow the helicase along each single-stranded region, which acts as a template for the synthesis of a new strand.
- The DNA polymerase assembles free DNA nucleotides into two new strands that are complementary to the template strands because of base pairing.
- The processes of unwinding followed by complementary strand synthesis progress along the whole length of the DNA molecule.
- The result is two DNA molecules that are identical to each other (and to the original molecule), each of which contains one strand from the original DNA molecule.

DNA helicase breaks the hydrogen bonds and the polynucleotide strands of DNA separate

Each strand acts as a template for the formation of a new molecule of DNA

Individual nucleotides line up with complementary bases on parent DNA strands

The nucleotides are joined together by DNA polymerase to form two molecules of DNA

Each molecule contains a strand from the parent DNA and a new strand

Although the idea of semi-conservative replication of DNA was proposed by Watson and Crick and generally accepted as the likeliest method of replication, there was no direct experimental evidence for it. In 1957, Matthew Meselson and Franklin Stahl carried out an investigation using the bacterium *Escherichia coli*, which provided strong evidence for the semi-conservative replication of DNA.

◄ The hydrogen bonds that hold the two strands of DNA together have approximately 5–10% of the strength of the bonds that hold the atoms together in the nucleotides. At room temperature, hydrogen bonds break more easily than other bonds. This is important in DNA replication.

Figure 9.5 Semi-conservative replication

In eukaryotic cells, DNA molecules occur in chromosomes in the nucleus. Each DNA molecule is highly coiled and surrounded by proteins (histones). When cell division occurs, by either mitosis or meiosis, each chromosome must first duplicate itself. For this to happen, each molecule of ◄ DNA must replicate itself.

Box 9.3 Meselson and Stahl's experiment

The basis of Meselson and Stahl's experiment is the technique of density-gradient centrifugation, which is very sensitive and can separate molecules of only slightly differing molecular masses.

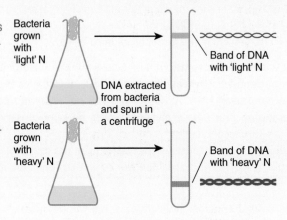

The element nitrogen exists as two isotopes. One isotope (the most common form) has an atomic mass of 14 (^{14}N).

The other isotope has an atomic mass of 15 (^{15}N). *E. coli* bacteria grown in a culture medium in which all the nitrogenous compounds contained ^{15}N produced DNA that was slightly 'heavier' than 'normal' DNA containing ^{14}N. This was reflected in the positions of the DNA in the centrifuge tube.

The investigation then proceeded as shown below.

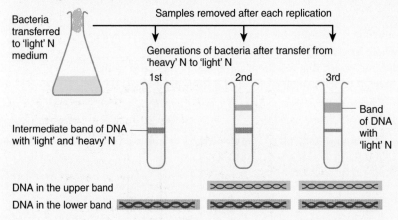

These results provided evidence for the semi-conservative replication of DNA.

> Semi-conservative replication means that when DNA replicates, one strand in each new DNA molecule has come from the original molecule.

The 'intermediate' band formed after the initial reproduction (first generation DNA) indicates that each molecule of DNA contains one 'heavy' strand (from the original molecule) and one light strand (formed using nitrogenous compounds containing ^{14}N in the new culture medium). This intermediate DNA then replicates. The strands separate and each strand acts as the template for a new complementary 'light' strand. Therefore, the second generation DNA is half intermediate and half light.

The detail of Meselson and Stahl's experiment is shown in the diagram opposite.

e Using a similar argument, you should be able to work out the proportions of light and intermediate DNA in the third generation.

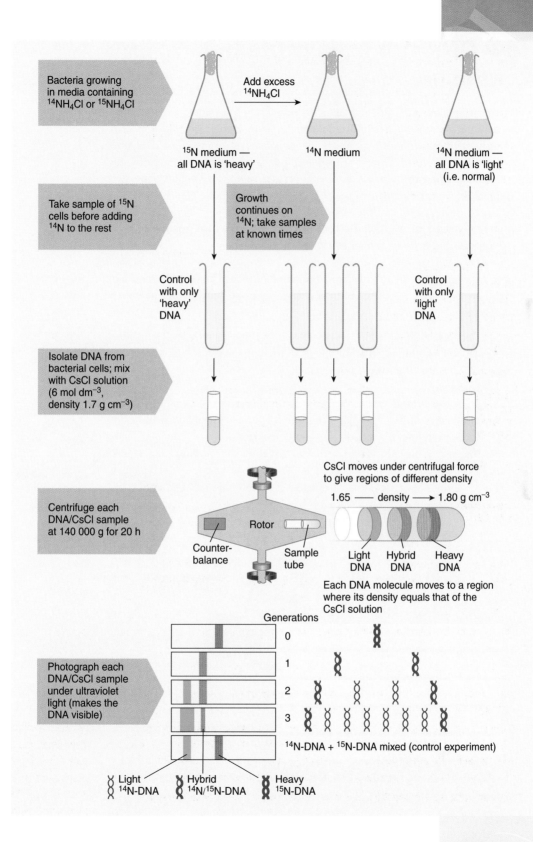

Bacteria growing in media containing $^{14}NH_4Cl$ or $^{15}NH_4Cl$

Add excess $^{14}NH_4Cl$

^{15}N medium — all DNA is 'heavy'

^{14}N medium

^{14}N medium — all DNA is 'light' (i.e. normal)

Take sample of ^{15}N cells before adding ^{14}N to the rest

Growth continues on ^{14}N; take samples at known times

Control with only 'heavy' DNA

Control with only 'light' DNA

Isolate DNA from bacterial cells; mix with CsCl solution (6 mol dm^{-3}, density 1.7 g cm^{-3})

Centrifuge each DNA/CsCl sample at $140\,000$ g for 20 h

Counter-balance

Rotor

Sample tube

CsCl moves under centrifugal force to give regions of different density

1.65 —— density —→ 1.80 g cm^{-3}

Light DNA   Hybrid DNA   Heavy DNA

Each DNA molecule moves to a region where its density equals that of the CsCl solution

Photograph each DNA/CsCl sample under ultraviolet light (makes the DNA visible)

Generations

0

1

2

3

^{14}N-DNA + ^{15}N-DNA mixed (control experiment)

Light ^{14}N-DNA   Hybrid $^{14}N/^{15}N$-DNA   Heavy ^{15}N-DNA

How DNA controls protein synthesis

Proteins are polymers of amino acids. Each protein has a unique tertiary structure because of the sequence of amino acids in its molecule. To control protein synthesis, DNA must be able to specify this sequence of amino acids. The 'one gene, one enzyme' hypothesis of Beadle and Tatum was not so far from the truth. Each gene controls the synthesis of a protein, although not all of these are enzymes. This provides us with a useful working definition of a gene.

> A gene is a sequence of DNA nucleotides that specifies (codes for) a sequence of amino acids that forms the primary structure of a protein.

As the sugar molecule and phosphate group are identical in all DNA nucleotides, it must be the sequence of bases in the gene that specifies the sequence of amino acids.

The code for a protein that is specified by DNA has to be carried to the ribosomes so that they can assemble the amino acids in the correct sequence to form the appropriate protein. However, DNA remains in the nucleus at all times. The following events occur:

- The DNA code is rewritten in a molecule of **messenger RNA** (mRNA) that travels from the nucleus through pores in the nuclear envelope to the ribosomes. This rewriting of the code is called **transcription**.
- Free amino acids are transferred from the cytoplasm to the ribosomes. This is carried out by molecules of **transfer RNA** (tRNA).
- The RNA code is read and the amino acids are assembled into a protein. This is called **translation** and is carried out by the ribosomes.

There is a third type of RNA called **ribosomal RNA** (**rRNA**). This is only found in the ribosomes. All three kinds of RNA are produced by transcription of DNA in the nucleus.

Figure 9.6 How DNA controls protein synthesis

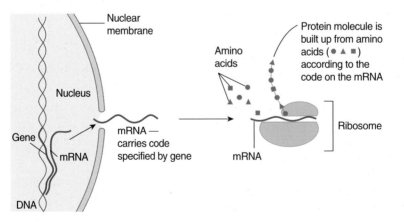

The genetic code

All the different proteins that are found in all the organisms on Earth are synthesised from just 20 amino acids. Different numbers and sequences of these amino acids produce an almost limitless range of proteins. Each protein is coded for by bases in a section of DNA but there are only four different bases available. How can this be? If each base coded for a single amino acid, then it would only be possible to specify four different amino acids. If two bases were needed to code for one amino acid, then 16 amino acids could be specified. This is still not enough. A sequence of three bases could code for 64 different amino acids. This is more than enough and is, in fact, the way in which the bases are organised to code for amino acids. The **genetic code** is a **triplet code**. It is also a **non-overlapping code**. This means that each triplet is distinct from all other triplets.

Hair contains the protein keratin. Bone contains the protein collagen. The protein in feathers is almost the same as that in the scales of dinosaurs.

A triplet of bases codes for each amino acid. There are 64 codes and only 20 amino acids, so what is the purpose of the other 44 codes? In fact, none of the codes is spare or redundant. Most amino acids have more than one code. Only methionine and tryptophan have just one triplet that codes for them; arginine has six. Three of the triplets (TAA, TAG and TGA) do not code for amino acids. They are 'stop' codes that signify the end of a coding sequence. Because there is this extra capacity in the genetic code, over and above what is essential, it is said to be a **degenerate code**.

The genetic code is a **universal code**. For example, the triplet TAT is the DNA code for the amino acid tyrosine in a human, a giant redwood tree, an *E. coli* bacterium or in any other living organism.

Box 9.4 The triplet code

If the genetic code were a singlet code, four bases could only specify four amino acids:

A = amino acid 1, T = amino acid 2,
C = amino acid 3, G = amino acid 4.

A doublet code could specify 16 amino acids. The possible codes are:

AA	AT	AC	AG
TA	TT	TC	TG
CA	CT	CC	CG
GA	GT	GC	GG

Notice that order matters. The code AT is not the same as the code TA.

In a triplet code, all sixteen of the doublet codes could have any of the four bases added to the start of the code. For example, the first line of the doublet code above becomes:

AAA	AAT	AAC	AAG
TAA	TAT	TAC	TAG
CAA	CAT	CAC	CAG
GAA	GAT	GAC	GAG

This generates 16 combinations, as do the three other lines, making a total of 64 combinations.

The DNA codes for all 20 amino acids are given in Table 9.1.

Table 9.1

First position	Second position				Third position
	T	C	A	G	
T	Phenylalanine Phenylalanine Leucine Leucine	Serine Serine Serine Serine	Tyrosine Tyrosine stop stop	Cysteine Cysteine stop Tryptophan	T C A G
C	Leucine Leucine Leucine Leucine	Proline Proline Proline Proline	Histidine Histidine Glutamine Glutamine	Arginine Arginine Arginine Arginine	T C A G
A	Isoleucine Isoleucine Isoleucine Methionine	Threonine Threonine Threonine Threonine	Asparagine Asparagine Lysine Lysine	Serine Serine Arginine Arginine	T C A G
G	Valine Valine Valine Valine	Alanine Alanine Alanine Alanine	Aspartic acid Aspartic acid Glutamic acid Glutamic acid	Glycine Glycine Glycine Glycine	T C A G

In Table 9.1, the first letter of each triplet specifies a horizontal band. The second letter specifies a column and the third letter specifies a horizontal line. Take, for example, the triplet CAG:

- **C** (the first position) specifies the second horizontal band across
- **A** (the second position) specifies the third column
- **G** (the third position) specifies the fourth horizontal line

To find which amino acid is coded for by CAG find the fourth line in the third column of the second band. CAG is the code for the amino acid glutamine. ATT is the code for isoleucine and GAG is the code for glutamic acid. Check the table and see if you agree!

Transcription

There are similarities between the transcription of DNA to RNA and the replication of DNA. However, both the scale of the process and the product formed are very different. When transcription takes place, only one of the strands of DNA is copied. This is because only one of the strands actually carries the genetic information for synthesising proteins. This is the **sense strand**. In practice, the bases on the complementary strand do not code for anything and it is tempting to call it the nonsense strand. Instead, biologists have dubbed it the **antisense strand**.

The structure of a messenger RNA molecule differs from a molecule of DNA in a number of important ways:

- mRNA is single stranded (DNA is double stranded).
- mRNA is much smaller. Its length corresponds to the number of bases in a single gene.

When DNA replicates, the sense strand forms the template for a complementary strand — an antisense strand. The new DNA molecule contains one sense strand and one antisense strand. The antisense strand forms a template for a new sense strand. Therefore, the new molecule of DNA based on the antisense strand also contains one strand of each ◀ type.

- mRNA contains the base **uracil**. It does not contain thymine.
- The pentose sugar in mRNA is ribose, not deoxyribose.

> 🅮 If you are asked to compare the structure of DNA and mRNA, make sure you give a genuine *comparison*. Simply saying, 'mRNA is single stranded' is not a comparison. Is the DNA also single stranded? Or maybe triple stranded? You must make your comparison clear.

Transcription takes place in the following way:
- A section of DNA unwinds. The sense strand of this section contains the gene that codes for a protein. However, copying this would produce a complementary sequence of bases, similar to those in the antisense strand, which would not code for anything.
- The enzyme DNA-dependent RNA polymerase moves along the *antisense* strand, using it as a template for the synthesis of mRNA.
- The polymerase assembles free RNA nucleotides into a chain in which the base sequence is complementary to the base sequence on the antisense strand of the DNA. This, therefore, carries the same triplet code as the sense strand (except that uracil replaces thymine).
- The completed mRNA molecule leaves the DNA; the strands of DNA rejoin and re-coil.

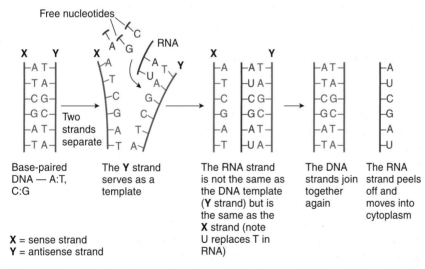

Figure 9.7 Stages in transcription of mRNA from DNA

The mRNA molecule now contains the code for the protein that originated in the gene (the section of the sense strand of the DNA). Again, three bases code for an amino acid, but in mRNA they are called **codons** rather than triplets. The base sequence is the same as that of the original sense strand, except that each thymine is replaced by uracil. The mRNA codes for all 20 amino acids are shown in Table 9.2.

As with the DNA from which the code shown in Table 9.2 is transcribed, most amino acids have more than one code. Some codes are 'stop' codes to tell the ribosome that this is the end of the reading sequence. The code for methionine,

Table 9.2

Second position

		U	C	A	G	
First position (5′ end)	U	UUU ⎤ Phe UUC ⎦ UUA ⎤ Leu UUG ⎦	UCU ⎤ UCC ⎥ Ser UCA ⎥ UCG ⎦	UAU ⎤ Tyr UAC ⎦ UAA stop UAG stop	UGU ⎤ Cys UGC ⎦ UGA stop UGG Trp	U C A G
	C	CUU ⎤ CUC ⎥ Leu CUA ⎥ CUG ⎦	CCU ⎤ CCC ⎥ Pro CCA ⎥ CCG ⎦	CAU ⎤ His CAC ⎦ CAA ⎤ Gln CAG ⎦	CGU ⎤ CGC ⎥ Arg CGA ⎥ CGG ⎦	U C A G
	A	AUU ⎤ Ile AUC ⎥ AUA ⎦ AUG Met	ACU ⎤ ACC ⎥ Thr ACA ⎥ ACG ⎦	AAU ⎤ Asn AAC ⎦ AAA ⎤ Lys AAG ⎦	AGU ⎤ Ser AGC ⎦ AGA ⎤ Arg AGG ⎦	U C A G
	G	GUU ⎤ GUC ⎥ Val GUA ⎥ GUG ⎦	GCU ⎤ GCC ⎥ Ala GCA ⎥ GCG ⎦	GAU ⎤ Asp GAC ⎦ GAA ⎤ Glu GAG ⎦	GGU ⎤ GGC ⎥ Gly GGA ⎥ GGG ⎦	U C A G

Third position (3′ end)

AUG, acts as a 'start' code. The reading section of all mRNA molecules begins with AUG and therefore the first amino acid in all polypeptide chains is methionine, although this may be removed at a later stage.

Translation

Translation of the mRNA code into a protein depends on the interaction within a ribosome between mRNA and tRNA. There are different types of tRNA, each being adapted to transfer one particular amino acid and to be recognised as carrying that amino acid. However, all tRNA molecules have the same basic structure.

Box 9.5 Promoters and introns

Transcription is really more complicated. In addition to the coding regions of a gene (exons) there are:

- **promoter regions** in the DNA that are not transcribed but serve as recognition sites for the polymerase — they indicate where to start copying the DNA
- non-coding sections of DNA called **introns**, separating the coding regions or **exons**; they do not code for any amino acids but are transcribed and are later 'cut out' of the mRNA molecule

In addition, the end of the mRNA is 'capped' with a different nucleotide that allows the ribosome to recognise it. Ribosomes cannot recognise non-capped mRNA.

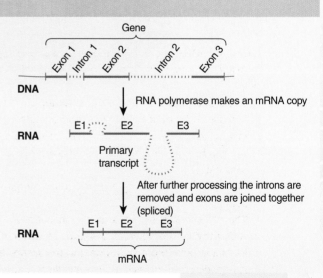

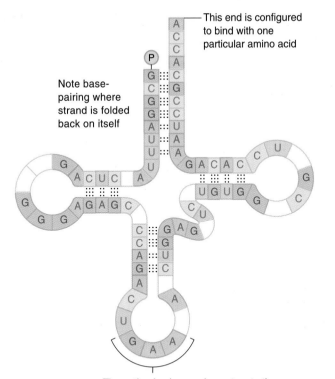

This end is configured to bind with one particular amino acid

Note base-pairing where strand is folded back on itself

The anticodon is complementary to the mRNA codon that specifies the amino acid carried by this tRNA

Figure 9.8 Structure of a tRNA molecule

Transfer RNA is single stranded (as is mRNA) but the single strand is conformed into a cloverleaf shape. It is held in this shape by hydrogen bonds between complementary bases. So, if you are asked to compare DNA and RNA, do not say that only DNA shows base pairing and/or hydrogen bonding.

Once the mRNA arrives at a ribosome and is recognised, it begins to thread itself between the small and large ribosomal subunits. Then, the following events take place:

- The first two codons of the mRNA enter the ribosome.
- Transfer RNA molecules (with amino acids attached) that have complementary anticodons to the first two codons of the mRNA bind to those codons.
- A peptide bond forms between the amino acids carried by these two tRNA molecules.
- The mRNA moves along by one codon, bringing the third codon into the ribosome.
- The tRNA that is freed returns to the cytoplasm.
- A tRNA with a complementary anticodon binds with the third codon, bringing its amino acid into position next to the second amino acid.
- A peptide bond forms between the second and third amino acids.

- The mRNA moves along by one codon, bringing the fourth mRNA codon into the ribosome.
- The process is repeated until a stop codon is in position and translation ceases.

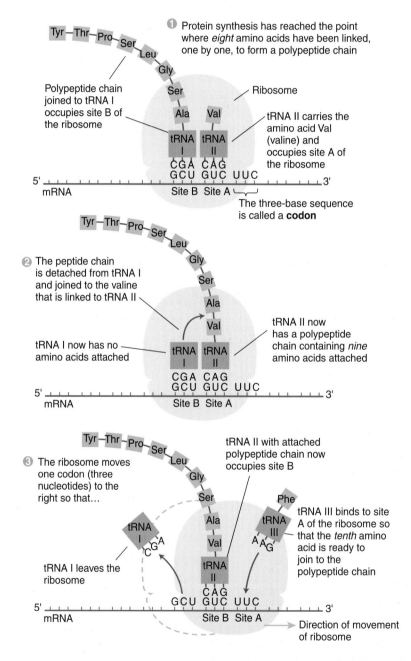

① Protein synthesis has reached the point where *eight* amino acids have been linked, one by one, to form a polypeptide chain

Polypeptide chain joined to tRNA I occupies site B of the ribosome

Ribosome

tRNA II carries the amino acid Val (valine) and occupies site A of the ribosome

The three-base sequence is called a **codon**

② The peptide chain is detached from tRNA I and joined to the valine that is linked to tRNA II

tRNA I now has no amino acids attached

tRNA II now has a polypeptide chain containing *nine* amino acids attached

③ The ribosome moves one codon (three nucleotides) to the right so that...

tRNA II with attached polypeptide chain now occupies site B

tRNA III binds to site A of the ribosome so that the *tenth* amino acid is ready to join to the polypeptide chain

tRNA I leaves the ribosome

Direction of movement of ribosome

Figure 9.9 How translation takes place

Protein synthesis is an important process in the flow of information that regulates a cell's metabolism. The main stages in the flow of information in a cell are shown in Figure 9.10.

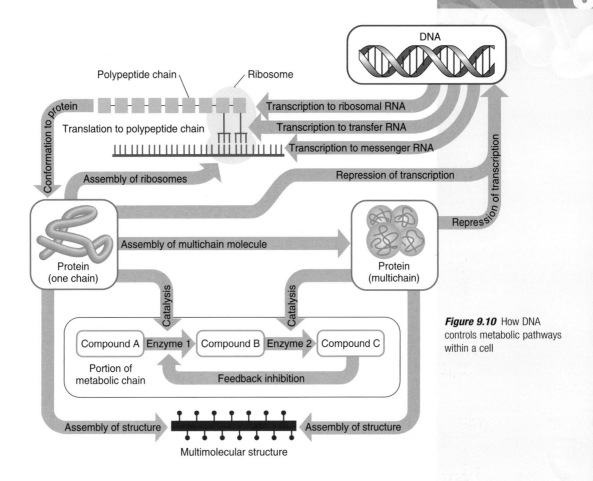

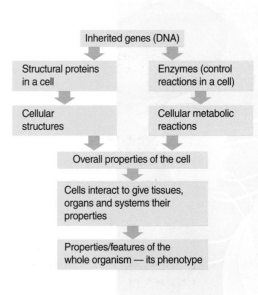

Figure 9.10 How DNA controls metabolic pathways within a cell

DNA and the next generation

DNA carries the code for the production of all the proteins that an organism will ever synthesise. Each cell will only make some of these proteins because different genes are transcribed in different cells:

- Some are structural proteins within a cell, such as ion-pore proteins.
- Others, for example keratin, are proteins that are components of larger structures, such as feathers.
- Some are enzymes that catalyse metabolic reactions that result in the organism being able to carry out a particular function or to have a particular structure.

The DNA an organism inherits determines the features that the organism will have — first at a cellular level and, as a result of interactions between cells, at a whole-organism level. This is the **phenotype** of the organism. These processes are summarised in the flowchart (right).

Summary

Structure of DNA

- In 1953 — using X-ray crystallography evidence supplied by Rosalind Franklin and ideas from Maurice Wilkins — James Watson and Francis Crick proposed the double-helix model for the structure of DNA.
- The DNA molecule is a double helix in which:
  - each strand is a polynucleotide consisting of four types of nucleotide
  - each nucleotide contains the pentose sugar deoxyribose, a phosphate group and an organic base
  - the four organic bases are adenine, thymine, cytosine and guanine
  - specific base pairing occurs between the strands; adenine is always paired with thymine and cytosine with guanine
  - each polynucleotide strand is held together by the 'sugar–phosphate backbone'; condensation links form between the phosphate group of one nucleotide and the deoxyribose sugar of the next
  - the two strands are held together by hydrogen bonds
- Only one strand of DNA holds coding information. This is the sense strand; the other strand is the antisense strand
- A gene is a section of a DNA molecule that codes for the synthesis of a specific protein.

DNA replication

- DNA replicates itself as a precursor to cell division.
- During the replication of DNA:
  - DNA helicase breaks the hydrogen bonds to separate the two strands and 'untwist' the helix
  - each separated strand forms a template for the synthesis of a new complementary strand
  - using free DNA nucleotides, the enzyme DNA polymerase assembles a complementary strand for each of the separated strands of the original molecule
  - the new strand binds with the original strand by forming hydrogen bonds between the complementary bases
  - two complete molecules of DNA are formed that are identical to each other and to the original molecule of DNA from which they were formed

DNA controls protein synthesis and cell activity

- The genetic code is a triplet code that is also degenerate, non-overlapping and universal.
- In protein synthesis:
  - a section of the antisense strand of DNA transcribes an mRNA copy of itself
  - the mRNA leaves the nucleus and threads its way through a ribosome
  - codons on the mRNA in the ribosome become bound to complementary anticodons on tRNA; each molecule of tRNA carries an amino acid specified by an mRNA codon

– a peptide bond forms between the amino acids in the ribosome
– the mRNA moves on by one codon and the process is repeated

- DNA regulates the activities of the cell by controlling protein synthesis. The protein could be, for example, an enzyme that catalyses a reaction, a structural protein that will be part of a membrane where reactions take place or an ion-pore protein to allow ions into the cell.

Questions

Multiple-choice

1 DNA consists of two polynucleotide strands in which:
   A the percentage of adenine is the same in each strand
   B the percentage of adenine is the same as that of thymine in each strand
   C the percentage of adenine is the same as that of thymine in the whole molecule
   D the percentage of adenine is 50% of that of thymine in the whole molecule

2 The two strands of DNA are held together by:
   A hydrogen bonds
   B ionic bonds
   C covalent bonds
   D van der Waals forces

3 A nucleotide consists of:
   A an organic base, a pentose sugar and three phosphate groups
   B an inorganic base, a pentose sugar and three phosphate groups
   C an inorganic base, a pentose sugar and one phosphate group
   D an organic base, a pentose sugar and one phosphate group

4 tRNA differs from DNA because it is:
   A smaller, single stranded and shows no base-pairing
   B smaller, single stranded with thymine replaced by uracil
   C smaller, single stranded and with deoxyribose instead of ribose
   D smaller, single stranded and linear in shape

5 The genetic code is:
   A a triplet code, degenerate and overlapping
   B a doublet code, degenerate and universal
   C a doublet code, degenerate and non-overlapping
   D a triplet code, degenerate and universal

6 When DNA replicates itself:
   A DNA polymerase 'unzips' the double strands and DNA helicase assembles new complementary strands
   B DNA helicase 'unzips' the double strands and DNA polymerase assembles new complementary strands
   C RNA polymerase 'unzips' the double strands and DNA helicase assembles new complementary strands
   D RNA helicase 'unzips' the double strands and RNA polymerase assembles new complementary strands

7 The DNA triplet AAT would code for an amino acid carried by tRNA with the anticodon:

A AAU

B TTA

C AAT

D UUA

8 In a ribosome, the two amino acids that are held adjacent to each other form a:

A hydrogen bond

B ionic bond

C ester bond

D peptide bond

9 Following transcription, mRNA must be modified to:

A remove non-coding sections

B alter its shape so that it can bind with ribosomes

C alter its shape so that it can bind with an amino acid

D remove unwanted amino acids

10 It is important that DNA is a stable molecule because:

A it should not take part in any chemical reactions

B alterations would result in mutations (changed genes) being passed on

C transcription should always produce the same mRNA and, therefore, the same protein

D all of the above

Examination-style

1 (a) The diagram represents the structure of the DNA molecule.

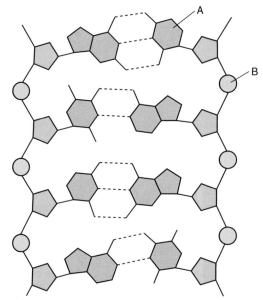

   (i) Name the structures labelled A and B.   *(2 marks)*

   (ii) Use the diagram to explain why the DNA molecule is sometimes described as consisting of two polynucleotide strands.   *(1 mark)*

(b) Complete the table to show three differences in structure between DNA and mRNA.

DNA	mRNA

(3 marks)

Total: 6 marks

2 Protein synthesis takes place in the ribosomes. The code for synthesis of a particular protein is specified by a section of the DNA molecule and is carried to the ribosomes by mRNA.

(a) (i) What do we call a section of DNA that codes for a protein? *(1 mark)*

(ii) The DNA code is sometimes called a degenerate code.
What does this mean? *(2 marks)*

(b) The diagram shows protein synthesis taking place in a ribosome.

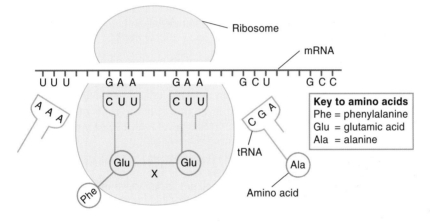

(i) Name the type of bond labelled X. *(1 mark)*

(ii) Use examples from the diagram to explain the terms codon and anticodon. *(2 marks)*

Total: 6 marks

3 Some viruses contain an enzyme called reverse transcriptase. This enzyme catalyses the reverse transcription of mRNA to DNA.

(a) Part of a molecule of mRNA has the base sequence:
    A A U G C C U U A G G U
What would be the sequence of the bases on the DNA strand formed by reverse transcription of this molecule of mRNA? *(1 mark)*

(b) Give *two* ways in which a molecule of DNA formed by reverse transcription would be different from a molecule of DNA in a typical eukaryotic cell. *(2 marks)*

(c) Give three differences between mRNA and DNA found in a typical eukaryotic cell. *(3 marks)*

Total: 6 marks

4   The table below gives information concerning the percentages of the four
    different bases (adenine, thymine, cytosine and guanine) in the DNA of five
    different organisms.

Organism	Adenine/%	Guanine/%	Cytosine/%	Thymine/%
A	21	29	29	21
B	32	18	18	32
C			14	
D	13	37	37	13
E	26	24	24	26

(a) What percentages would you expect for adenine, guanine and
    thymine in the DNA of organism C?   *(1 mark)*

(b)(i) Explain why, in DNA, the ratio of the percentages of the bases
    adenine plus guanine to cytosine plus thymine (A + T:C + G)
    is always equal to 1.   *(3 marks)*

   (ii) Explain why, in mRNA, the ratio of the bases adenine plus
    guanine to cytosine plus uracil (A + G:C + U) is rarely
    equal to 1.   *(2 marks)*

(c) Explain why two organisms can have almost identical
    percentages of the four bases in their DNA and yet be very
    different organisms.   *(2 marks)*

                                                    Total: 8 marks

5   Read the following passage concerning protein synthesis.

    A section of DNA in the nucleus 'unzips' in a similar way as in replication, but
    different enzymes control the process. Molecules of free RNA nucleotides are
    assembled into a strand of mRNA using one of the single DNA strands as a
    template. The resulting molecule of mRNA contains the same genetic
    information as the section of DNA from which it was copied. It then leaves the
    nucleus through a pore in the nuclear envelope and moves into the cytoplasm,
    where it encounters ribosomes. Here, using tRNA as a sort of adaptor molecule,
    the coded information is used to synthesise a protein.

(a)(i) Name the two enzymes involved in DNA replication and
    briefly describe the function of each.   *(3 marks)*

   (ii) Name the enzyme involved in producing the mRNA molecule
    from a section of DNA.   *(1 mark)*

(b)(i) Name the process by which mRNA is produced.   *(1 mark)*

   (ii) Why is only one of the strands of DNA used to produce
    mRNA?   *(2 marks)*

(c) Using the DNA triplet ATC as an example, explain how the
    mRNA formed carries the same genetic information as the
    DNA from which it was copied.   *(3 marks)*

(d) Describe how mRNA and tRNA are used in protein synthesis
    in the ribosomes.   *(5 marks)*

                                                   Total: 15 marks

Chapter 10

The cell cycle, mitosis and meiosis

This chapter covers:
- the main events of the cell cycle
- the structure of chromosomes
- the main stages of mitosis
- a brief outline of meiosis
- the roles of meiosis and mitosis in life cycles

Cell theory states that all cells are formed from pre-existing cells and that this occurs by cell division. The daughter cells formed by this division must contain all the organelles necessary to carry on functioning. They must contain a sufficient number of mitochondria to produce enough ATP to release the energy to 'drive' the metabolic reactions of the cell, and they must have enough ribosomes to synthesise proteins. If they are cells from the mesophyll of a plant leaf, they must have a sufficient number of chloroplasts to carry out photosynthesis. They must have the correct amount and type of DNA for a cell of that species in order to control all the reactions of the cell. This chapter looks at the events that occur during the life history of a cell that lead up to it being able to divide by mitosis or by meiosis, and the roles of these two types of division in the life history of some different organisms.

◄ Strictly, mitosis and meiosis are processes that bring about the division of the nucleus, *not* the whole cell.

Why cells divide

Human life begins as a single cell (a **zygote**), which is the product of **fertilisation**. The billions of cells that make up the body develop from that cell. They are all formed by cell division — nearly all by cell division involving **mitosis**. Only the sex cells are formed by cell division involving **meiosis**. Cell division involving mitosis produces growth.

Some of the cells in the human body retain the ability to divide to replace those lost. Cells are continually being scraped off the lining of our gut as food passes through it. Tens of millions are lost each day from the stomach lining alone. About 1% of red blood cells die and are replaced each day — this amounts to a staggering 250 000 000 000 red blood cells. Cells are lost from the surface of the skin each time something is touched. These cells are replaced by other cells that divide mitotically. There are some cells that have become so specialised that they have lost the ability to divide. For example, nerve cells do not normally divide, although some treatments can induce limited nerve regrowth.

Stem cells in the bone marrow divide mitotically to form more stem cells and other cells that will develop into red blood cells. This ensures that there are always stem cells present to divide to form more red blood cells.

◀ Adult fish can produce new brain cells. The brown ghost fish can produce 50 000 per hour. It had been thought that cells in the human brain never divide, but recent research has shown that new brain cells are formed, albeit very slowly. This has opened up the possibility of treatment for degenerative nerve conditions.

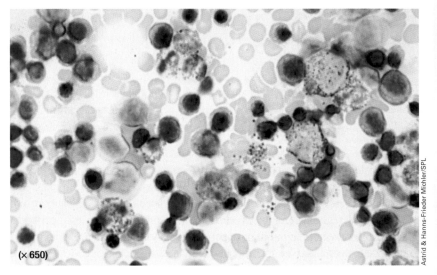

(× 650)

Astrid & Hanns-Frieder Michler/SPL

Red blood cells are formed in the bone marrow

Mitotic cell division in plants is primarily associated with growth. There are three main places where this takes place:
- near the tips of roots and shoots
- in buds
- in a ring of cells beneath the cortex of older roots and shoots

The ring of dividing cells in a root

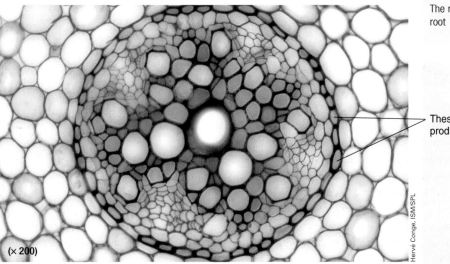

These cells divide to produce lateral roots

(× 200)

Hervé Conge, ISM/SPL

The cell cycle

Cells that divide repeatedly, such as stem cells in bone marrow or cells in the skin that divide to replace those lost from the surface, go through a cycle of events called the **cell cycle**. These events eventually allow the cell to divide to form two cells by mitotic division. One of these cells becomes a specialised cell; the other completes the cell cycle so that the process can be repeated. The cell cycle is shown in the flowchart below, using a stem cell in bone marrow as the example.

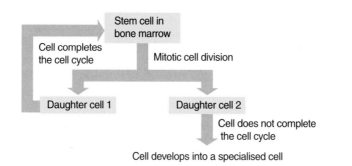

The situation is not always so straightforward; 'daughter cell 2' may go through other divisions before it becomes the specialised cell. An example of this is in the formation of sex cells in the testis (or ovary). This process is summarised in the flowchart below, which starts with the division of an epithelial cell in a testis.

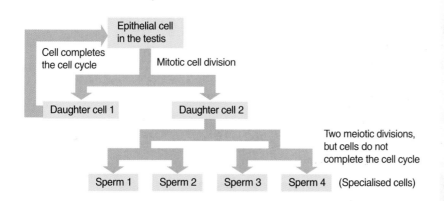

A cell that has just been produced by cell division must go through the following stages if it is to divide again:

- It must grow. Initially, the cell is half-sized, with only half the organelles of a full-size cell. During this phase, more organelles are synthesised and the cell enlarges. Nucleotides are synthesised in preparation for DNA replication later in the cycle. This is the **G1 phase** of the cell cycle.
- DNA must replicate itself and combine with newly synthesised histone proteins to double the amount of chromatin in the nucleus. The cell continues to grow. This is the **S phase** of the cell cycle.

Chromatin is the name given to the DNA–histone complex that makes up chromosomes.

- The cell must prepare itself for mitosis. Specialised proteins called tubulins are synthesised. These are used to make the spindle apparatus, which will eventually separate the chromosomes. This is the **G2 phase** of the cell cycle.

The G1, S and G2 phases are collectively known as **interphase.** The nucleus of the cell now divides by mitosis. Once mitosis is complete, the cell divides into two cells by **cytokinesis.**

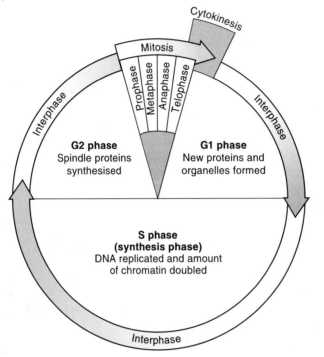

Figure 10.1 The cell cycle

The DNA content of a cell changes during the cell cycle. Replication of DNA in the S phase means that the amount doubles. The amount of DNA remains at this 'double' level until cytokinesis because, until then, the DNA is still contained within one cell.

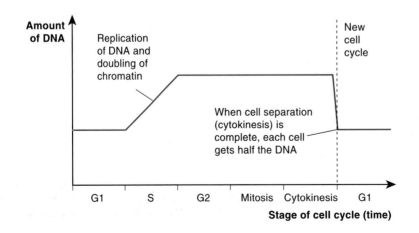

Figure 10.2 Changes in DNA content during the cell cycle

Mitotic cell division

Mitotic cell division involves two main stages:
- division of the *nucleus* by mitosis
- division of the *cell* by cytokinesis

Mitosis

The division of the nucleus by mitosis essentially concerns the distribution of the chromosomes between the two daughter nuclei. As a result of mitosis, each daughter nucleus contains exactly the same number and type of chromosomes as the other daughter nucleus and as the parent nucleus from which they were formed. Each chromosome contains one molecule of DNA. Therefore, each daughter nucleus contains exactly the same amount and type of DNA as the other daughter nucleus and as the parent nucleus from which they were formed. This happens because, before mitosis, each molecule of DNA replicates itself (Chapter 9) and the chromosome that was a single structure becomes a double structure. Each of the two structures is a **chromatid**; the two chromatids that make up one chromosome are called '**sister chromatids**'. They are held together by a **centromere**.

The difference in chromosome structure before and after DNA replication is shown in Figure 10.3.

◀ We owe the name 'mitosis' to the German cell biologist Walther Flemming. He observed cell division and described the chromosomes as 'mitosen' (from the Greek 'mitos', meaning thread).

Box 10.1 The centromere

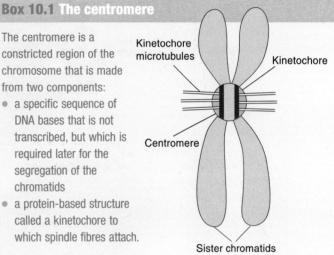

The centromere is a constricted region of the chromosome that is made from two components:
- a specific sequence of DNA bases that is not transcribed, but which is required later for the segregation of the chromatids
- a protein-based structure called a kinetochore to which spindle fibres attach.

Kinetochore microtubules

Kinetochore

Centromere

Sister chromatids

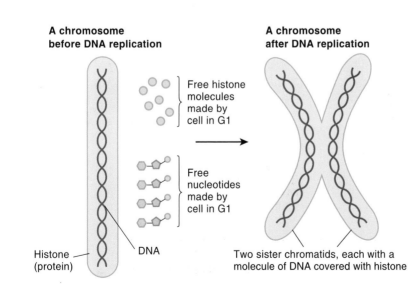

A chromosome before DNA replication

Free histone molecules made by cell in G1

Free nucleotides made by cell in G1

Histone (protein)

DNA

A chromosome after DNA replication

Two sister chromatids, each with a molecule of DNA covered with histone

Figure 10.3 Prior to mitosis, a chromosome becomes a double structure

Box 10.2 The structure of chromosomes

The different levels of organisation in a metaphase chromosome are shown in the diagram.

Chromosomes are composed of DNA and proteins called histones. The DNA–histone complex is called chromatin. During interphase (the period between nuclear divisions), the chromatin is loosely organised throughout the nucleus as loops of chromatin fibres. Individual chromosomes cannot be distinguished. The 'loose' organisation allows the genes to be active. As a cell prepares to enter mitosis, the chromatin loops (by now duplicated) become compacted to form a chromosome that is visible (when stained) under a light microscope. The compact state of the chromatin in such a chromosome means that the genes are too tightly packed to be active.

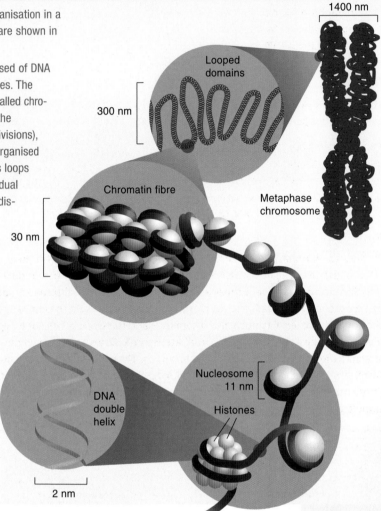

Mitosis is a continuous process but there are four phases:
- prophase
- metaphase
- anaphase
- telophase

Study the photograph of onion root tip cells on page 173. Most of the cells shown here are in interphase. This is because growth of the cell, replication of DNA and production of the spindle proteins take longer than mitosis and cytokinesis. The approximate durations as a percentage of the total time for a cell cycle are:
- interphase — 80%, of which:
  - G1 phase = 25%
  - S phase   = 25%
  - G2 phase = 30%

- mitosis — 17%, of which:
  - prophase = 6%
  - metaphase = 4%
  - anaphase = 3%
  - telophase = 4%
- cytokinesis — 3%

On a microscope slide showing 300 cells, one would expect to find 4% in metaphase, i.e. 12 cells.

The figures are approximations and there is considerable variation in the duration of cycles. However, the principle of calculating the number of cells in any one stage holds true.

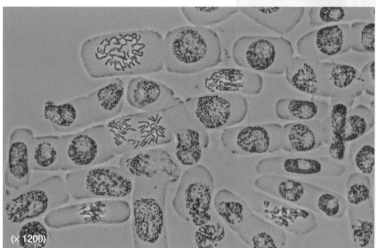

(× 1200)

Cells from the root tip of an onion, stained to show the chromosomes

Prophase

By the start of **prophase**, the chromosomes are double structures because, during the S phase of interphase, DNA has replicated. The two chromatids making up the chromosome are held together by a centromere. The chromatin becomes condensed during prophase, with the result that the chromosomes become shorter and thicker. The nucleolus disappears and the nuclear envelope begins to break down. Towards the end of prophase, **spindle fibres** appear, some of which attach to the centromeres of the chromosomes. These spindle fibres radiate from structures at the two poles of the cell called **microtubule-organising centres**. These organise the tubulin molecules into microtubules, which, in turn, form the spindle fibres.

◀ The DNA in the seven pairs of chromosomes in a cell of the garden pea has a total length of about 7 m. By the end of prophase, the total chromosome length is just 350 μm. The length has been reduced by a factor of 20 000!

(× 4000)

A bluebell cell during prophase of mitosis

Metaphase

During **metaphase**, the spindle apparatus develops fully. Most of the spindle fibres do not attach to a chromosome, but extend from one pole to the other. These fibres (called **polar fibres**) provide a structure in which the fibres that are attached to the chromosomes can function and give the spindle its characteristic shape (Figure 10.4). During metaphase, the chromosomes become aligned along the centre of the spindle. This is an important stage in mitosis, as it determines how the chromatids will be segregated later.

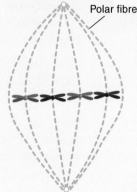

Figure 10.4 The spindle apparatus

Polar fibre

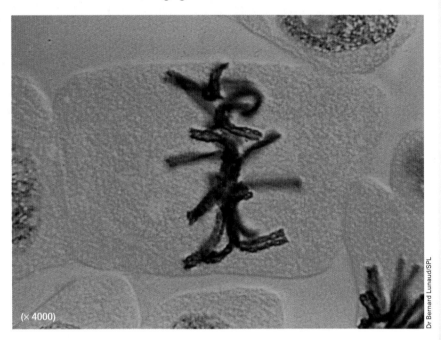

(× 4000)

Dr Bernard Lunaud/SPL

A bluebell cell in metaphase of mitosis

Anaphase

Anaphase is the shortest phase of mitosis. For each chromosome, it involves:
- the splitting of the centromere
- the separation of the two sister chromatids
- the movement of the sister chromatids to opposite poles of the cell

The spindle fibres pull the two chromatids from each chromosome to opposite poles of the cell. As the spindle fibres are attached to the centromere, the centromere forms the leading part of each chromosome. If the centromere is near the centre of the chromosome, then the chromosome has a 'V' shape as it is pulled to the pole. If it is near one end, then the chromosome has more of a 'J' shape. By the end of anaphase, there are two groups of chromosomes, one at each pole of the cell.

◀ Technically, once the centromere has split and the chromatids are separate, they are no longer chromatids but chromosomes, because each now has its own centromere.

The accuracy of DNA replication means that sister chromatids contain identical molecules of DNA — each carries the same genetic information. At the end of anaphase, the two groups of chromosomes formed contain one from each pair of sister chromatids. Therefore, the two groups of chromosomes carry the same genetic information — they are genetically identical.

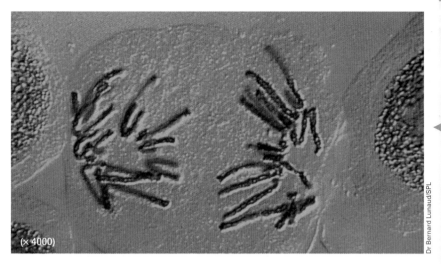

(× 4000)

A bluebell cell in late anaphase of mitosis

◀ The mechanism by which the spindles pull the chromosomes apart remains uncertain. The most likely explanation is that the kinetochore shortens the spindle fibre to which it is attached by breaking off molecules of tubulin.

Dr Bernard Lunaud/SPL

Telophase

During **telophase**, many of the events of prophase seem to be thrown into reverse:

- The spindle apparatus is dismantled.
- A nuclear envelope forms around each daughter nucleus.
- Nucleoli appear in each daughter nucleus.
- The chromosomes steadily elongate as the chromatin extends itself from its condensed state until there is, once again, just a diffuse mass of chromatin fibres.

By the end of telophase, the cell contains two fully formed daughter nuclei. They are genetically identical to each other and to the original nucleus from which they were formed.

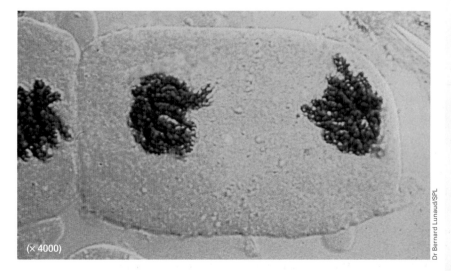

(× 4000)

A bluebell cell in early telophase of mitosis

Dr Bernard Lunaud/SPL

Telophase marks the end of mitosis. The original nucleus has divided into two genetically identical daughter nuclei. Next, the cell must divide into two.

Cytokinesis

During **cytokinesis**, the original cell divides into two. In animal cells, this involves the plasma membrane forming a constriction across the centre of the cell. This becomes narrower and narrower, finally pinching off the cytoplasm into two cells. Plant cells must, in addition, synthesise two new cell walls across the centre of the original cell. Initially, a 'cell plate' is formed in the centre of the cell. This grows outwards and fuses with the cell wall, forming the two new cell walls and separating the two daughter cells.

Although the chromosomes are segregated in a precise manner during mitosis, the organelles of the original cell are distributed at random between the two daughter cells. Their position at the time of cytokinesis decides which daughter cell they enter.

Box 10.3 Mitotic cell division

The key features of a mitotic cell division are that:
- it involves only one nuclear division
- two daughter cells are formed
- the daughter cells are diploid (p. 177)
- the daughter cells are genetically identical (contain the same number and type of chromosomes and therefore contain the same genes)

Meiotic cell division

Unlike mitosis, division of a nucleus by meiosis does not produce genetically identical daughter nuclei, but nuclei that show genetic variation. In mammals and higher plants, meiosis is involved only in the formation of sex cells.

Chromosome number

It is common knowledge that most human cells contain 46 chromosomes. However, there are some exceptions:
- Red blood cells contain none because they have no nucleus.
- Some liver cells contain 92.
- Sperm cells and oocytes contain 23.

The actual number of chromosomes does not tell the whole story. The 46 chromosomes in, for example, a skin cell are in fact made up of 23 pairs — there are two sets of 23 different chromosomes. Each pair of chromosomes is called a **homologous pair**. Each chromosome within a homologous pair carries genes that control the same features in the same sequence. However, many genes can exist in two (or more) different forms called **alleles**. While the chromosomes of a homologous pair carry genes controlling the same feature, they may carry different alleles of those genes. However, the sister chromatids that make up one chromosome from the S phase of the cell cycle onwards are genetically identical and, therefore, carry the same alleles of the genes in the same sequence.

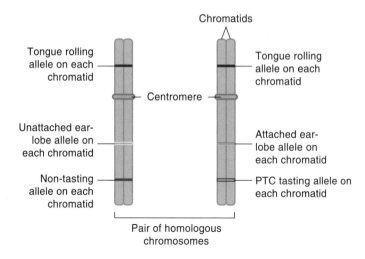

Chromatids

Tongue rolling allele on each chromatid

Tongue rolling allele on each chromatid

Centromere

Unattached ear-lobe allele on each chromatid

Attached ear-lobe allele on each chromatid

Non-tasting allele on each chromatid

PTC tasting allele on each chromatid

Pair of homologous chromosomes

Figure 10.5 Homologous chromosomes carry genes controlling the same feature in the same sequence; they might not carry the same alleles of those genes

Cells that contain two sets of chromosomes are called **diploid** cells. Sperm cells and oocytes contain 23 chromosomes and therefore have only one set of chromosomes, i.e. they have one chromosome from each homologous pair. These cells are **haploid** cells.

The 23 pairs of chromosomes from the cell of a human male

Box 10.4 Chromosome pairs

Of the 23 pairs of chromosomes in most human cells, 22 pairs are autosomes (chromosomes not related to sex determination) and one pair are sex chromosomes. Cells from males have two different sex chromosomes, the **X** and the **Y** chromosomes. Cells from females have two **X** chromosomes.

The chromosomes are numbered by their size and shape. Of the autosomes, chromosome 1 is the largest and chromosome 22 is the smallest.

Different species have different numbers of chromosomes. Humans have 46 (two sets of 23), fruit flies have 8 (two sets of 4), garden peas have 14 (two sets of 7). The number of chromosomes in a 'set' is the haploid number and is represented by the letter n. The diploid number is therefore $2n$. So in humans, $2n = 46$.

CNRI/SPL

Meiosis

You will not be examined at AS on the *details* of meiosis. That is part of the A2 content. However, you must have an understanding of the outcome of meiotic cell division and the ways in which it is different from mitotic cell division.

As with mitotic cell division, meiotic cell division involves division of the nucleus (**meiosis**) and division of the cell (cytokinesis). However, there are a number of significant differences between the two processes. Meiosis is summarised in Figure 10.6.

  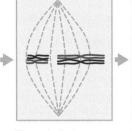 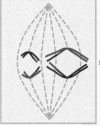 

Figure 10.6 The main stages of meiosis

The DNA has already replicated and each chromosome consists of two chromatids. The cell contains two sets of chromosomes.

The spindle starts to form. Homologous chromosomes pair and exchange DNA.

The spindle is complete and the nuclear envelope has disintegrated. The bivalents are arranged around the middle of the spindle.

Homologous chromosomes start to separate from each other.

There is one complete set of chromosomes at each end of the cell. The two cells resulting from meiosis I are therefore haploid.

Meiosis II separates the chromatids, forming four haploid cells.

Box 10.5 Meiotic cell division

The key features of a meiotic cell division are that:
- it involves two nuclear divisions
- four daughter cells are formed
- the cells formed are haploid (p. 177)
- the daughter cells show genetic variation (contain the same number and type of chromosomes but in different combinations)

Mitosis, meiosis, life cycles and chromosome numbers

Members of the same species have the same number and types of chromosome. The individuals vary because of the different combination of alleles that each possesses. In a species that reproduces sexually, mitosis and meiosis are important in keeping this chromosome number constant from one generation to the next. The roles of mitosis and meiosis in the life cycles of a mammal and of a flowering plant are shown in Figure 10.7.

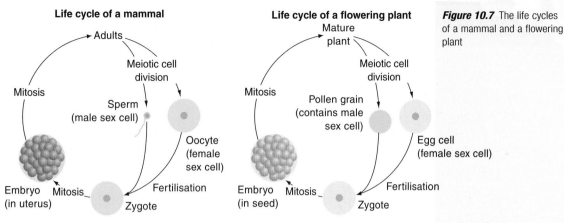

Life cycle of a mammal

Life cycle of a flowering plant

Figure 10.7 The life cycles of a mammal and a flowering plant

In both these life cycles:

- cells in the sex organs divide meiotically to form haploid sex cells
- fertilisation produces a zygote in which the normal diploid number of chromosomes has been restored
- from the zygote, mitotic cell division produces all the diploid cells of the adult organism

Summary

Why cells divide

- In mammals and higher plants, cells divide mitotically to allow growth to take place and to replace cells that are lost or damaged.
- In mammals and higher plants, cells divide meiotically to produce sex cells.

Cell cycle

- Stem cells go through the cell cycle repeatedly; other cells lose the ability to divide when they become specialised.
- The main phases of the cell cycle are:
  - the G1 phase — the cell grows and produces more organelles
  - the S phase — growth continues, DNA replicates and each chromosome is duplicated to become a pair of sister chromatids, held together by a centromere
  - the G2 phase — the cell prepares for mitosis by producing tubulins (the proteins needed to assemble the spindle fibres)
  - mitosis — the nucleus divides into two genetically identical daughter nuclei
  - cytokinesis — the cell splits into two daughter cells
- The G1, S and G2 phases are known collectively as interphase.
- Chromosomes are made of chromatin, which is a complex of DNA and histone (a protein).

Mitotic cell division

- There are four stages in mitosis:
  - prophase — chromatin condenses, making the chromosomes shorter and thicker; the nucleolus and nuclear envelope disappear and assembly of the spindle apparatus commences
  - metaphase — assembly of the spindle apparatus is completed and chromosomes attach to the centre of the spindle by their centromeres
  - anaphase — spindle fibres shorten, split the centromere and pull sister chromatids (now called chromosomes again) to opposite poles of the cell
  - telophase — the two groups of chromosomes form daughter nuclei; the spindle is dismantled, nuclear envelopes and nucleoli appear and the chromosomes become longer and thinner as the chromatin becomes less condensed
- Telophase is followed by cytokinesis, which involves:
  - in animal cells, the plasma membrane forming a constriction that eventually 'pinches off' the cytoplasm, forming two new cells
  - in plant cells, a cell plate forming in the centre of the cell, which grows outwards and forms two new cell walls that separate the daughter cells
- A single mitotic division produces two daughter cells that are diploid and genetically identical.

Meiotic cell division and chromosome number

- As a result of the two meiotic divisions, four daughter cells are produced that are haploid and show genetic variation.
- The chromosome number is kept constant from generation to generation by:
  - meiosis halving the number of chromosomes in the sex cells
  - fertilisation restoring the diploid number of chromosomes in the zygote
  - mitosis producing the diploid cells of the body of the adult organism

Questions

Multiple-choice

1 A mitotic cell division produces:
   A two haploid cells
   B two diploid cells
   C four haploid cells
   D four diploid cells

2 The sequence of phases in the cell cycle is:
   A G1 → G2 → S → mitosis → cytokinesis
   B G1 → G2 → mitosis → cytokinesis → S
   C G1 → S → G2 → cytokinesis → mitosis
   D G1 → S → G2 → mitosis → cytokinesis

3 A homologous pair of chromosomes is:

   A a pair of sister chromatids held together by a centromere

   B a pair of non-sister chromatids

   C a pair of chromosomes carrying genes for the same features in the same sequence

   D a pair of chromosomes carrying genes for different features

4 During prophase:

   A the nucleolus and nuclear envelope disappear and chromatin becomes much less condensed

   B the nucleolus appears, the nuclear envelope disappears and chromatin condenses

   C the nucleolus appears, the nuclear envelope appears and chromatin condenses

   D the nucleolus and nuclear envelope disappear and chromatin condenses

5 The role of meiosis in life cycles is to:

   A restore the diploid chromosome number in the zygote

   B produce the haploid chromosome number in the zygote

   C produce the haploid chromosome number in the gametes

   D produce the diploid number of chromosomes in the gametes

6 During the S phase of the cell cycle, the DNA content of a cell:

   A doubles

   B halves

   C remains the same

   D none of the above

7 When the spindle apparatus is fully assembled:

   A all of the fibres are attached to chromosomes

   B all of the fibres run from one pole to the other

   C some fibres are attached to chromosomes, others run from one pole to another

   D all of the fibres are fully contracted

8 During cytokinesis in animal cells:

   A a cell plate is formed

   B new organelles are synthesised

   C DNA replicates

   D a constriction forms in the middle of the cell

9 Haploid cells have:

   A only one chromosome from each homologous pair

   B half the normal number of chromosomes for that species

   C both of the above

   D neither of the above

10 In mammals, meiotic cell division differs from mitotic cell division in that:

   A the original nucleus is haploid, not diploid

   B the nucleus of each daughter cell is haploid, not diploid

   C there is only one nuclear division, not two

   D there are two daughter cells formed, not four

Examination-style

1 Figure 1 shows a cell in a stage of mitosis. The cell contains just two pairs of homologous chromosomes.

Figure 1

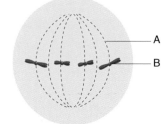

(a) (i) What are homologous chromosomes? *(1 mark)*

(ii) Identify the structures labelled A and B on Figure 1. *(2 marks)*

(iii) Name the stage of mitosis represented in this diagram. Give a reason for your answer. *(1 mark)*

Figure 2 shows the life cycle of a mammal.

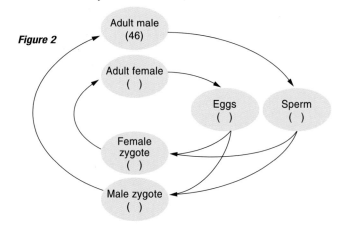

Figure 2

(b) (i) Mark on Figure 2 one stage where meiosis takes place and one stage where mitosis takes place. *(2 marks)*

(ii) Complete the empty boxes to show the number of chromosomes per cell. *(1 mark)*

Total: 7 marks

2 (a) The diagram shows the four stages of mitosis.

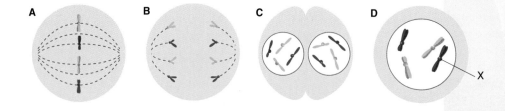

(i) Name the structure labelled X. *(1 mark)*
(ii) List the letters representing the stages in the order in which the stages occur during mitosis. *(1 mark)*
(iii) Describe fully what happens during stage B. *(3 marks)*
(b) Describe three differences between mitosis and meiosis. *(3 marks)*

Total: 8 marks

3 The graph shows the changes in the amount of DNA in a cell during the stages of the cell cycle.

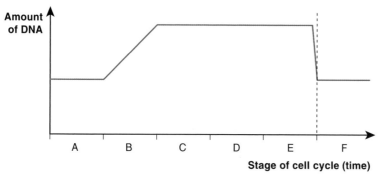

Explain the change in the amount of DNA during:
(a) (i) stage B *(2 marks)*
(ii) stage E *(2 marks)*
(b) (i) Name the stage of the cell cycle labelled C. *(1 mark)*
(ii) Describe the events that take place in the stage labelled A. *(2 marks)*

Total: 7 marks

4 (a) Complete the table below to compare mitosis and meiosis.

Feature of the process	Mitosis	Meiosis
Number of nuclear divisions		
Number of cells formed		
Genetic variability of daughter cells (Yes/No)		
Diploid or haploid daughter cells formed		

(2 marks)

(b) The graph shows the change in distance between the centromere of one chromosome and a pole of the cell.

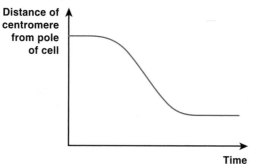

(i) Describe the change in position of the chromosome. *(1 mark)*

(ii) Explain how this change in position is brought about. *(2 marks)*

(c) Explain why individual chromosomes are not visible when an interphase nucleus is viewed through a light microscope. *(2 marks)*

Total: 7 marks

5 (a) The table below shows the relative amounts of DNA in some mammalian cells.

Cell	Relative amount of DNA/ arbitrary units
Skin cell	30
Muscle cell	30
Red blood cell	0
Sperm	
Oocyte	
Zygote	

(i) Give an explanation for the amount of DNA in a red blood cell. *(2 marks)*

(ii) How much DNA would you expect there to be in:
- **A** a sperm?
- **B** a zygote?

Explain your answers. *(4 marks)*

(b) Some anticancer drugs inhibit spindle formation in mitosis. Suggest why patients given such drugs often develop anaemia. *(3 marks)*

Total: 9 marks

Chapter 11

Manipulating genes

This chapter covers:
- the isolation of genes from donor cells
- the transfer of genes into host cells
- the synthesis of genes starting from mRNA and from proteins
- the culture of host cells to ensure that they contain the transferred gene
- some applications of genetic engineering
- some of the moral and ethical issues raised by genetic engineering

The discovery of the structure of DNA in 1953 led to an explosion of discoveries and the development of new techniques. At about the same time, biologists discovered the presence of restriction enzymes in bacteria. The genetic code was deciphered in 1966 and in 1970 the true nature of the restriction enzymes was realised. In 1976, Fred Sanger and his team of researchers developed the technique of gene sequencing that allowed them to work out the sequence of bases in a fragment of DNA. Within a year, a genetically engineered bacterium containing the gene for human insulin was created. The first purified insulin from this source was available in 1982. In 1987, the technology of the polymerase chain reaction was developed. In 1990, the human genome project was set up and the first draft of the human genome was published in 2001. Other developments have led to our current ability to alter the genome of many organisms. The basic principles of how this is achieved are covered in this chapter.

A genome is the complete set of genetic information of an organism.

Why create transgenic organisms?

A **transgenic organism** is an organism that has had genetic material from another type of organism transferred to it. It has been **genetically modified** or **genetically engineered** to create a specific change in its genome. The new gene is usually carried into the organism by a **vector**. Altering the genotype of an organism also alters its **phenotype**. The altered phenotype is the result of the nature of the new protein coded for by the gene. The new protein could be an enzyme or a structural protein and could result in:

- new substances that are useful to humans being synthesised in microorganisms
- increased resistance to disease (in plants now, and possibly humans in the future)
- increased resistance to the effects of herbicides, insects, drought or spoilage in plants
- crops with increased amounts of some nutrients — one genetically engineered strain of rice contains more lysine (or amina acid) than usual; golden rice contains a high concentration of beta-carotene, which can be converted to vitamin A

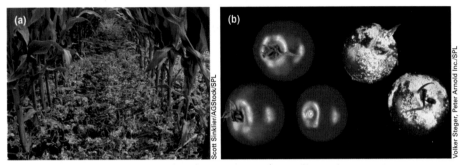

How about a blue rose, a tobacco plant that glows in the dark and a potato that makes plastic? All these already exist.

(a) Genetically modified maize after exposure to herbicide. When the crop is treated with herbicide, the maize is unaffected but the weeds are killed.
(b) Tomatoes genetically engineered for resistance to spoilage (left) and normal tomatoes after the same period of time (right).

The main reasons for genetically engineering any organism are nearly always based on benefits, direct or indirect, to human beings. Insulin from genetically engineered bacteria can save human lives and can make diabetes more manageable for many. Bovine somatotrophin from genetically engineered bacteria can significantly improve the milk yield of cattle. This should give an economic benefit to the farmer or to the large organisations that buy from the farmer and retail most of the milk. The benefit of crops being resistant to attack by insects is improved yields of the resistant plants and hence higher returns for the producer.

There is a much debate about the rights and wrongs of producing food from genetically modified plants and animals — GM food. There is much less debate about using insulin from genetically modified bacteria. Is this consistent thinking?

Creating transgenic organisms

Much of the original research into genetic engineering was carried out on single-celled organisms, such as bacteria and brewer's yeast. Genetically engineered bacteria continue to be of importance in research. Because of the many products these transgenic organisms produce, they now have great economic importance too. The key stages in the genetic engineering of bacteria are shown in the flow-chart below.

| Identify the gene to be transferred and:
• remove the gene from a donor cell *or*
• create the gene from mRNA using reverse transcriptase *or*
• create the gene from a known base sequence | → | Insert the gene into a vector | → | Transfer the vector to the host bacterial cell | → | Culture the host bacterial cells and extract any product |

Isolating the gene of interest

There are a number of ways in which the gene of interest can be prepared for insertion into a vector.

Creating the gene from a known base sequence

With the advent of 'gene machines', it is now possible to synthesise a gene from free nucleotides. This is a really direct method of obtaining a gene. How do we know the nature of the gene to be synthesised? Genes are transferred from one organism to another because of the effect of the protein for which they code. The genetic code in DNA is a triplet code in which three bases codes for an amino acid. So, if the sequence of amino acids in the protein for which the gene codes is known, then the required sequence of bases can be worked out. In fact, there will be many possible base sequences because the code is **degenerate** with most amino acids being coded for by more than one triplet.

Protein analysis to find the sequence of amino acids	→	Work out the sequence of bases that will code for this sequence of amino acids	→	Synthesise the gene in a gene machine from free nucleotides and DNA polymerase

This procedure has the added advantage that the gene of interest need not be identified in a donor organism and then extracted from that organism. However, in reality, this technique is only practicable for proteins that have relatively small molecules. For larger proteins, the initial analysis currently takes too long and is too costly.

Creating the gene from mRNA

Most eukaryotic cells are diploid (p. 177) and contain two copies of a gene controlling a particular feature. They may have two different alleles and so only carry one functional copy of the gene. The gene of interest, however, might be expressed in certain cells only. For example, the gene controlling the synthesis of insulin is only expressed in islet cells in the pancreas. These cells contain thousands of molecules of the mRNA that codes for insulin. This mRNA is comparatively easy to extract and gives a high yield of the source for the gene from relatively few cells.

Remember that to initiate protein synthesis, a section of the antisense strand of a DNA molecule is transcribed into mRNA that has a complementary base sequence to the DNA transcribed (uracil replacing thymine). If the appropriate mRNA were available and transcription could be thrown into reverse, then a section of DNA that was complementary to the mRNA would be created. This complementary DNA (cDNA) would be equivalent to the antisense strand of a DNA molecule for the gene of interest.

To achieve this, the extracted mRNA is incubated with free DNA nucleotides and an enzyme called **reverse transcriptase**. This enzyme throws the transcription process into reverse and creates the cDNA strand. However, cDNA is single-stranded. To be of any use, the sense strand is also needed. The mRNA is 'washed' out and the newly synthesised cDNA is incubated with free DNA nucleotides and DNA polymerase. The cDNA strand forms the template for, and then binds with, a strand that is complementary to it. This is the sense strand of the gene of interest (Figure 11.1). The two-stranded section of DNA can now be transferred into another organism.

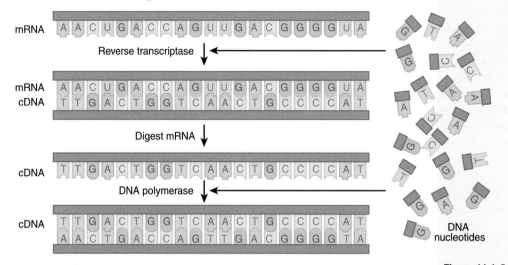

Figure 11.1 Creating the gene from mRNA

Extracting the gene from a donor cell

After isolating DNA from donor cells, enzymes called **restriction endonucleases** are used to extract the gene.

These enzymes 'cut' the DNA molecule at places called **restriction sites**. Each restriction site is a short sequence of 4–8 nucleotides. The enzymes can be used to cut out any gene of interest. Different bacteria make many different restriction enzymes, each of which recognises a different restriction site. One of these enzymes is called *Eco*R1. It recognises the sequence G–A–A–T–T–C, cutting the strand between the G and the A nucleotides wherever it finds the sequence (Figure 11.2).

◄ Restriction endonucleases are often simply called restriction enzymes.

◄ *Eco*R1 is so named because it was the first restriction enzyme (R1) to be isolated from the *E. coli* bacterium (*Eco*).

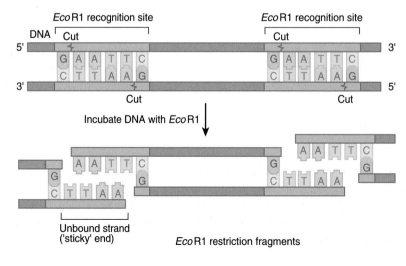

Figure 11.2 The restriction enzyme *Eco*R1 cuts DNA at specific restriction sites

Box 11.1 Finding the gene of interest

A restriction enzyme will cut DNA *wherever it finds its restriction site*. There are unlikely to be just two of these, conveniently placed at the start and end of the gene of interest. By chance alone, the sequence will occur once every 4000 nucleotide pairs and there are millions of nucleotide pairs in the human genome. So, treating a sample of human DNA with a restriction enzyme cuts it into many fragments — called a gene library. Only one of the fragments will contain the gene of interest. Finding that gene is the most time-consuming part of the whole process. It involves the following steps:

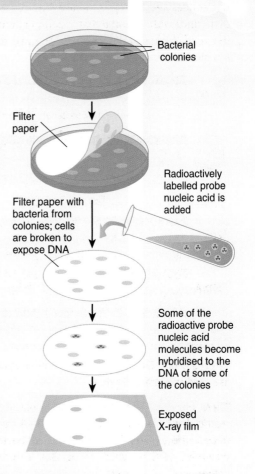

Bacterial colonies

Filter paper

Filter paper with bacteria from colonies; cells are broken to expose DNA

Radioactively labelled probe nucleic acid is added

Some of the radioactive probe nucleic acid molecules become hybridised to the DNA of some of the colonies

Exposed X-ray film

- Incubate the DNA fragments with plasmids (small, circular sections of DNA) that have been previously cut open by the same restriction enzyme. Each fragment is taken up by a plasmid to form a recombinant plasmid.
- Incubate the recombinant plasmids with bacteria. The ratio of plasmids to bacteria is low so that it is unlikely that any one bacterium will take up more than one plasmid.
- Dilute the bacterial suspension and culture it on agar gel in petri dishes. Each bacterium will occupy a unique location in a petri dish.
- Incubate the petri dish at a suitable temperature. The bacteria will multiply; each bacterium will form a colony of millions, all containing copies of the recombinant plasmid taken up by the original bacterium.
- 'Blot' each petri dish with filter paper. This will transfer a few cells from each colony to the filter paper. The cells will be in the same relative positions as the colonies in the petri dish. Break open the cells to expose the DNA and split the two strands of DNA.
- Incubate with a radioactive gene probe that has a sequence that is complementary to at least part of the gene of interest. DNA from cells with the gene will bind with the probe and become radioactive.
- Locate the radioactive DNA by producing an X-ray photograph.
- The position of the radioactive DNA on the X-ray photograph correspond to the colonies of bacteria containing the gene of interest.

◀ A gene probe is a short length of single-stranded DNA or mRNA that is radioactive or fluorescent. The sequence of bases is complementary to at least part of the sequence of bases in the gene of interest. By base pairing, a gene probe can pair with complementary DNA, provided the two strands of the DNA molecule have been separated (Figure 11.3).

Notice that complementary base pairing means that the sequence occurs on both strands, but running in opposite directions. By cutting between the G and the A on both strands, the enzyme makes a zigzag cut and the section of DNA that is cut out has overlapping ends. The single-stranded portions at each end of the section of the cut-out DNA will be able to form hydrogen bonds with a complementary DNA sequence. They are called **sticky ends**.

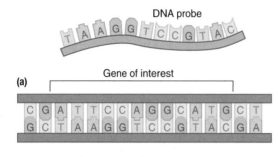

DNA probe

Gene of interest

(a)

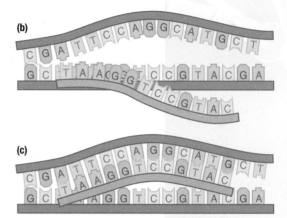

(b)

(c)

Some restriction enzymes do not make zigzag cuts — they make straight cuts across the two strands of DNA. The fragments of DNA produced have 'blunt ends' and do not join as easily to other DNA molecules, although techniques now exist for facilitating this.

Transferring the gene of interest to a vector

Vectors are carriers. In the genetic modification of a bacterium, a vector carries the gene of interest into a bacterial cell. There are two main types of vector:

- **plasmids** are small circular fragments of DNA found naturally in bacteria; they replicate independently of the main bacterial DNA molecule
- **bacteriophages** (phages) are viruses containing DNA as their genetic material that can infect bacterial cells

The DNA of the plasmid must first be made receptive to the gene DNA. This is carried out by cutting open the plasmid DNA using the same restriction enzyme used to cut out the gene. The single-stranded ends of the two types of DNA will contain complementary base sequences. Incubating the two together will cause the plasmid DNA and the gene DNA to **anneal** (join). The rate and extent of this reaction is increased by the enzyme **DNA ligase**. The reaction takes place in two stages:

- Hydrogen bonds form between the bases in the sticky ends, weakly holding the gene DNA in place in the plasmid.
- Catalysed by ligase, covalent bonds form between the sugar–phosphate backbones of the plasmid DNA and gene DNA; the gene has now been firmly **spliced** into the plasmid.

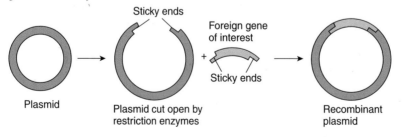

Sticky ends

Foreign gene of interest

Sticky ends

Plasmid

Plasmid cut open by restriction enzymes

Recombinant plasmid

Figure 11.3
(a) The gene of interest and a DNA probe
(b) The strands in the DNA of the gene of interest are split apart
(c) Complementary base paring allows the probe to bind with the sense strand of the gene

◀ The principle of introducing the gene of interest using a bacteriophage is the same as when using a plasmid.

◀ In the case of genes that have been synthesised, rather than extracted, sticky ends have to be added by a special technique.

Figure 11.4 A gene is spliced into a plasmid to form a recombinant plasmid

Any DNA that has had 'foreign DNA' inserted into it is called **recombinant DNA**. The plasmid is now a **recombinant plasmid**.

This sounds quite straightforward, but there is a little more to it. Many plasmids will not take up any new DNA; they will remain exactly as they were at the start. Later, when the bacteria have taken up the plasmids, we need to be able to tell which have taken up the recombinant plasmid and which have taken up the original plasmid and are, therefore, of no use.

Bacteria contain many different plasmids, each of which contains a different combination of genes. Some plasmids contain genes that confer resistance to a particular antibiotic — for example, ampicillin or tetracycline. Some plasmids contain genes that confer resistance to two antibiotics — for example, both ampicillin *and* tetracycline.

Choosing a plasmid that contains genes giving resistance to tetracycline *and* ampicillin allows the bacteria that have taken up the plasmid to be identified. These plasmid genes are called **marker genes**. Introducing a foreign gene into such a plasmid splits the gene for tetracycline resistance and makes it inactive. So, bacteria that have taken up the original plasmid are resistant to both antibiotics; bacteria that have taken up the recombinant plasmid are resistant to ampicillin only (see below).

Introducing the gene of interest into a host bacterial cell

Obtaining plasmids from bacterial cells is relatively simple — the cells are broken open and the plasmids isolated from the other components. Putting plasmids into bacterial cells is rather more difficult because the bacteria must continue to live. The process usually involves treating the bacteria with a solution of calcium chloride. This alters the bacterial cell wall, making it permeable to plasmids. Following this treatment, recombinant plasmids can be introduced into the host by incubating the bacteria with the plasmids. However, there are two important points to note:

- The frequency of plasmid take-up by the bacteria may be as low as 1 in 10 000.
- Of those bacteria that do take up plasmids, some will take up recombinant plasmids and others will take up the original, non-recombinant plasmids. Those that take up the recombinant plasmids are called **transformed bacteria**.

So how do we know which is which? This is where the initial choice of plasmid and host bacterium is crucial. For example, incubating plasmids that contain genes giving resistance to ampicillin and tetracycline with host bacteria that have *no resistance* will result in the following types:

- those that take up no plasmids and are not resistant to either antibiotic
- those that take up the original plasmids and are therefore resistant to both antibiotics
- those that take up the recombinant plasmids and are therefore resistant to ampicillin only

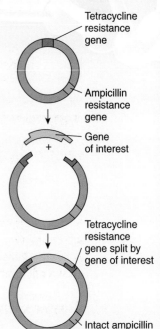

Figure 11.5

The bacteria are cultured on media containing ampicillin or tetracycline. Those that survive on the ampicillin culture *only* are the transformed bacteria. These bacteria can now be cultured and their product harvested (see Chapter 8).

Genetic engineering of bacteria: the whole story

Figure 11.6 summarises the production of human insulin using genetically engineered bacteria.

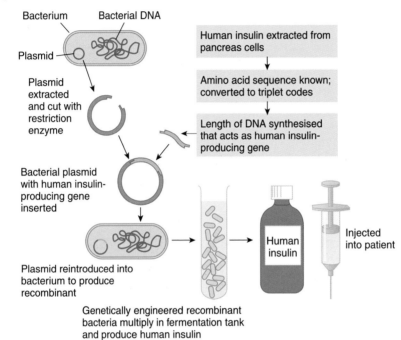

Figure 11.6 Production of human insulin using genetically modified bacteria

Applications of genetic engineering

So far, we have only considered the genetic engineering of bacteria — not the possible alteration of the genome of multicellular organisms. There has been more progress in creating genetically modified plants than genetically modified animals, although some genetically modified animals have been produced. Genetically modified *Tilapia* fish grow bigger and faster than the non-modified fish and could prove to be an important source of protein in some regions of Africa.

Many genetically modified crop plants have been produced and are the subject of much debate. Initially, it proved difficult to transform the genome of plant cells. This was because plant DNA cannot be recombined with foreign DNA by the direct use of restriction enzymes and ligases. However, it was discovered that the bacterium *Agrobacterium tumefaciens* can act as a 'natural genetic engineer'. This bacterium infects plant cells and is able to transfer a plasmid (the

T_i plasmid) into the DNA of the host cells. Therefore, the solution is to modify the T_i plasmid by adding the desired gene (e.g. one for herbicide resistance) and then allow the bacterium to do the rest.

This only produces relatively few genetically modified cells, so these cells are then cultured to produce herbicide- resistant plants.

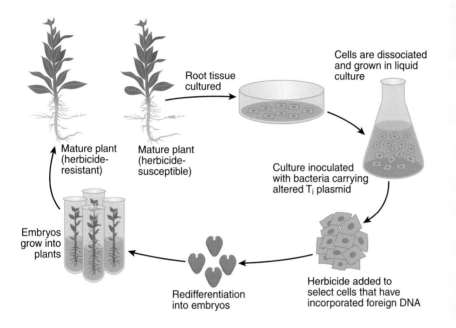

Figure 11.7 Production of herbicide-resistant plants

Root tissue cultured

Cells are dissociated and grown in liquid culture

Culture inoculated with bacteria carrying altered T_i plasmid

Mature plant (herbicide-resistant)

Mature plant (herbicide-susceptible)

Embryos grow into plants

Redifferentiation into embryos

Herbicide added to select cells that have incorporated foreign DNA

Unfortunately, *Agrobacterium* will not infect cereals. To genetically modify these plants, a new technique was developed — the gene gun. This fires tiny pellets (1 μm diameter) of gold fragments with DNA attached into plant tissue. Research has shown that if young, delicate plant tissue is used, there is a good take-up of the DNA. Modified cells can then be cultured into plants in much the same way as shown in Figure 11.7.

The gene gun has allowed biologists to produce a genetically modified rice called 'golden rice'. Golden rice has three genes — two from daffodils and one from a bacterium — added to its normal DNA content. Together, these genes allow the rice to make beta-carotene, which is the chemical that gives carrots their colour. It also colours the rice — hence the name 'golden rice'. Beta-carotene is converted into vitamin A when eaten. In less economically developed regions of the world, millions of children go blind because they have no source of vitamin A in their diet. Golden rice could save their eyesight.

Golden rice

Golden Rice Humanitarian Board

Current applications

- Genetic modification of bacteria produces a range of products, including:
  - enzymes for the food industry
  - thermostable enzymes for washing powders
  - human insulin
  - human growth hormone
  - vaccines (e.g. for prevention of hepatitis B)
  - bovine somatotrophin (to increase milk yield and muscle development in cattle)
- Genetic modification of crop plants gives higher yields, increased shelf-life and improved flavour
- Genetic modification of plants produces:
  - human antibodies ('plantibodies'), which could be used as boosters in people who are failing to produce enough themselves
  - antigens similar to those from viruses and bacteria ('plantigens') to form the basis of vaccines; there would be no risk of contracting the disease from these antigens, whereas there is a risk that a live virus in a vaccine could become virulent
- genetic modification of some animals to give increased growth rates

Potential benefits in the future

- **Gene therapy** may become practicable. This involves changing the genetic code of some cells or, maybe, a whole organism. Some conditions, for example cystic fibrosis, are genetically determined but have a localised effect. It might be possible to alter the genes of the affected cells only, so that they no longer produce the faulty protein that causes the symptoms. Trials are underway, but a timescale of 20–25 years seems likely before this sort of treatment is in regular use.
- It might be possible to produce **gene chips**. Strands of cDNA are immobilised on a glass chip. When a sample of DNA is passed over the chip, any that has complementary sequences to the cDNA binds and can be detected. The cDNA strands on the chip could be tailored to pick out DNA from a virus or a bacterium. This could have real benefits in terms of the fast diagnosis of disease. In addition, the variability in the genome of humans is responsible for different responses to the same drug treatment. By identifying the DNA type of a person, drug treatment could be tailored to individuals.
- It is likely that the production of 'plantigens' and 'plantibodies' will be expanded, and that antibodies will be produced by other genetically engineered organisms too.
- In future, biotechnologists will study the nature of the human **proteome** — the range and nature of the proteins in the human body. This will be more difficult than elucidating the genome as the techniques currently available for

Box 11.2 Two hormones produced by genetically modified bacteria

Human growth hormone is produced by the pituitary gland at the base of the brain. Before growth hormone from genetically modified bacteria was available, the only source of the hormone was human corpses. Obtaining growth hormone involved a rather gruesome procedure and carried health risks. A number of children treated with the hormone from corpses developed Creutzfeldt–Jakob disease (the human form of 'mad cow' disease). When this became apparent, the treatment was withdrawn.

Before human insulin was available from genetically modified bacteria, the only form for treatment of diabetes was non-human insulin. This had to be obtained from other animals. Insulin from genetically engineered bacteria has not just saved the lives of people.

sequencing proteins are much less efficient than those used for sequencing DNA. However, once known, differences in protein content of healthy and diseased tissue could be investigated. It may then be possible to design drugs to interact with the proteins and alter the course of the disease.

- Antisense treatments may be developed. The technology is currently in use, but in its infancy. It involves producing antisense mRNA from the sense strand of the gene that controls production of the protein causing the condition. The antisense mRNA is complementary to the sense mRNA. Therefore, the two will bind. This means that the sense mRNA cannot bind with a ribosome and so the problem protein is not produced (Figure 11.8). Antisense technology has been used to produce tomatoes that do not go mushy when left to ripen to develop their full flavour.

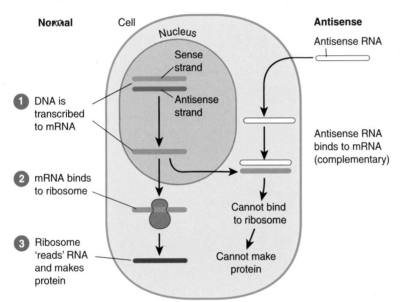

Figure 11.8 Antisense RNA can block protein synthesis

Moral and ethical considerations

Is genetic engineering right or wrong? A debate about right and wrong involves the principles of ethics and morality.

- Morality is our personal sense of what is right, or acceptable, and what is wrong. Morality is not necessarily linked to legality.
- Ethics also involve a sense of right and wrong. However, ethics are not individual opinions. They represent the 'code' adopted by a particular group to govern its way of life.

Many people have passionate views about genetic engineering. Some hold an unshakeable belief in the technology, which they see as something that will bring great benefits to humankind. Other people hold the equally strong belief that genetic engineering is tampering with nature and is likely to cause serious ecological and physiological problems. Some of the issues people are concerned about are discussed below.

- A species is sacrosanct and should not be altered genetically in any way.
  This is a personal, moral viewpoint. People who take this moral stance usually do so on the basis that the genes from one species would not normally find their way into another species. However, genes have been 'jumping' from one species to another (albeit at a very low frequency) for millions of years.

- Not enough is known about the long-term ecological effects of introducing genetically modified organisms into the field. They may out-compete wild plants and take over an area.
  This is also a moral viewpoint. The effects of any new crop cannot be determined without field trials. Ten thousand years ago, the early farmers who cross-bred wild wheat plants to produce the forerunner of today's strains could not have known what impact these would have. Does this make it wrong?

- If plants are genetically engineered to be resistant to herbicides, the gene could 'jump' into populations of weeds and other wild plants.
  This is perfectly true — it could. However, non-genetically modified herbicide-resistant strains of plants already exist. The gene could just as easily jump from these.

- Gene technology might give doctors the ability to create designer babies. It could become possible to obtain a newly fertilised human egg, determine its genotype and ask the parents which genes they would like to be modified. Initially, only genes that cause disease might be replaced. Subsequently, the technology might be used to replace other genes.
  Most doctors would find this morally *and* ethically unacceptable. They might consider replacing genes that cause disease but not replacing genes merely to improve a child's image in the eyes of its parents. However, if such practices become possible, who will define for doctors what is ethically acceptable? What will be the dividing line between cosmetic gene therapy and medical gene therapy?

- Using **genetic fingerprinting** to combat crime will only be useful if there is a genetic database — a file of the genetic fingerprints of everyone in the country. Once all the genes have been identified by the human genome project, who will have access to this information?
  There are concerns that a genetic database would be subject to misuse and that evidence could be manufactured. If insurance companies had access to the genetic database, they might refuse insurance (or charge higher premiums) to people with an increased risk of, say, heart disease. Employers could (covertly) refuse employment to people because their 'genetic profiles' did not meet particular requirements.

◀ The human genome project has identified all the base sequences in the human genome. However, much of this is 'junk' DNA and the exact start and end points of many genes are not yet known.

Consider also the fact that biotechnology (including gene technology) is sometimes merely a refinement of less controversial practices. Organic farmers use the naturally occurring soil bacterium *Bacillus thuringiensis* as a non-chemical insecticide. Genetic engineers have extracted a gene from this bacterium and transferred it to cotton plants to make them resistant to attack by insects. People have known for centuries that rubbing a certain blue mould onto cuts can stop them turning septic. In 1922, Alexander Fleming discovered penicillin in the blue mould *Penicillium*.

e You must make up your own mind about genetic engineering. Be sure of the facts before you do.

Summary

- The genome of an organism is the complete set of genetic information in that organism.
- A transgenic organism has had genes from a different type of organism (usually a different species) added to its genome.
- The methods for obtaining a gene for transfer to another organism involve:
  - analysing the protein for which the gene codes, to find the amino acid sequence, deducing the base sequence for the gene and then synthesising it in a 'gene machine'
  - using mRNA as a template and synthesising single-stranded cDNA from free DNA nucleotides using the enzyme reverse transcriptase; the cDNA is then used (with more nucleotides and DNA polymerase) to make the complementary second strand of DNA
  - cutting the DNA into fragments using a restriction enzyme and isolating the gene
- Restriction enzymes cut DNA at specific sequences, called restriction sites, to leave overlapping, sticky ends.
- A gene is inserted into a plasmid using a ligase enzyme.
- Plasmids are chosen that contain marker genes, such as resistance to an antibiotic, which allow identification of the bacteria that have taken up the gene of interest.
- Once the gene has been successfully inserted and the transformed bacteria identified, they are cultured and the product is harvested.

Questions

Multiple-choice

1 An organism that has had genes transferred to it from another organism is best defined as:
- **A** a genome modified organism
- **B** a trans-specific organism
- **C** a transgenic organism
- **D** a complementary organism

2 The genome of an organism is:
- **A** the genes that can be transferred to another organism
- **B** the set of genes that regulate the physiology of the organism
- **C** the genes that control mitosis
- **D** all the genetic information of the organism

3 A ligase is an enzyme that:
- **A** cuts DNA molecules, leaving sticky ends
- **B** joins sticky ends of DNA fragments
- **C** copies DNA fragments
- **D** separates DNA fragments

4 It is possible to create a gene using protein as a starting point because:

  A the protein can be used to make nucleotides

  B the amino acids in the protein can be used to make nucleotides

  C the sequence of the amino acids in the protein is determined by the sequence of the sugars in the nucleotides

  D the sequence of the amino acids in the protein is determined by the sequence of the bases in the nucleotides

5 Reverse transcriptase is an enzyme that makes:

  A a cDNA copy of mRNA

  B an mRNA copy of DNA

  C an mRNA copy of cDNA

  D a DNA copy of mRNA

6 A gene probe could be:

  A a short length of single-stranded DNA that has been made radioactive

  B a tRNA molecule that has been made radioactive

  C a short length of double-stranded DNA that has been made radioactive

  D all of the above

7 Bacteriophages and plasmids are examples of:

  A vectors

  B transformed bacteria

  C restriction enzymes

  D viruses

8 It is often preferable to create a gene from mRNA rather than extract the gene from the donor cell because:

  A it saves the tedious process of isolating the gene from many DNA fragments

  B there can be thousands of copies of mRNA in cells where the gene is active

  C it creates a copy of the gene without any introns

  D all of the above

9 When plasmids are incubated with bacteria, the rate of take-up of plasmids by the bacteria is:

  A 100%

  B 0%

  C quite high

  D very low

10 Concerns about genetically modified food are:

  A completely justified

  B completely unjustified

  C either of the above, depending on your moral stance

  D either of the above, depending on your ethical stance

Examination-style

1 Bovine somatotrophin (BST) is a hormone that is produced by genetically engineered bacteria and injected into dairy cattle. The hormone increases the milk output of the cattle.

  (a) Outline how the gene for BST could be transferred from a donor cell to a bacterium. You need only give the main stages. *(4 marks)*

(b) The table gives information about the amount of feed given to a herd of cattle and their milk yield, with and without the administration of BST.

Condition	Feed/kg d⁻¹	Milk yield/kg d⁻¹	Milk-to-feed ratio
Without BST	34.1	27.9	0.82
With BST	37.8	37.3	0.99

(i) Explain why the farmer's costs increased when BST was administered to the herd. *(2 marks)*

(ii) Explain why the farmer's profits could have increased when he administered BST, despite the increased cost. *(3 marks)*

Total: 9 marks

2 The flowchart shows the main stages in genetic engineering.

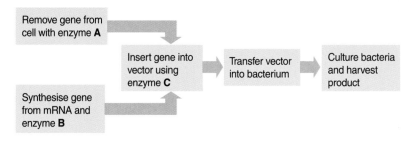

(a) (i) Name the enzymes A, B and C. *(3 marks)*

(ii) Name two possible vectors. *(2 marks)*

(b) Explain the benefits of using genetically engineered bacteria to produce human insulin. *(2 marks)*

Total: 7 marks

3 The diagram shows how the action of enzyme X cuts a molecule of DNA.

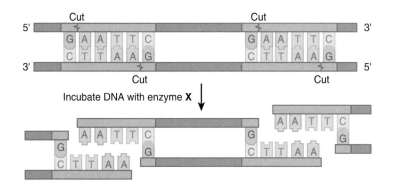

(a) (i) Name the type of enzyme that cuts DNA in this way. *(1 mark)*

(ii) What name is given to the places where the enzyme makes the cuts? *(1 mark)*

(iii) Explain the importance of the type of cut made by this
        enzyme.   (3 marks)
  (b) Suggest why it may be preferable to obtain the gene from
       mRNA, rather than from DNA.   (2 marks)
                                                         Total: 7 marks

4 Antisense technology can be used to prevent the expression of a gene. A
   molecule of antisense mRNA is created that prevents the translation of the
   normal mRNA.
   (a) Explain what is meant by the term 'translation'.   (2 marks)
   (b) The sense strand of the DNA had the following base sequence:
        T T G A A C C G C T T A
       Give the base sequence of:
       (i) the sense mRNA molecule
       (ii) the antisense mRNA molecule   (2 marks)
   (c) Explain how the use of antisense mRNA prevents the synthesis
       of the protein coded for by the gene.   (3 marks)
                                                         Total: 7 marks

5 The diagram shows the process of introducing a foreign gene into a bacterial
   plasmid.

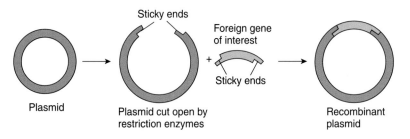

   (a) Name the enzyme used to:
       (i) produce the 'sticky ends'
       (ii) insert the foreign gene into the plasmid.   (2 marks)
   (b) The plasmids are then introduced into host bacteria with no resistance to
       antibiotics. What would be the result of culturing the transformed bacteria
       on Petri dishes of agar containing:
       (i) tetracycline?
       (ii) ampicillin?
       Explain your answers.   (4 marks)
   (c) Bacteria naturally 'swap' plasmids in a process called conjugation.
       Suggest how this might have given rise to bacteria resistant to
       many antibiotics.   (2 marks)
                                                         Total: 8 marks

Chapter 12

Immunology and genetic fingerprinting

This chapter covers:
- the different levels of defence against infection in the human body
- the nature of antigens and antibodies
- the antibody-mediated immune response
- the cell-mediated immune response
- the basis of the ABO blood grouping system and its use in forensic science
- genetic fingerprinting
- the polymerase chain reaction (PCR)

Biotechnology is used increasingly in criminal investigations. It may be used to eliminate a person from suspicion or to provide extra evidence to secure a conviction. Some forensic evidence depends on the fact that, apart from identical twins, the DNA of each person is slightly different. As a consequence of this, there is variation in the range of proteins that each person produces. Some of these proteins — antigens and antibodies — form the basis of immune responses and of the blood groups. The genetic fingerprint and blood group of a person can be important evidence in ascertaining whether or not that individual was present at the scene of a crime.

The basis of immunity

Resisting infection caused by pathogenic microorganisms is possible because of:
- species resistance
- physical and chemical barriers that help to exclude microorganisms from the body
- immune responses that destroy microorganisms that have succeeded in entering the body

◀ A pathogenic microorganism is one that causes disease.

Species resistance

Species resistance in the case of humans is resistance to disease simply because we are *Homo sapiens*. We do not contract many diseases that are common in other species. For example, a human is unlikely to suffer from Dutch elm disease or from canine distemper. This is usually because the conditions in the human body do not provide a suitable environment for such pathogens. In other cases, it is because the pathogen cannot easily infect human cells or tissues.

Methods of excluding microorganisms

The main methods of excluding microorganisms from the body are shown in Figure 12.1.

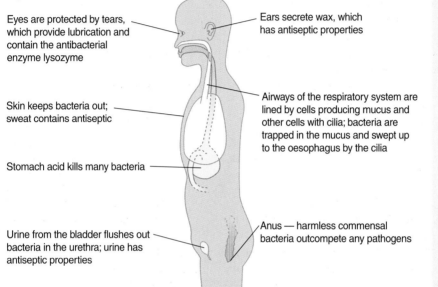

Eyes are protected by tears, which provide lubrication and contain the antibacterial enzyme lysozyme

Ears secrete wax, which has antiseptic properties

Skin keeps bacteria out; sweat contains antiseptic

Airways of the respiratory system are lined by cells producing mucus and other cells with cilia; bacteria are trapped in the mucus and swept up to the oesophagus by the cilia

Stomach acid kills many bacteria

Urine from the bladder flushes out bacteria in the urethra; urine has antiseptic properties

Anus — harmless commensal bacteria outcompete any pathogens

Figure 12.1 Ways of excluding microorganisms

Box 12.1 Blood clotting

Blood clotting at a wound is another important way of keeping out pathogenic microorganisms. The chain of events that leads to blood clotting and the formation of a scab at a wound is called the extrinsic pathway. This is shown in the diagram below.

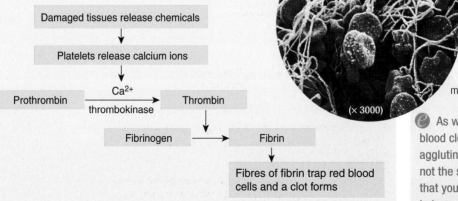

When blood clots, red blood cells become trapped in a mesh of fibrin fibres

e As we shall see later, blood clotting and the agglutination of blood are not the same. Be sure that you can distinguish between the two.

Methods of destroying microorganisms

If pathogenic microorganisms manage to get past the physical and chemical barriers, the body can put into operation a number of **immune responses**. Some of these are general, or non-specific, immune responses; others are specific.

Non-specific immune responses

Non-specific immune responses are not dependent on the presence of a specific foreign antigen in the body.

- **Fever** raises the temperature of the body. This happens because many pathogens release chemicals that stimulate the hypothalamus to 'reset' the body's thermostat to a higher temperature — perhaps to 40°C rather than 37°C. The higher temperature causes more damage to the cells of the pathogen than to the cells of the body.

  During a fever, because the body thermostat has been reset, attempts to reduce the temperature will be resisted by the body's temperature regulation systems. Once the pathogen has been destroyed, it is usually best to let the fever 'break' naturally.

- **Inflammation** due to infection has four classic signs:
  - redness
  - pain
  - swelling
  - heat

  The consequence of inflammation is that capillaries in the infected area become more permeable. More white blood cells, antibodies and 'complement proteins' can escape from the capillaries.

- **Phagocytosis** (Figure 12.2) involves the ingestion and subsequent digestion of microorganisms by a range of white blood cells. The most common white blood cells that act as phagocytes are **neutrophils** and **macrophages**. When tissue is damaged by infection, chemicals called mediators are released, which attract phagocytic cells by chemotaxis. Often, they can escape more easily into the tissues because of the increased permeability due to inflammation. They engulf bacteria by enclosing them in phagosomes formed by pseudopodia. Lysosomes then migrate to the phagosome and secrete hydrolytic enzymes to digest the microorganism.

Complement proteins are a group of about 20 proteins that cause a cascade of reactions leading to the lysis (bursting) of bacterial cells. The complement proteins can also be activated by ◄ specific immune responses.

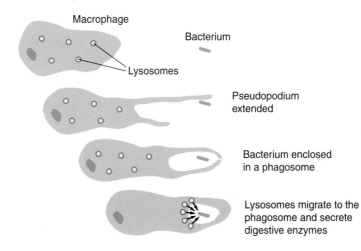

Macrophage

Bacterium

Lysosomes

Pseudopodium extended

Bacterium enclosed in a phagosome

Lysosomes migrate to the phagosome and secrete digestive enzymes

Figure 12.2 Phagocytosis

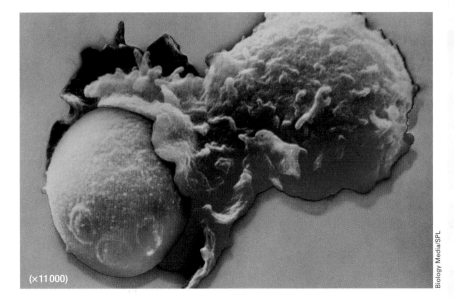

(×11000)

Biology Media/SPL

A yeast cell being engulfed by a white blood cell

Specific immune responses

Non-specific responses do not give any lasting immunity to a pathogen. If the same type of bacterium were to enter the body the day after being destroyed by a combination of non-specific responses, the whole process would take place again, in exactly the same way. Specific immune responses, in addition to destroying the pathogen, usually result in an **immunological memory** that gives lasting protection against that particular pathogen. There are two types of specific immune response:

- the humoral, or antibody-mediated, response
- the cell-mediated response

Antigens and antibodies

Both the humoral and cell-mediated responses occur when a foreign antigen is detected in the body. Many different types of molecule can act as antigens — proteins, carbohydrates, even DNA — but most antigens are proteins.

> An antigen is any molecule that produces an immune response.

The antigen can be the pure chemical itself, or it might be carried on the surface of a pollen grain, a bacterial cell, a virus or a human cell. An immune response is only stimulated when a foreign or **non-self-antigen** is detected in the body. Each person has an individual 'set' of antigens called **self-antigens**. Normally, the cells of the immune system do not attack self-antigens. Often, it is not the whole antigen molecule that stimulates the immune response but certain parts of it, called **antigenic determinants**.

Production of antibodies in the humoral response

Antibodies belong to a class of proteins called **immunoglobulins**. They are produced by cells derived from B-lymphocytes and each can bind with a specific antigen. Each antibody molecule is basically 'Y'-shaped. Part of the molecule is

e You are required to know in detail about the humoral response only.

Occasionally, the immune system begins to attack some self-antigens, resulting in **autoimmune disease**. Iritis (serious inflammation of the iris) can be an autoimmune condition, as can some types of ◀ diabetes.

Antibodies are able to bind with antigens because the shape of the variable portion of the antibody molecule is ◀ complementary to one or more of the antigenic determinants in the antigen.

the same in all antibodies — the constant region. The part that binds with the antigen is different in different antibodies — the variable region (Figure 12.3).

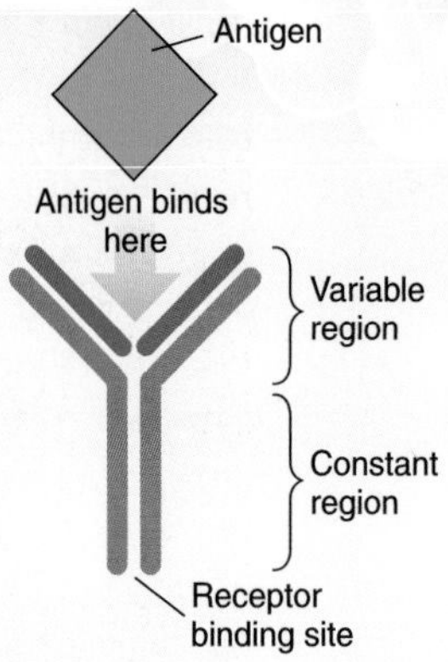

An antibody is a protein produced by a B-lymphocyte in response to a specific antigen.

The B-lymphocytes that are responsible for the antibody-mediated response develop just before and just after birth from stem cells in the bone marrow. At this stage, they are inactive, but they 'present' antibody molecules on their plasma membranes. Each B-lymphocyte produces a slightly different antibody. The inactive B-lymphocytes then migrate to lymph nodes, the liver and spleen where they remain, unless stimulated by an antigen to which their antibody can bind. In this case, the B-lymphocytes become active and divide rapidly by mitosis to form millions of either:

- **plasma cells** — large cells that actually secrete the antibody into the blood, or
- **memory cells** — B-lymphocytes that are stored in the lymph nodes and, on any subsequent exposure to the same antigen, quickly divide to form many plasma cells

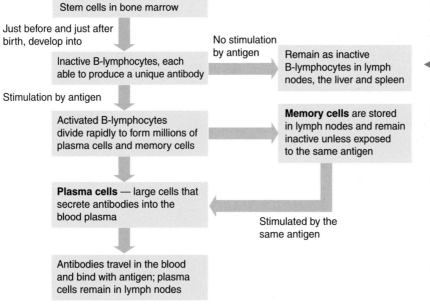

Figure 12.3 Structure of an antibody

Figure 12.4 Production of antibodies

◀ B-lymphocytes do not have antibodies that bind with self-antigens. When they are undergoing their initial development, any B-lymphocytes that contain antibodies that bind with self-antigens are destroyed. This leaves only those B-lymphocytes that do not react with self-antigens. Therefore, the antibodies they produce will bind with non-self-antigens.

What triggers a particular B-lymphocyte to start developing into plasma cells and memory cells? When the B-lymphocyte encounters a microorganism with an antigen complementary to its antibody, it binds with the antigen and then engulfs it by phagocytosis. Using special proteins, called **MHC proteins**, it displays the antigen on its surface. Now another type of lymphocyte, called a **helper T-lymphocyte,** which must also have MHC proteins that can bind with the antigen, attaches itself. The helper cell is stimulated to divide and produce chemicals called **cytokines**, which stimulate the B-cell to divide and form plasma cells and memory cells.

The initial production of antibodies by plasma cells derived directly from B-lymphocytes is called the **primary immune response**. Since it depends on the initial stimulation of relatively few cells, it takes some time for the inactive B-lymphocytes to form sufficient plasma cells for the antibody to have a real impact on the antigens. During this period, the bacterium or virus carrying the antigen multiplies and illness results.

The later production of antibodies by plasma cells derived from memory cells (on reinfection by a microorganism with the same antigen) is the **secondary immune response**. There are many more memory cells than there were original inactive B-lymphocytes, so this response is much faster and many more antibodies are produced.

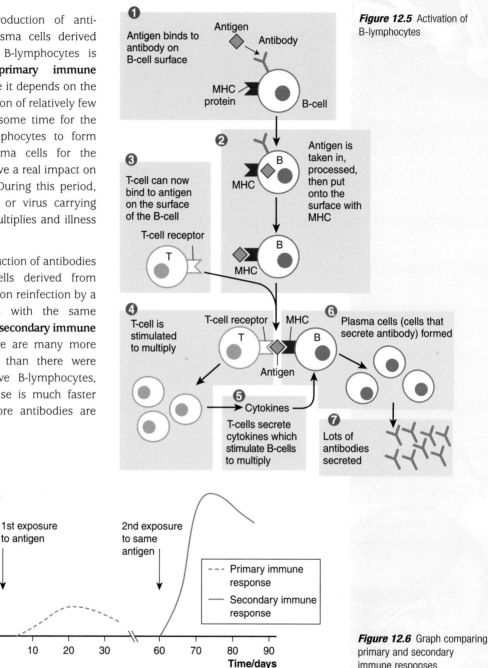

Figure 12.5 Activation of B-lymphocytes

Figure 12.6 Graph comparing primary and secondary immune responses

Action of antibodies

Different antibodies act in different ways. The most common effects on antigens are:

- inactivation — antibodies of this type neutralise toxins produced by bacteria
- binding them together — this causes antigen-carrying bacteria to form clumps, which makes them more susceptible to attack by other cells of the immune system (Figure 12.7)

- facilitating phagocytosis
- stimulating the complement proteins, which leads to lysis of the bacterium

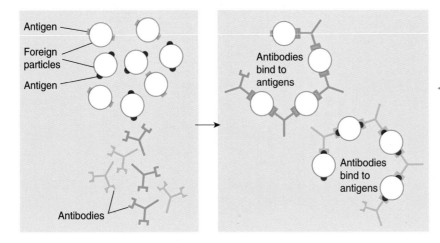

Figure 12.7 Some antibodies bind antigens together, causing clumps of bacteria to form

◀ Immunological research could help to develop our understanding of cancer — why does the body recognise and destroy some cancer cells but not others? In the future, it may also help the development of effective vaccines against malaria and HIV.

The cell-mediated response

The cell-mediated response is brought about by **T-lymphocytes**. These cells are also formed from stem cells in the bone marrow, but they are modified in the thymus gland (hence T-) before migrating to the lymph nodes, liver and spleen. The action of T-lymphocytes is different from that of B-lymphocytes, as is the way in which they are activated. Their initial recognition of a foreign antigen depends on a macrophage engulfing the antigen and presenting it on its surface. A T-lymphocyte with a complementary surface receptor then binds to the presented antigen. This sensitises the T-cell, enabling it to recognise the antigen without its being displayed by a macrophage. It also stimulates the T-cell to reproduce.

Different T-lymphocytes act in different ways. Some kill virus-infected cells by binding to the viral antibodies on the plasma membrane and then releasing chemicals that perforate the membrane, killing the cell within seconds. Others coat cells with chemicals that mark them out as requiring phagocytosis. As with the B-lymphocytes, some become memory cells. However, they are not confined to the lymph nodes (as are B-lymphocytes). T-lymphocyte memory cells circulate freely in the blood and preferentially visit those areas in which they first encountered the antigen. This is known as **T-cell homing**.

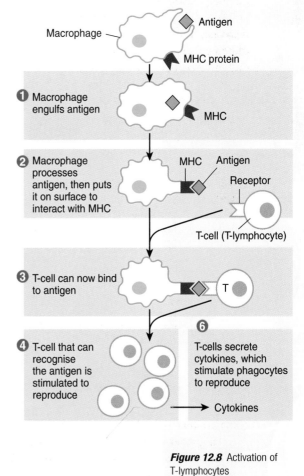

Figure 12.8 Activation of T-lymphocytes

ABO blood groups

Although there are several systems of blood grouping, for example the rhesus system and the M/N system, most people are only aware of the **ABO system.** They might know whether they are blood group A, B, AB or O. In the ABO system, blood group is determined by the presence (or absence) of two antigens on the surface of red blood cells. These antigens are carbohydrates and are named A and B.

Most antibodies are produced in response to an infection by a microorganism that is carrying a non-self-antigen. However, the antibodies that cause **agglutination** on binding with the blood-group-determining antigens are present all the time in the plasma.

Antibody **a** binds with antigen **A**, causing agglutination (clumping) of cells carrying that antigen. Antibody **b** binds with antigen **B**, causing agglutination.

The system has evolved so that the plasma contains only antibodies that could bind to non-self antigens and none that could bind to self antigens. This is summarised in Figure 12.9.

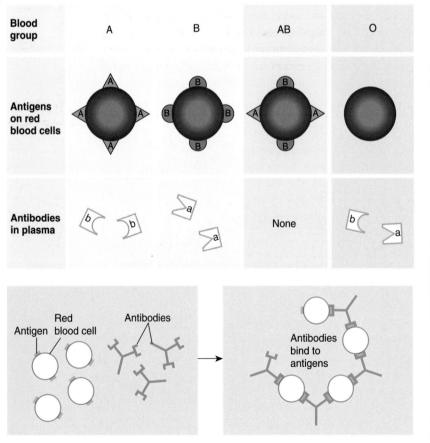

Figure 12.9 Antigens and antibodies in different ABO blood groups

Figure 12.10 How agglutination occurs

Agglutination is a potential hazard when blood transfusions are carried out. When whole blood is stored, the antibodies present in the plasma quickly become ineffective, but the antigens on the red blood cells are largely unaltered. So, if, for example, group A blood were given to someone of group B, agglutination would occur. This would happen because the **a** antibodies in the plasma of the recipient (person receiving the blood) would bind with the **A** antigens on the red blood cells of the transfused blood. Blood is always carefully cross-matched before routine transfusions to ensure that there is no reaction between the antibodies of the recipient and the antigens in the donor blood. The outcomes of the possible transfusions are summarised in Table 12.1.

Table 12.1

Blood group of donor (antigen in brackets)	Blood group of recipient (antibodies in brackets)			
	A (b)	B (a)	AB (neither)	O (a + b)
A (A)	No agglutination	Agglutination	No agglutination	Agglutination
B (B)	Agglutination	No agglutination	No agglutination	Agglutination
AB (A + B)	Agglutination	Agglutination	No agglutination	Agglutination
O (neither)	No agglutination	No agglutination	No agglutination	No agglutination

Blood group O is called the universal donor, because neither antigen **A** nor antigen **B** is present to stimulate agglutination. Blood group AB is called the universal recipient. People with this blood group have neither antibody **a** nor antibody **b** in the plasma to cause agglutination. Therefore, they can receive blood of any group.

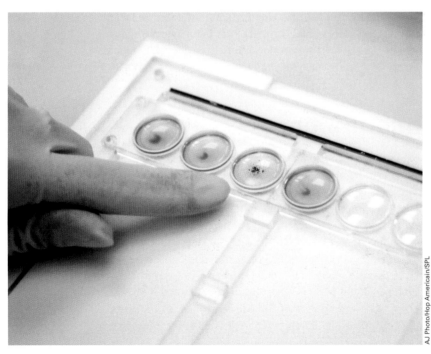

Agglutination has occurred in the sample second from right

AJ Photo/Hop Americain/SPL

Box 12.2 Determining blood group

Blood groups can be determined using blood grouping cards. These cards have three panels, as shown in the diagram. One panel carries the **a** antibody; the second panel carries the **b** antibody. The third panel carries neither antibody and so acts as a control.

A sample of blood is placed on each panel. Care must be taken not to transfer material from one panel to another. If any agglutination occurs, then there has been a reaction between the antibody and the corresponding antigen. There should be no agglutination on the control panel. Agglutination on this panel means that material has been transferred from another panel and the test is not valid. Possible results are shown in the table.

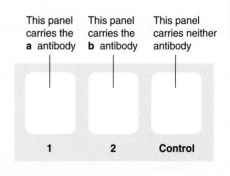

Blood group	Panel 1 (antibody a)	Panel 2 (antibody b)	Control (no antibody)
A	Agglutination	No agglutination	No agglutination
B	No agglutination	Agglutination	No agglutination
AB	Agglutination	Agglutination	No agglutination
0	No agglutination	No agglutination	No agglutination

Table 12.2

As there are only four different blood groups in the ABO system, it is clear that matching the blood group of a suspect with the blood group from a sample taken from the scene of a crime does not necessarily place that person at the scene. Millions of people share the same blood group. However, having a *different* blood group from that taken from the scene could help to eliminate a person from a list of suspects.

Genetic fingerprinting

Fingerprints have been used for many years to help place a suspect at the scene of a crime. They continue to provide strong evidence because, with the exception of identical twins, an individual's fingerprints are unique. They do not change throughout life. **Genetic fingerprinting** has nothing to do with actual fingerprints. It is a technique for comparing the DNA of different people, without the need to know anything about the function of the DNA. Much of the DNA in the cells of the body is non-coding or junk DNA. The non-coding DNA found between genes contains base sequences that are repeated, sometimes many times over. These repeating sequences of non-coding DNA are called **mini-satellites** and it is these that form the basis of a genetic fingerprint. The mini-satellites are inherited along with the coding DNA from one or other parent.

The DNA to be used for analysis can be obtained from a sample of blood (white blood cells could supply the DNA), skin or semen — in fact, from any type of cell

The coding DNA within the genes is unlikely to vary a great deal between individuals. For example, the base sequence in the gene for normal haemoglobin is the same in all of us, as is the base sequence in the gene for pepsin.

that has a nucleus. If the sample does not contain sufficient DNA for analysis, then the amount can be amplified using the **polymerase chain reaction** (PCR), which is described on page 212.

The main stages in preparing a genetic fingerprint are as follows:
- DNA is isolated from the cells.
- The DNA is cut into fragments using one or more restriction enzymes. These are chosen to cut, where possible, outside the repeating sequences of non-coding DNA.
- The fragments that are obtained are treated with alkali to separate the strands of each DNA fragment.
- The fragments are separated by gel electrophoresis (Chapter 2, pp. 39–40). Smaller fragments (with a lower molecular mass) move further than larger fragments.
- The (invisible) pattern of separated DNA fragments is transferred from the gel to a nylon membrane. The membrane is placed over the gel in a tray of 'flow-buffer' and is held in place by paper towels and a weight. The buffer soaks up through the gel, carrying the fragments of DNA with it. The buffer can pass through the membrane (to be absorbed by the paper towels), but the DNA cannot. It remains in the nylon membrane in the same relative position as it was in the gel.
- A radioactive gene probe is applied to the membrane. This is designed to bind with base sequences in the mini-satellite regions.
- Placing the membrane over a piece of X-ray film reveals the positions of those fragments that have base sequences complementary to the probe (Figure 12.11).

◄ The size of DNA molecules is usually measured in kilobase pairs (thousands of pairs of bases). These fragments are single stranded, so there are no base pairs. Their size is measured in kilobases.

◄ The technique of transferring DNA fragments from the gel to the nylon membrane was devised by Professor E. M. Southern and is called Southern blotting. A similar technique can be used to transfer mRNA fragments to a nylon membrane. It is known as Northern blotting — but no Professor Northern was involved!

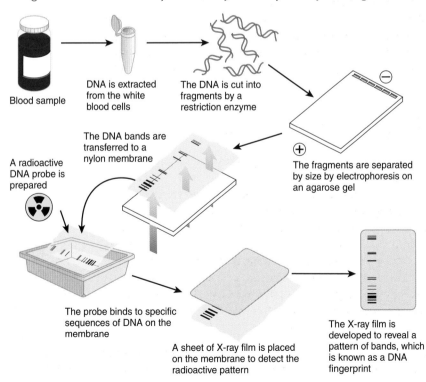

Blood sample

DNA is extracted from the white blood cells

The DNA is cut into fragments by a restriction enzyme

The fragments are separated by size by electrophoresis on an agarose gel

The DNA bands are transferred to a nylon membrane

A radioactive DNA probe is prepared

The probe binds to specific sequences of DNA on the membrane

A sheet of X-ray film is placed on the membrane to detect the radioactive pattern

The X-ray film is developed to reveal a pattern of bands, which is known as a DNA fingerprint

Figure 12.11 Stages in preparing a genetic fingerprint

Remember that the mini-satellites are inherited along with the coding DNA. Genetic fingerprints can, therefore, be used to help resolve disputed parentage — each fragment of DNA in the fingerprint must have come from one or other parent.

The polymerase chain reaction

The **polymerase chain reaction (PCR)** is an automated technique that mimics the process of DNA replication occuring in living cells. It allows a tiny sample of DNA to be amplified many times in a short period of time — over a million copies can be made in just a few hours. Essentially, there is a repeating cycle of separation of the two DNA strands, followed by synthesis of a complementary strand for each. The amount of DNA doubles with each cycle. However, there are a few technical problems:

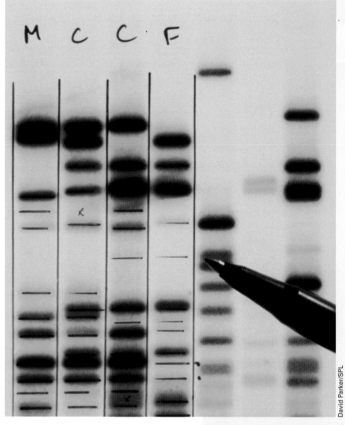

David Parker/SPL

- There is no suitable helicase to separate the strands. This is achieved by heating to 95°C.
- The DNA polymerase cannot work on DNA that is completely single stranded. There must be double stranded regions at the start of the sequence to be copied on each strand. This means that:
  - special primers (short sequences of DNA), complementary to the bases at the start of the region to be amplified, must be included; these bind to the DNA and provide a 'starting point' for DNA polymerase
  - to synthesise these primers, the base sequences at the start of the sequences to be copied must be known
- To avoid having to keep adding fresh DNA polymerase, the enzyme used must be thermostable. Originally, the DNA polymerase used was obtained from bacteria that lived in hot water springs. Now it is produced by genetically modified bacteria.
- The replication must be carried out at 72°C because this is the optimum temperature of the DNA polymerase used.

Great care is needed to ensure that:
- the nucleotides used are of the highest purity
- the DNA is not contaminated in any way (any foreign DNA would also be copied)

Genetic fingerprints of two children and their parents. Each fragment of DNA (dark bands) in the children is also present in one or both of the parents.

◀ There are two sequences to be copied because the sequences on the two strands are complementary, not identical. Therefore, two different primers are needed.

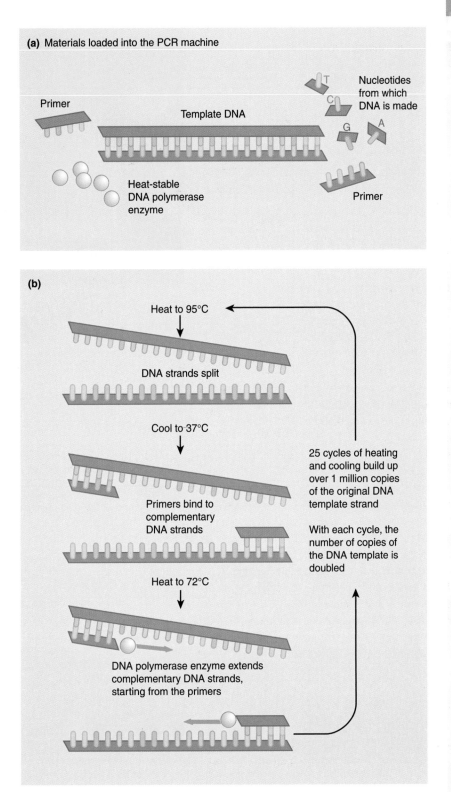

(a) Materials loaded into the PCR machine

Primer

Template DNA

Nucleotides
from which
DNA is made

Heat-stable
DNA polymerase
enzyme

Primer

(b)

Heat to 95°C

DNA strands split

Cool to 37°C

Primers bind to
complementary
DNA strands

Heat to 72°C

DNA polymerase enzyme extends
complementary DNA strands,
starting from the primers

25 cycles of heating
and cooling build up
over 1 million copies
of the original DNA
template strand

With each cycle, the
number of copies of
the DNA template is
doubled

Figure 12.12 Main stages of
the polymerase chain reaction

Theoretically, each cycle doubles the amount of DNA. After two cycles, the amount of DNA should have quadrupled. After four cycles, there will be eight times as much DNA. The total number of molecules produced is given by the formula:

$$T = N \times 2^c$$

where T = total number of DNA molecules formed, N = number of DNA molecules at the start, and c = number of cycles.

After 25 cycles, starting with just one molecule of DNA, there should be $1 \times 2^{25} = 33\,554\,432$ molecules of DNA!

In practice, no process is 100% efficient and this number is not achieved. However, 25 cycles can produce well over 1 million copies of the initial DNA sample. As each cycle takes about 7–8 min, this takes place in less than 3 h 20 min. Then the analysis of the DNA can begin.

A PCR machine does not take up much space in a forensic laboratory

Summary

Immunity

- Resistance to infection by pathogenic microorganisms is possible because of species resistance, physical and chemical barriers that exclude microorganisms from the body, and immune responses that destroy microorganisms that have entered the body.
- Physical and chemical barriers include:
  - the skin (sweat contains an antiseptic)
  - wax in the ears — a physical barrier and also a mild antiseptic
  - mucus in the airways of the lungs
  - tears that lubricate the conjunctiva and contain lysozyme
  - stomach acid that kills many bacteria
  - commensal bacteria in the anus and rectum
  - urine flushing bacteria out of the urethra
  - clotting of blood at a wound
- Non-specific responses to infection include:
  - phagocytosis — microorganisms are engulfed and destroyed by macrophages
  - fever — the increased temperature limits the reproduction of microorganisms
  - inflammation — the increased permeability of capillaries allows more macrophages, antibodies and complement proteins to escape from the capillaries
- In the antibody-mediated immune response process:
  - an inactive B-lymphocyte with complementary antibodies on its surface binds to a foreign (non-self) antigen on a microorganism
  - the B-lymphocyte engulfs the antigen and displays it on its surface
  - a helper T-lymphocyte binds with the displayed antigen on the B-lymphocyte and is stimulated to reproduce

- the T-lymphocytes produce chemicals that stimulate the B-lymphocyte to reproduce and form millions of plasma cells and memory cells
- the plasma cells secrete antibodies into the bloodstream
- the memory cells remain in lymph nodes but form plasma cells if the same antigen is detected in the future (due to a second infection by the same microorganism)
- The response to an initial infection is the primary immune response; the response to a subsequent infection is the secondary immune response.
- The secondary immune response is quicker than the primary immune response and produces a higher concentration of antibodies in the blood.
- The cell-mediated response is brought about by the activation of T-lymphocytes.

ABO blood groups

- The ABO blood grouping system is based on the presence, or absence, of two antigens (**A** and **B**) on the plasma membrane of red blood cells.
- There are naturally occurring antibodies to the two antigens; antibody **a** causes agglutination of cells carrying antigen **A**, while antibody **b** causes agglutination of cells carrying antigen **B**.
- The antigens and antibodies of the different blood groups are shown in Table 12.3.
- In a transfusion, care must be taken to ensure that antibodies in the recipient's blood will not cause agglutination of the donated blood by reacting with its antigens.

Table 12.3

Blood group	Antigen on plasma membrane of red blood cells	Antibody in blood plasma
A	A	b
B	B	a
AB	A + B	Neither
0	Neither	a + b

Genetic fingerprinting

- In genetic fingerprinting:
  - a DNA sample is cut into fragments by restriction enzymes
  - the fragments are denatured by separating the two strands
  - the fragments are separated by gel electrophoresis and transferred to a nylon membrane by Southern blotting
  - a radioactive gene probe is added to the membrane and the pattern of complementary sequences is revealed using X-ray film

Polymerase chain reaction

- In the polymerase chain reaction:
  - the template DNA (the sample) is placed in a PCR machine with free DNA nucleotides, DNA primers and thermostable DNA polymerase
  - the strands of the template DNA are separated by heating to 95°C
  - the mixture is cooled to 37°C to allow the primers to bind
  - the mixture is heated to 72°C to allow replication at the optimum temperature of the DNA polymerase
  - the cycle repeats itself many times, each cycle taking about 7–8 minutes

Questions

Multiple-choice

1 Species resistance is:
   A resistance to disease shared with other species
   B a type of specific immune response
   C resistance to diseases that are common in other species
   D a type of non-specific immune response

2 Inflammation allows:
   A more phagocytes to leave the blood
   B fewer complement proteins to leave the blood
   C both of the above
   D neither of the above

3 Blood group A cannot be safely transfused to a person with blood group B because:
   A the antibodies in the donated blood would cause agglutination of the recipient's red blood cells
   B the antibodies in the recipient's blood would cause agglutination of the red blood cells in the donated blood
   C the antigens in the donated blood would cause agglutination of the recipient's red blood cells
   D the antigens in the recipient's blood would cause agglutination of the donated red blood cells

4 Antigens are, most commonly:
   A proteins or glycoproteins that stimulate an immune response
   B foreign DNA that stimulates an immune response
   C bacteria
   D viruses

5 Antibodies are best described as:
   A J-shaped proteins
   B J-shaped proteins with a common region and a variable region
   C Y-shaped proteins
   D Y-shaped proteins with a common region and a variable region

6 Compared with the secondary antibody-mediated immune response, the primary response is:
   A slower but produces more antibodies
   B quicker and produces more antibodies
   C slower and produces fewer antibodies
   D quicker but produces fewer antibodies

7 The DNA used in producing a genetic fingerprint is:
   A coding DNA
   B non-coding DNA
   C both of the above
   D neither of the above

8 In gel electrophoresis of DNA:
   A the DNA fragments migrate towards the positive electrode and are separated according to their molecular mass

B the DNA fragments migrate towards the negative electrode and are separated according to their molecular mass

C the DNA fragments migrate towards the negative electrode and are separated according to their electric charge

D the DNA fragments migrate towards the positive electrode and are separated according to their electric charge

9 In the polymerase chain reaction, the sample of DNA is mixed with:

A free DNA nucleotides

B free DNA nucleotides and DNA primers

C free DNA nucleotides, DNA primers and thermostable DNA polymerase

D free DNA nucleotides, DNA primers and thermolabile DNA polymerase

10 At one stage in the polymerase chain reaction, the mixture is cooled to 37°C in order to:

A split the two strands of DNA

B attain the optimum temperature for DNA polymerase

C allow hydrogen bonds to form between the separated strands of DNA and the free nucleotides

D allow the primers to bind

Examination-style

1 The polymerase chain reaction (PCR) is a method of obtaining large amounts of DNA from a small initial sample. The diagram shows the main stages in the polymerase chain reaction.

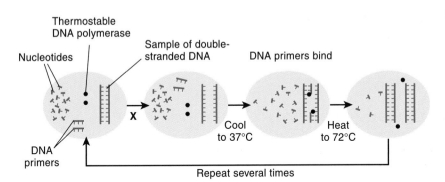

(a) (i) What must be done to separate the strands of DNA (process X)? *(1 mark)*

(ii) What are primers? *(2 marks)*

(b) (i) What is meant by 'thermostable DNA polymerase'? *(2 marks)*

(ii) What is the main advantage of using a thermostable DNA polymerase in this process? *(1 mark)*

Total: 6 marks

2 Genetic fingerprinting involves the analysis of sections of non-coding DNA. Unlike blood grouping, which can only ever prove the innocence of a suspect, genetic fingerprinting can establish guilt with a high degree of certainty.

(a) (i) What is meant by non-coding DNA? *(1 mark)*

Chapter 12 Immunology and genetic fingerprinting　　**217**

(ii) Explain why only non-coding DNA is used in genetic fingerprinting? *(2 marks)*

(iii) Why can blood grouping alone not establish the guilt of a suspect? *(1 mark)*

(b) Three suspects were tested to see which blood group each was. The results of the tests are shown in the diagram. The blood found at the scene of the crime was blood group B.

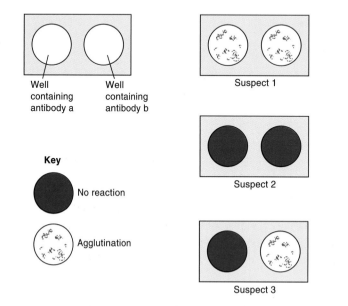

(i) Which of the three suspects should the police eliminate from their enquiries? *(1 mark)*

(ii) Explain the result obtained for suspect 1. *(2 marks)*

Total: 7 marks

3 (a) When a pathogenic bacterium enters the body, a person is often ill for a few days before starting to feel better. During this time, the person may feel feverish. Explain the reason for:

(i) the time delay between being infected and starting to feel better *(3 marks)*

(ii) feeling feverish *(2 marks)*

(b) AIDS is caused by the human immunodeficiency virus (HIV). HIV infects helper T-lymphocytes. Explain why AIDS sufferers commonly contract other serious illnesses. *(4 marks)*

Total: 9 marks

4 In an investigation into immune responses, some volunteers were injected with an antigen. The level of antibodies against that particular antigen in their bloodstream was monitored over several weeks. Some time later, a second injection with the same antigen was given, together with a second antigen. The level of antibodies against both antigens was monitored. The results are shown in the graph below.

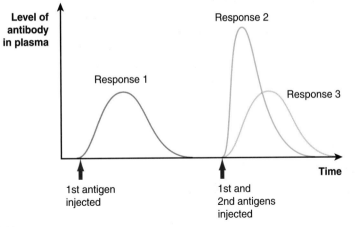

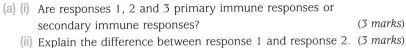

(a) (i) Are responses 1, 2 and 3 primary immune responses or
secondary immune responses? *(3 marks)*

(ii) Explain the difference between response 1 and response 2. *(3 marks)*

(b) Suggest a reason for injecting the second antigen at the same
time as the second injection of the first antigen. *(2 marks)*

Total: 8 marks

5 A couple have three children. However, the father believes that the third child
is not his, but that of another man. Genetic fingerprints are produced from
samples of blood taken from the three adults and the three children. These
are shown below.

Father	Mother	Other man	Child 1	Child 2	Child 3

(a) (i) Which blood cells would be used to provide the DNA
sample? Give a reason for your answer. *(2 marks)*

(ii) Explain why it was not necessary to use the polymerase
chain reaction. *(2 marks)*

(b) Explain how genetic fingerprinting is carried out. *(6 marks)*

(c) (i) Explain how the fingerprints confirm that child 1 is the
child of the parents. *(2 marks)*

(ii) Is the other man the father of child 3? Explain your answer. *(3 marks)*

Total: 15 marks

Chapter 13

Crop production: getting the best yields

This chapter covers:
- the role of photosynthesis in the growth of crop plants
- factors affecting photosynthesis
- the role of fertilisers in improving crop yields and the environmental impact of fertilisers
- methods of reducing the damage done by pests to crop plants
- the principles of integrated crop management
- the adaptations of some crop plants to their environments

By observing which environmental conditions gave the best crop yields, early farmers found out when to plant their crops and in which areas. They found that adding fertiliser, in the form of compost or manure, improved the growth of crops and they found ways of controlling the pests that reduce yields. The biological principles behind these practices have not changed for centuries. However, the development of modern technology has revolutionised farming over the last century.

Farming has become highly mechanised

Jeremy Walker/SPL

Photosynthesis and crop yields

The process of photosynthesis

Photosynthesis is one of the few processes that produce complex organic molecules from simple inorganic molecules. All plants can photosynthesise, as can all algae, some unicellular protoctistans and some bacteria. No animals can photosynthesise and neither can any fungi.

Box 13.1 Chemosynthesis

Some bacteria have developed chemosynthesis. They use energy derived from chemical reactions to drive other reactions that result in the synthesis of organic molecules. One type lives deep in the oceans, where no light penetrates, close to vents on the ocean-bed that release hydrogen sulphide. The bacteria oxidise the hydrogen sulphide to release energy. They then use this energy as plants use light energy — to 'fix' the carbon in carbon dioxide into organic molecules.

From GCSE, you will probably be familiar with the following equation:

$$6CO_2 \; + \; 6H_2O \xrightarrow[\substack{\text{chlorophyll} \\ \text{suitable temperature}}]{\text{light energy}} C_6H_{12}O_6 \; + \; 6O_2$$

This is a useful summary equation, which gives the following information:

- Carbon dioxide and water are required for the process — they are the raw materials.
- Glucose and oxygen are produced — they are the products.
- Light energy, absorbed by chlorophyll, is needed to 'drive' the process.
- The process is temperature dependent.

However, this equation also has limitations, two important ones being that:

- it suggests that photosynthesis is a single-step chemical reaction, whereas it is a multi-step process
- it suggests that either all the oxygen produced is derived from carbon dioxide or some comes from carbon dioxide and some from water — in fact, all the oxygen produced is derived from water

There are two main stages in photosynthesis. The initial reactions are 'driven' by the light energy absorbed by chlorophyll; these are called the **light-dependent reactions**. In these reactions, water molecules are split to produce the oxygen that is given off. The hydrogen from the water is used to reduce other chemicals. ATP is also produced in these reactions. These reduced chemicals and the ATP are used in another set of reactions called the **light-independent reactions**. These reactions, in which the carbon dioxide is used, are 'driven' by the reduced chemicals from the light-dependent reactions; they do not need light. The reduced chemicals are reoxidised and made available for reuse in the light-dependent reactions. The hydrogen from these chemicals, together with carbon dioxide, is used to produce glucose from organic molecules that already exist in the plant.

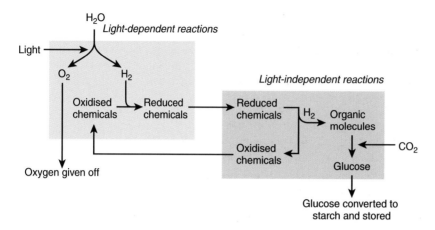

Figure 13.1 The light-dependent and light-independent reactions of photosynthesis

The influence of environmental factors on the rate of photosynthesis and crop yield

As photosynthesis requires a suitable temperature, light, and supplies of carbon dioxide and water, it follows that changes in any of these could affect the rate of photosynthesis. These factors influence photosynthesis in different ways. Light intensity determines how many water molecules are split and, therefore, how many molecules of the reduced chemicals are produced in the light-dependent reactions. The concentration of carbon dioxide determines how quickly the light-independent reactions proceed. Like all biological processes, the reactions of photosynthesis are controlled by enzymes, which are influenced by temperature.

Photosynthesis is the starting point for the production of all the organic molecules in a plant; changes in the rate of photosynthesis can have a direct effect on plant growth and, therefore, on crop yield.

Limiting factors and the rate of photosynthesis

Imagine some lettuce plants being grown in a glasshouse under a range of conditions of light intensity, temperature and carbon dioxide concentration. How do the conditions interact to influence the rate of photosynthesis? The data below are all invented, but they serve to illustrate a point.

- Suppose that carbon dioxide enters a leaf at a rate that supplies:
  - at a low atmospheric carbon dioxide concentration, 1000 molecules s^{-1}
  - at a high atmospheric carbon dioxide concentration, 2000 molecules s^{-1}
- Suppose that the maximum possible rates at which carbon dioxide molecules can be used at different temperatures are:
  - at 10°C, 500 molecules s^{-1}
  - at 20°C, 1000 molecules s^{-1}
  - at 30°C, 1500 molecules s^{-1}
- Suppose that the maximum possible rates at which carbon dioxide molecules can be used at different light intensities are:
  - at low light intensity, 750 molecules s^{-1}
  - at high light intensity, 1500 molecules s^{-1}

◀ The rate at which carbon dioxide molecules are used is a measure of the rate of photosynthesis.

So, at 10°C, with a high concentration of carbon dioxide in the air and high light intensity, the temperature would limit the rate of photosynthesis to 500 molecules of carbon dioxide used per second. There is insufficient kinetic energy for the reactions to take place any faster. Under these conditions, the only way to increase the rate of photosynthesis would be to increase the temperature.

If the temperature were increased to 20°C, then even at a low carbon dioxide concentration, 1000 molecules of carbon dioxide could be used per second, provided the light intensity was high. If the light intensity were low, the rate of photosynthesis would be limited to the use of 750 molecules of carbon dioxide per second. Under these conditions, the only way to increase the rate of photosynthesis would be to increase the light intensity.

This is the **principle of limiting factors**. To increase the rate of photosynthesis, the availability of the limiting factor must be increased. If increasing a factor produces an increase in the rate of photosynthesis, then that factor was the limiting factor.

◄ Think of the rate of the process as the speed of a group of people cycling together. Individuals cycle at various speeds but the speed of the group is determined by the slowest cyclist.

Box 13.2 Why grow crops in glasshouses?

Growing crops in glasshouses, rather than in fields, gives the producer some control over the environment. Glasshouses are naturally well illuminated because glass is transparent. They can also be fitted with fluorescent lights to effectively extend the day in winter. The 'greenhouse effect' (shown in the diagram below) makes them naturally warm. Glasshouses can be made warmer by burning fossil fuel (oil or gas is the most convenient). This also enriches the air in the glasshouse with carbon dioxide.

Growing crops in glasshouses allows production of some crops throughout the year, whereas their natural growing season would be more limited.

Lettuce plants growing in a glasshouse

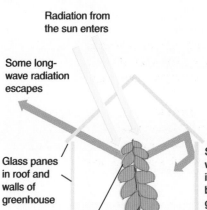

Radiation from the sun enters

Some long-wave radiation escapes

Glass panes in roof and walls of greenhouse

Some long-wave radiation is reflected back into the greenhouse — which warms up

Some shorter-wavelength radiation is absorbed — the radiation reflected is of a longer wavelength

Rosenfeld Images Ltd/SPL

Graphical representation of the principle of limiting factors

Consider the effect of changing light intensity on the rate of photosynthesis. As light intensity increases, the rate of photosynthesis increases — until some other factor begins to limit the rate.

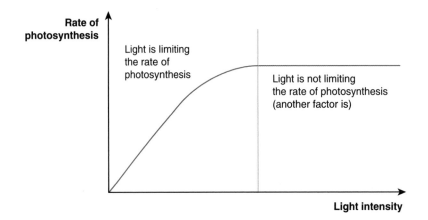

Figure 13.2 Effect of light intensity on the rate of photosynthesis

The graph of the effect of light intensity on photosynthesis always has, more or less, the shape shown in Figure 13.2. The curve levels off because some other factor, for example carbon dioxide, is limiting the rate. The point at which this occurs will vary, depending on the environmental conditions. For example, an increase in carbon dioxide concentration increases the rate of photosynthesis, but once again becomes limiting, albeit at a higher light intensity.

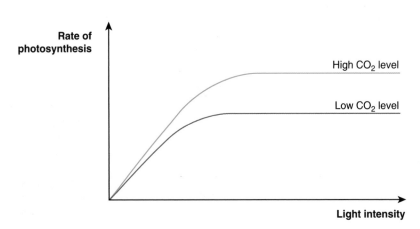

Figure 13.3 Effect of light intensity on the rate of photosynthesis at two different carbon dioxide concentrations

On taking into account the effect of temperature as well, the situation becomes more complex. The most favourable conditions for photosynthesis are higher temperature and increased carbon dioxide concentration. The light intensity at which the rate becomes limited is higher under these conditions. When compared with graph D, the limiting factors for the graphs in Figure 13.4 are:

- Graph A — temperature and carbon dioxide
- Graph B — temperature
- Graph C — carbon dioxide

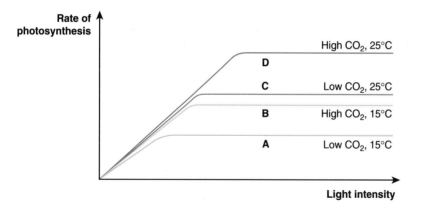

Temperature affects photosynthesis largely through its effect on the enzymes that control the reactions. Therefore, there is a point at which increasing the temperature will actually decrease the rate of the process because the enzymes become denatured. Assuming that all other factors are present at non-limiting levels, the effect of temperature on the rate of photosynthesis is as shown in Figure 13.5.

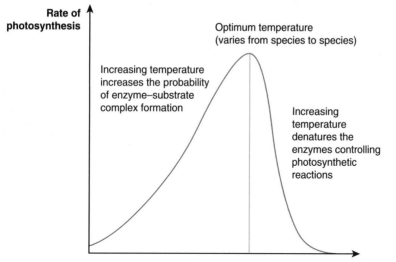

Figure 13.5 Effect of temperature on the rate of photosynthesis

◀ The optimum temperature of the enzymes that control photosynthesis is not the same in all plants because plants are adapted to their environment. Enzymes in plants growing in the Arctic have a lower optimum temperature than those in plants growing in the tropics.

Using fertilisers to improve crop yields

Why do plants need mineral ions?

Photosynthesis produces carbohydrates from carbon dioxide and water. These carbohydrates are organic molecules and form the starting point for the synthesis of all other organic molecules in the plant. Proteins, lipids and nucleic acids cannot be synthesised from inorganic molecules; they are synthesised directly or indirectly from the carbohydrates produced in photosynthesis. The element nitrogen, in the form of ammonia, must be added to synthesise amino acids and, subsequently, proteins. The ammonia is produced from nitrate ions obtained from the soil. Phosphates, also from the soil, are needed to synthesise nucleotides.

Figure 13.6 Pathways for the synthesis of the main groups of organic chemicals in plants

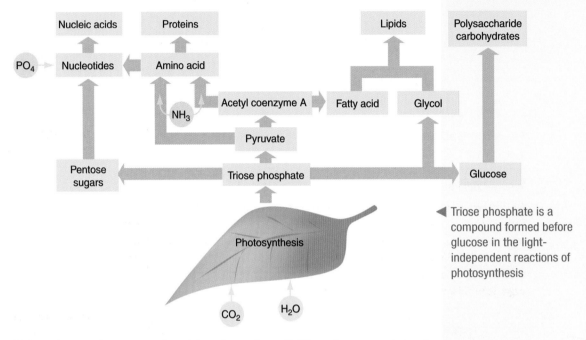

◀ Triose phosphate is a compound formed before glucose in the light-independent reactions of photosynthesis

Plants also require many **mineral ions** from the soil. These have a variety of functions (Table 13.1).

Table 13.1

Mineral element	Mineral ion	Function in plants	Effect of deficiency
Nitrogen	Nitrate (NO_3^-)	Found in nucleic acids, proteins, chlorophyll	Chlorosis (lack of chloro-phyll); stunted growth
Phosphorus	Phosphate (PO_4^{3-})	Found in nucleic acids, ATP, phospho-lipids; promotes enzyme activity	Stunted growth and delayed maturity
Potassium	Potassium (K^+)	Controls opening of stomata; activates many enzymes; needed for starch formation	Weak stems and roots; parts of plant die; chlorosis
Calcium	Calcium (Ca^{2+})	Cell walls; important in responses to environment	Death of root and shoot tips
Magnesium	Magnesium (Mg^{2+})	Part of chlorophyll molecule	Chlorosis and reddening of leaves

Mineral ions are circulated between living tissue and the soil in cycles — for example, the nitrogen cycle and the carbon cycle. Some ions are lost from the soil when heavy rainfall washes them out. This is known as leaching. The ability of a soil to supply mineral ions to plants is its **fertility**.

The natural circulation of mineral elements is illustrated in Figure 13.7.

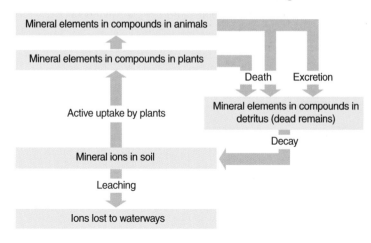

◀ The particles of clay in soils are negatively charged and bind with positively charged ions (e.g. K^+, Mg^{2+} and Ca^{2+}). Therefore, these ions are not easily leached from the soil. Negatively charged ions (e.g. NO_3^- and PO_4^{3-}) are not bound by the clay particles and are more easily lost.

Figure 13.7 The natural circulation of mineral elements

Why do farmers need to use fertilisers?

On a farm, the natural cycles that return mineral elements to the soil are interrupted as farmers harvest their crops and send their livestock for slaughter. Mineral ions are taken out of the soil by plants but not returned by the death and decay of the plants and animals. To make up for this, farmers add fertilisers to the soil to replace the mineral ions. There are two main types of fertiliser — **organic fertilisers** and **inorganic fertilisers.**

(a) Farmyard manure is an organic fertiliser
(b) Different inorganic fertilisers contain different combinations and amounts of ions

Organic fertilisers are formed from the dead remains and/or excretory products of a range of plants and animals. They include farmyard manure, poultry manure, dried blood, seaweed and sewage sludge. As decomposers in the soil decay the organic fertiliser, mineral ions are released.

Inorganic fertilisers are mixtures of inorganic compounds (such as potassium nitrate and ammonium nitrate) that have been formulated to yield a specific amount of nitrogen, when applied as instructed.

Many fertilisers are referred to as NPK fertilisers. This is because they supply the elements nitrogen (N), phosphorus (P) and potassium (K). Three numbers printed on the sack refer to the proportions of these elements. For example, 12 6 6 means that the fertiliser contains, by mass, 12% nitrogen, 6% phosphorus and 6% potassium. ◀

The circulation of mineral elements on a typical farm is illustrated in Figure 13.8.

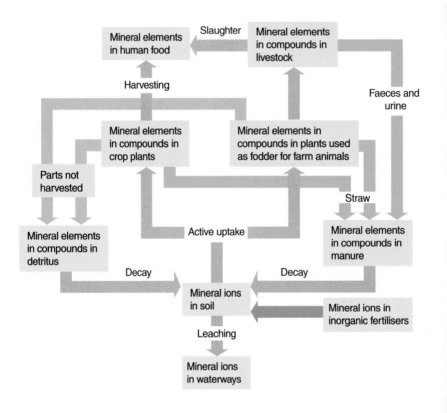

Figure 13.8 The circulation of mineral elements on a farm

Which type of fertiliser should farmers apply?

Organic fertilisers and inorganic fertilisers both add mineral ions to the soil, so why should it matter which type a farmer uses? An important difference between the two is that in order to release mineral ions, the organic compounds in organic fertilisers have to be decomposed by soil microorganisms. Therefore, they are **slow-release fertilisers**. The mineral ions in inorganic fertilisers are available immediately — they are **quick-release fertilisers**. In addition, organic fertilisers release only a small quantity of mineral ions per kilogram, whereas inorganic fertilisers are a much more concentrated source. However, organic fertilisers do not only improve the fertility of a soil. They also improve soil structure, which helps:

- the drainage of clay soils
- the water-holding capacity of sandy soils

Organic fertilisers are often dark in colour and so absorb more radiation from the sun. This helps the soil to warm up more quickly in spring, which allows seeds to germinate a little earlier.

Inorganic fertilisers produce none of these effects.

The main differences between organic and inorganic fertilisers are summarised in Table 13.2.

Some inorganic fertilisers act as 'intermediate-release' fertilisers. Ammonium nitrate (NH_4NO_3) supplies nitrogen in two ways. Nitrate is available for immediate uptake; ammonium must first be converted to nitrate by nitrifying bacteria before plants can take it up. This takes time.

Table 13.2

Feature of fertiliser	Organic fertilisers	Inorganic fertilisers
Solubility	Low	High
Release of mineral ions	Slow	Quick
Quantity of mineral ions released kg^{-1}	Low	High
Leaching of ions to nearby waterways, causing eutrophication	Unlikely	Likely, if overused
Increased drainage of clay soils	Yes	No
Increased water holding by sandy soils	Yes	No
Increased absorption of radiation by soil	Yes	No

If the farmer needs to supply ions quickly, then an inorganic fertiliser is appropriate, but this will not improve the structure and fertility of the soil in the long term. Applying an organic fertiliser will have long-term benefits, but will not make ions available immediately. An organic fertiliser needs to be applied some time in advance of the time when the ions need to be available to the crop.

Potential environmental problems of overuse of fertilisers

Overuse of either type of fertiliser can lead to environmental problems, but these are more likely with the overuse of inorganic fertilisers. The large amounts of soluble mineral ions in inorganic fertilisers mean that overuse can easily lead to ions, for example nitrate and phosphate, being leached into waterways. When these ions run into waterways, they cause increased growth — but not of crop plants. The following sequence of events can occur:

- Algae multiply rapidly, because increased synthesis of organic molecules such as proteins and nucleic acids is possible.
- The increased algal population forms a mat over the surface of the water (filamentous algae) or an algal bloom (unicellular algae), or both.
- The algal bloom or mat reduces the transmission of light to lower levels of the waterway.
- Plants growing at these lower levels cannot photosynthesise, and die.
- Algae start to die as the mineral ions are used up.
- Microorganisms start to decompose the dead plants and algae, and reproduce rapidly as the amounts of dead plants and algae increase.
- The microorganisms use up oxygen, in aerobic respiration, in increasing amounts as their populations increase.
- The levels of oxygen in the water fall dramatically and many animals die.

The process is known as **eutrophication**. Eutrophication refers specifically to the build-up of nutrients in a waterway. It can occur naturally. The problem with eutrophication caused by leaching of ions from fertilisers is the speed at which the build-up of ions occurs.

Eutrophication is *more* likely to occur in hot weather because:

- the mineral ions become more concentrated through increased evaporation of water
- metabolic processes are speeded up due to increased enzyme activity

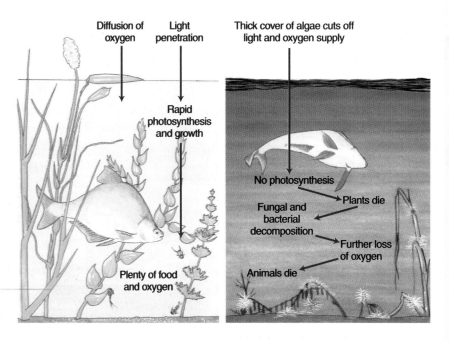

Figure 13.9 Effects of eutrophication

Labels in figure: Diffusion of oxygen | Light penetration | Thick cover of algae cuts off light and oxygen supply | Rapid photosynthesis and growth | No photosynthesis | Plants die | Fungal and bacterial decomposition | Further loss of oxygen | Animals die | Plenty of food and oxygen

> Be quite clear that it is *bacteria* that use the oxygen, *not* the algae. Algae can photosynthesise and, as they reproduce, their increased photosynthesis *adds* oxygen to the water. It is only when they die and are decomposed by bacteria that oxygen is lost.

Eutrophication is *less* likely to occur in moving water because:
- the mineral ions are rapidly diluted
- the water is being re-oxygenated continuously

Organic fertilisers are less likely to cause these problems because they are less soluble and release mineral ions slowly over a period of time. However, **organic pollution** of waterways can have serious effects. If sewage, or other organic matter, enters a waterway, the following events may occur:
- Microorganisms start to decompose the organic matter and reproduce rapidly.
- The microorganisms use up oxygen, in aerobic respiration, in increasing amounts as their population increases.
- The level of oxygen in the water falls and animals may die.

This is, effectively, what happens in the latter stages of rapid eutrophication of a waterway. As with eutrophication, organic pollution has more serious consequences in hot weather and in still water.

Controlling pests

What are pests and why are they a problem?

Pests are organisms that reduce the productivity of crops, without causing disease. Viruses, bacteria and fungi that cause diseases in plants are pathogens, rather than pests. As far as the farmer is concerned, a pest is simply an organism in the wrong place. Most farmers do not dislike, for example, the cabbage white butterfly. However, when the larvae (caterpillars) destroy a cabbage crop, they are pests and must be dealt with. Not only animals are pests — weeds (plants) are also pests, as are some fungi.

Weeds

Weeds and the crop plants compete for:

- mineral ions and water from the soil
- light
- carbon dioxide from the air

This type of competition is called **interspecific competition**. The seeds of many weeds germinate earlier in the year than those of crop plants and the young weed plants grow more quickly. Therefore, they become established before the crop plants and are able to obtain more of the available resources. This reduces the growth of the crop plants and therefore reduces crop yield.

To control weeds effectively, they should be treated (with whatever control method is to be used) as early as possible — before they become established. The crop plants are then able to grow. This restricts the growth of the weeds, because the crop plants often have:

- bigger roots and, therefore, absorb more water and mineral ions
- bigger leaves and, therefore, shade the weeds, reducing their photosynthesis

Poppies and other weeds in a field of wheat

Animal pests

Many different kinds of animal are pests, including insects, molluscs (slugs and snails) and nematodes (a type of roundworm). Animal pests can reduce the yield of crops in the following ways:

- Some feed directly on the organ of the plant that forms the crop. For example, carrot fly larvae feed on the young roots of carrot plants (the carrots); larvae (caterpillars) of the pea moth feed on young peas maturing in the peapod.
- Some (e.g. the larvae of many butterflies) feed on the leaves, which reduces leaf area and, therefore, lowers the photosynthetic capacity of the plant. Less organic material is produced and the yield falls as a result.
- When roots are not the crop-forming organ, pests that feed on and damage roots reduce the uptake of mineral ions and water, which are essential for growth. For example, cabbage root fly larvae feed on the roots of cabbages, stunting their growth.

Box 13.3 Interspecific competition and plant density

Interspecific competition is affected by the density of the competing species. If there are only a few plants of each type in a large area, there will be enough mineral ions, water and carbon dioxide for all the plants and there will, in effect, be no competition. However, if there are large numbers of plants of different species in the same area, then the same levels of resources cannot provide for all the plants. The plants most able to absorb water, mineral ions and carbon dioxide will be successful, at the expense of the others.

- Aphids and some other insects use piercing and sucking mouthparts to tap into the phloem and draw out the liquid, which contains sugars and amino acids. This prevents the transfer of these nutrients to appropriate organs for growth or for storage and so reduces the yield.

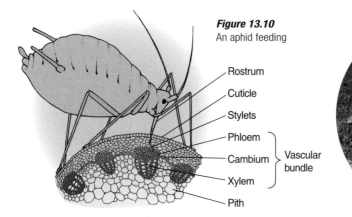

Figure 13.10
An aphid feeding

Rostrum
Cuticle
Stylets
Phloem
Cambium } Vascular bundle
Xylem
Pith

- An insect pest may transfer viruses or bacteria to a crop plant. The resulting disease will further reduce the yield because the disease-causing organisms use up nutrients and may produce toxins that damage the plant.

(a) Slug on a leek
(b) Damage to a wheat crop caused by rabbits

Methods of controlling pest populations

Pests are only a problem to the farmer when their population increases to a level at which the yield of the crop is reduced to such an extent that economic damage is caused. A few whiteflies in a glasshouse of tomato plants are unlikely to do this, but a few thousand probably would. Pest populations can be controlled in a number of ways. They can be treated with **pesticides** or their numbers can be reduced using **biological control**. Some agricultural practices encourage the build-up of pests; avoiding such practices will discourage that build-up.

Using pesticides

Pesticides are chemicals that kill pests. There are different types, designed to kill different kinds of organism:
- **Herbicides** kill weeds (they are weedkillers).
- **Insecticides** kill insects.
- **Molluscicides** kill molluscs.
- **Fungicides** kill fungi.

Spraying a field of cabbages with pesticide

They are usually applied to fields of crops by spraying.

Some pesticides can have effects on other organisms in the environment. These effects include:
- **non-selectivity**. Few insecticides kill only one type of insect. Using an insecticide could kill insects that are pollinators or species that are natural predators of pests. Killing pollinators reduces the ability of some plants to produce seeds. If these plants are crop plants, then the yield of that crop will be reduced.

- **non-biodegradability**. Pesticides may persist in the environment for many years before being broken down. A single application of DDT (an insecticide) can remain in the soil for up to 25 years. Now, more pesticides are designed to be biodegradable. Those that are not can affect many organisms while they are active and might also enter food chains.

- **bioaccumulation**. Pesticides that remain in the soil could be taken up by plants and stored. Over a period of time, the pesticide is accumulated (hence the term 'bioaccumulation'). When the plants are eaten, the herbivores eating the plants may also store the pesticide — typically in fatty tissue. This is repeated at the next link in the food chain — the carnivore eats several herbivores and so stores more pesticide than did an individual herbivore. This increase in concentration of the pesticide along the food chain is called **biomagnification**. It was a particular problem with the insecticide DDT, as the food chains below illustrate:

Dead elm leaves	$\rightarrow$	Earthworms	$\rightarrow$	Robin
(24 ppm DDT)		(86 ppm DDT)		(109 ppm DDT)

Plankton	$\rightarrow$	Crustaceans	$\rightarrow$	Small fish	$\rightarrow$	Large fish	$\rightarrow$	Osprey
(0.000 000 3 ppm DDT)		(0.04 ppm DDT)		(0.5 ppm DDT)		(2 ppm DDT)		(25 ppm DDT)

There were serious effects in the organisms at the top of the food chains because of the high concentrations of DDT they had accumulated. Many robins and ospreys were infertile or produced eggs that did not hatch.

Pesticides never kill all the pests, particularly when applied to large areas by spraying. There are two main reasons for this:

- The pesticide does not contact all the pests. If a large field is sprayed, there are areas that are missed. The pests in these areas will reproduce and could restore the pest population.

- As a result of mutations, some pests become **resistant** to the pesticide. When the pesticide is used, the resistant organisms survive and reproduce. Some of the non-resistant types also survive and reproduce (because of non-contact or limited contact with the pesticide). However, the proportions of the two types will change. There will be an increased proportion of resistant types in the pest population. The next time the pesticide is used, the process is repeated with fewer pests being killed initially because more are resistant. Successive applications of the pesticide kill fewer and fewer pests as the proportion of resistant types in the population increases. Eventually, most of the population could be resistant and the pesticide will be of limited use.

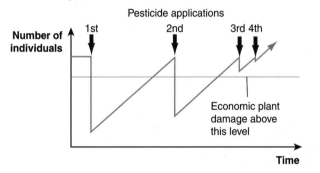

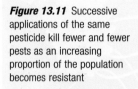

Figure 13.11 Successive applications of the same pesticide kill fewer and fewer pests as an increasing proportion of the population becomes resistant

e Be careful not to confuse becoming *resistant* with becoming *immune*. An organism is resistant to a pesticide because of a mutation in a gene. The organism will always have been resistant and could pass on this resistance to its offspring. If a pest population is sprayed with that pesticide, natural selection will operate, ensuring that resistant types survive to reproduce in greater numbers than non-resistant types. Over several generations, the proportion of resistant types in the population will increase.

An organism becomes immune as a result of exposure to a particular antigen. The immune system manufactures antibodies and memory cells. Immunity is not passed on to offspring.

Box 13.4 Pest resurgence

Sometimes spraying a crop with an insecticide can result in the pest population reaching even higher levels than before spraying. This is known as **pest resurgence**. It happens when the pesticide, besides killing some of the pests, also kills some of the natural predators of the pest. When the surviving pests reproduce, there are fewer predators to keep their population in check and it increases to a level higher than the original. Pest resurgence is shown graphically below.

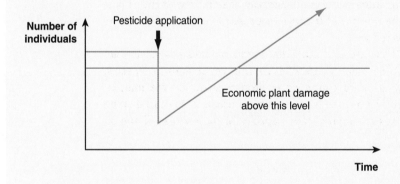

Using biological control

Many people now view **biological control** as a more ecologically friendly method of controlling pests and the practice is being adopted by a growing number of organic farmers.

Biological control makes use of a natural biological agent. A feature of nearly all methods of biological control is that the pest population is reduced — *not* eradicated — to below a level at which economic damage might occur. There is always a residual pest population present.

Methods of biological control include:
- introducing a **predator**. Ladybirds and their larvae are natural predators of aphids and have been used to control aphid populations in orange groves. The effect of introducing a predator is shown in Figure 13.12.

Adult ladybirds feeding on aphids. Their larvae also feed on these pests.

Claude Nuridsany & Marie Perennou/SPL

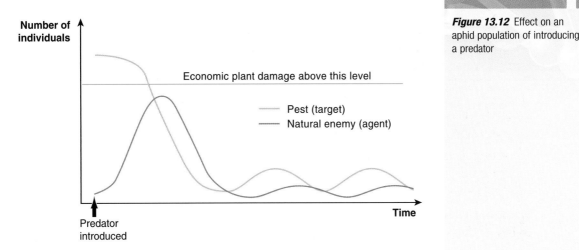

Figure 13.12 Effect on an aphid population of introducing a predator

- introducing a **herbivore** to control weeds. A moth native to South America was introduced into Australia to control the prickly pear cactus, which was taking over many areas of arable land.
- introducing a **parasite**. The larvae of the wasp *Encarsia* parasitise whitefly and are used to control whitefly populations in glasshouses.
- introducing **sterile males**. Sterile males can mate with females but do not produce any offspring. Introducing large numbers of sterile males into a pest population reduces the number of matings that result in offspring. Therefore, the pest population is reduced.
- using **pheromones**. These are chemicals that attract animals of the opposite sex. They are most commonly used to control populations of insects. Releasing a pheromone into a controlled environment attracts the male or female insects (depending on which pheromone is used), which can then be destroyed. This reduces the reproductive capacity of the population and so numbers decrease.

Pesticides and biological control compared

Advantages of the use of pesticides
- They are often easier and, initially, cheaper to use.
- They can be used to control pests in stored products.

Disadvantages of the use of pesticides
- Pests could develop resistance.
- Pest resurgence could occur.
- Bioaccumulation and biomagnification could occur.
- Some pesticides are non-selective and could kill natural predators of a pest.

Advantages of biological control
- Pests cannot develop resistance to the control agent.
- Biological control is usually much more specific than pesticide control — the agent usually targets the pest only.
- Once a biological control agent has been successfully introduced to an area, no further reintroductions are necessary.

Disadvantages of biological control

- The research necessary to identify a potential control agent and verify that it will adapt to the new conditions and kill only the pest are time-consuming and costly.
- The reduction in numbers of the pest may allow another organism to fill the niche of the pest. This could make the situation worse.
- Biological control is not appropriate for controlling pests in stored products such as grain. The grain would be contaminated by the dead bodies of pest and control agent alike.

Using integrated management systems

The reality is that the use of pesticides and of biological control has limitations. Integrated crop management makes use of both methods of pest control and employs a number of other strategies that help to maximise the crop yield. Some, or all, of the following strategies are used:

- Crops that are adapted to the conditions on the farm are selected. For example, if the soil was slightly acidic, it would be unwise to plant a crop that needs an alkaline soil, because this would either:
  - lead to a reduced yield or
  - involve considerable expense to alter the pH of the soil (probably by adding lime)
- Selecting, where possible, crops that have some degree of resistance to pests found in the area.
- Evaluating the potential ecological and financial advantages and disadvantages of both biological control and the use of specific pesticides before choosing the method of pest control appropriate to the crop.
- Using crop rotation.
- Using a combination of organic and inorganic fertilisers as appropriate to the particular crop and the soil.
- Improving and maintaining soil structure and fertility.

◀ Many plants have specific adaptations. This is true of crop plants such as cereals.

Box 13.5 Crop rotation

If the same crop is grown in a field year after year, increasing pest levels can occur because the life cycles of pests frequently coincide with those of the crops. Many pests lie dormant in the soil over winter as eggs or pupae. Their emergence in spring coincides with the germination of crops. Since a particular pest may require a specific crop, crop rotation can help prevent the build-up of pests. If, when the pest emerges, there is a different crop growing, fewer pests will survive in that area.

Some crop rotations also improve the fertility of the soil. One such rotation is shown below.

Root crops and cereals make different demands on the soil for mineral ions, but both remove a significant amount of nitrate ions. Clover is a legume — it has nodules on its roots that contain **nitrogen-fixing bacteria**. These bacteria convert nitrogen gas in the soil air into ammonium ions that are used by the plant to form amino acids and, subsequently, proteins. At the end of the season, the clover is ploughed into the soil. After decomposition, the nitrogen-containing ammonium ions are converted into nitrate ions by nitrifying bacteria. By following this practice, the level of nitrate ions in the soil is restored without needing to add fertiliser.

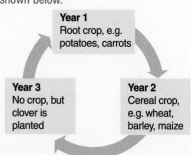

Year 1
Root crop, e.g. potatoes, carrots

Year 2
Cereal crop, e.g. wheat, barley, maize

Year 3
No crop, but clover is planted

A crop rotation. Young maize plants growing on soybean stubble. Soybeans can fix nitrogen; maize cultivation drains the soil of nutrients, especially nitrogen.

Russ Munn/Agstock/SPL

Adaptations of cereals: the right crop for the right place

Cereals form the staple diet for billions of people world-wide. They have all been developed by selective breeding from ancient varieties of grass. Cereals contain more protein than many crop plants (between 9% and 14% of the dry mass) and the protein is of the 'right type', i.e. it contains reasonable amounts of all the **essential amino acids**. These are the amino acids that have to be obtained from the diet. The non-essential amino acids are manufactured in the cells of the body from amino acids present in the diet and from organic acids. Cereals also contain significant amounts of starch and the B-group vitamins. They contain little sugar or fat. There are many different cereals, but we shall consider just three: rice, sorghum and maize.

Rice

Rice originated in Asia. It has been a staple food in China for 5000 years and in India for almost as long. Different varieties are now being grown in parts of Africa, South America, Australia and Europe. Rice forms the basis of many oriental and Indian dishes, the Spanish paella and the Italian risotto.

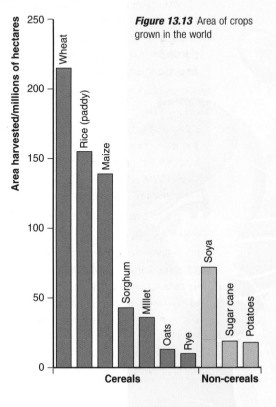

Figure 13.13 Area of crops grown in the world

Ninety per cent of all rice is grown in areas of standing water called **paddy fields**. In the paddy fields, much of the plant is underwater, but the upper shoot (stem, leaves and flowers) remains out of the water. The water level is raised during the growing period and the paddy fields are drained just before harvesting takes place.

◀ The remaining 10% ('upland rice') is a different variety and is grown on dry land like other crop plants.

Figure 13.14
Rice growing in standing water

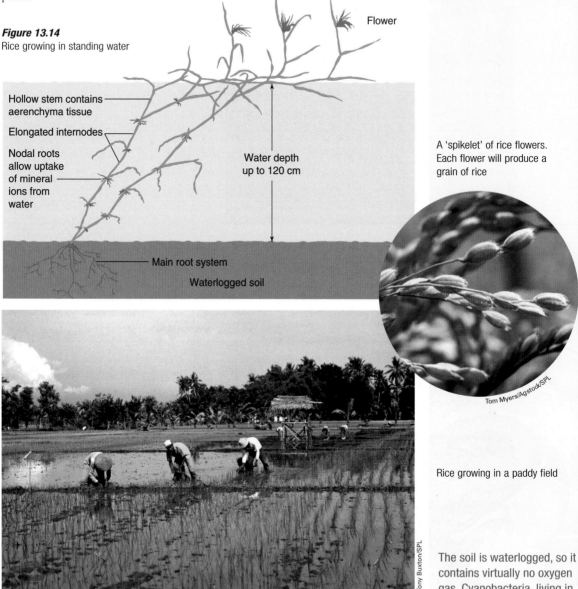

Flower

Hollow stem contains aerenchyma tissue

Elongated internodes

Nodal roots allow uptake of mineral ions from water

Water depth up to 120 cm

Main root system

Waterlogged soil

A 'spikelet' of rice flowers. Each flower will produce a grain of rice

Tom Myers/Agstock/SPL

Rice growing in a paddy field

Tony Buxton/SPL

Rice is adapted to growing in standing water in a number of ways:

● Much of the stem and some of the root tissue is **aerenchyma**. This is a specialised tissue, which contains many large air spaces. Since the plant grows in water, it does not need the extra support usually provided by, for example, xylem tissue. The stem is hollow, so oxygen, taken in by the aerial parts, can diffuse through it to the roots in the waterlogged, anaerobic, soil.

The soil is waterlogged, so it contains virtually no oxygen gas. Cyanobacteria, living in the anaerobic conditions, fix nitrogen gas into organic compounds. When the cyanobacteria die and are decomposed, the fertility of the soil is increased, which
◀ benefits the rice plants.

- The plant grows rapidly; the stem can elongate by as much as 10 cm in a day. This is possible because the stem is largely made from aerenchyma and is, therefore, hollow. Fewer cells need to be produced to elongate the stem by 10 cm than would be the case if there were no air spaces.
- Rice is ethanol tolerant. Sometimes the level of water in the paddy fields rises rapidly (due to flooding) and the whole plant becomes submerged. The cells can no longer receive oxygen and so respire anaerobically, producing ethanol. Over a period of several days, the amount of ethanol in the plant increases. **Ethanol tolerance** allows the plant to survive until the water level falls and aerobic respiration can be resumed.
- Additional roots, called nodal roots, develop from submerged regions of the stem. These roots absorb mineral ions from the surrounding water.

Rice is an important crop plant. However, it has a slightly lower protein content than many other cereals. When rice forms the bulk of the diet, unless the whole grain is eaten, a deficiency disease called beri-beri can result. This is due to a lack of vitamin B_1, which is present only in the husk of the rice grain.

Sorghum

Sorghum (also known as kaffir corn and great millet) probably originated in Africa. The plant is similar to maize in appearance and grows to between 1 m and 5 m tall, with a well-developed root system. It is now cultivated in southern and western Africa, northern India, China, the USA and Australia. Most sorghum is used to produce 'meal' to supplement livestock feeds. Little is used for human food, although one bitter-tasting variety is used to produce beer and a sweet-tasting variety is used to produce a kind of syrup.

Martyn F. Chillmaid/SPL
Peter Menzel/SPL

(a) Sorghum — notice the maize-like leaves
(b) An 'ear' of seeds formed from a spikelet

Sorghum is a **xerophyte** — a plant adapted to grow in a hot, dry climate:
- It has a deep, extensive root system, which allows the plant to absorb as much water as possible from the dry soil.
- It photosynthesises using the 'C4' pathway. **C4 photosynthesis** is more efficient than the usual system at low carbon dioxide concentrations and at high temperatures, such as those in the tropics.

- Both the adult plants and the embryos can tolerate high temperatures.
- It has many large leaves, which provide an extensive area for the absorption of sunlight to drive the reactions of photosynthesis.
- The leaves have several adaptations:
  - The upper surfaces are covered in a thick, waxy cuticle, which reduces water loss.
  - The number of stomata is reduced, which further reduces water loss.
  - They have thin-walled cells in the lower surfaces that lose water rapidly under dry conditions. As a consequence, the leaves roll up to form a tube, with the lower surface on the inside. The space inside the tube becomes saturated with water vapour, which greatly reduces any further water loss because of the reduced water potential gradient.

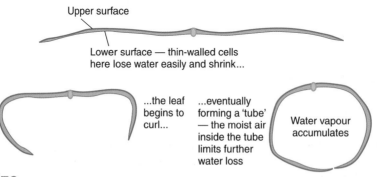

Upper surface

Lower surface — thin-walled cells here lose water easily and shrink...

...the leaf begins to curl...

...eventually forming a 'tube' — the moist air inside the tube limits further water loss

Water vapour accumulates

Figure 13.15 Under dry conditions, the leaves of sorghum roll up to form a tube, thereby reducing water loss

Maize

Maize (commonly known as corn or sweetcorn) was originally an American crop. It was brought to Europe by Christopher Columbus. Its seeds form the familiar corn-on-the-cob, although this is far from the only way in which maize is used for food. The dried seeds can be ground to a meal, which is used to make tortillas in Latin America and as a staple food in some parts of Africa. Commercial cornflour is a kind of maize meal. Maize is also used to make popcorn and cornflakes. In the USA (the world's largest producer), most of the crop is used to feed livestock, particularly pigs.

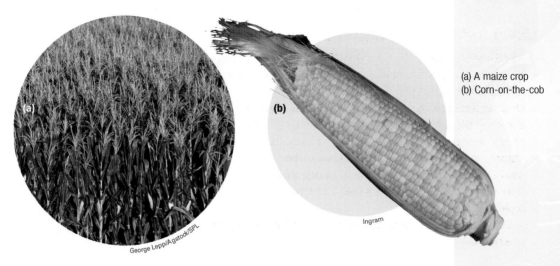

(a) A maize crop
(b) Corn-on-the-cob

George Lepp/Agstock/SPL

Ingram

Maize is adapted to its environment in the following ways:
- It has many large leaves which provide a big area to absorb sunlight for photosynthesis.
- Like sorghum, maize uses C4 photosynthesis.
- It needs less water than many other cereal crops.

Summary

Photosynthesis and crop yield

- The process of photosynthesis can be represented by the summary equation:

$$6CO_2 \ + \ 6H_2O \ \xrightarrow[\substack{\text{chlorophyll} \\ \text{suitable temperature}}]{\text{light energy}} \ C_6H_{12}O_6 \ + \ 6O_2$$

- The rate of photosynthesis is influenced principally by:
  - light intensity
  - concentration of carbon dioxide
  - temperature
- The principle of limiting factors states that when a process or reaction is influenced by several factors, the rate is determined by the limiting factor; other factors would allow a faster rate.
- Increasing the availability of a limiting factor raises the rate of a reaction/process; increasing a non-limiting factor has no effect on the rate of the reaction/process.
- The reactions of photosynthesis are controlled by enzymes.
- Raising the temperature up to the optimum value for the enzymes to operate increases the rate of photosynthesis. Further increases in temperature cause the rate to decrease because the enzymes denature.
- Nitrate ions, obtained from the soil, are needed for the synthesis of amino acids (and subsequently proteins) from the carbohydrates produced in photosynthesis.

Using fertilisers to improve crop yield

- Fertilisers are used to restore the fertility of a soil by adding mineral ions.
- Inorganic fertilisers are quick-release, concentrated products that are specially formulated mixtures of inorganic ions.
- Organic fertilisers are slow-release products made from the dead remains/excretory products of a range of organisms. On decomposition, they release much lower concentrations of ions than inorganic fertilisers.
- Organic fertilisers improve soil structure. They increase the drainage of clay soils and the water-holding capacity of dry, sandy soils.
- If inorganic fertilisers are overused, ions may leach into waterways and cause rapid eutrophication:
  - The increased concentration of nitrate ions stimulates increased growth of algae.

- This blocks out light, so plants growing at lower levels in the waterway cannot photosynthesise and, therefore, die.
- The algae die as the nitrate ions are used up.
- Plants and algae are decomposed by bacteria. The increasing population of bacteria uses up more and more oxygen in aerobic respiration.
- The oxygen levels fall and many organisms die.
- Organic pollution results in an increase in the population of decomposers. These use increasing amounts of oxygen from the water in aerobic respiration.

Controlling pests

- Interspecific competition between weeds and crop plants results in competition for:
  - mineral ions and water from the soil
  - light
  - carbon dioxide from the air
- Animal pests can reduce the yields of crops by:
  - feeding directly on the organ of the plant that forms the crop
  - feeding on the leaves, which reduces the leaf area and, therefore, the photosynthetic capacity
  - feeding on the roots, which reduces the uptake of mineral ions and water
  - feeding on the sap in the phloem (e.g. by aphids), which prevents the transfer of these nutrients to other organs
  - transferring pathogenic viruses or bacteria
- Pesticides are chemicals that are used to kill pests. They are rarely 100% effective because:
  - the application does not contact all individuals
  - some individuals may be resistant
- Methods of biological control include:
  - introducing a predator
  - introducing a herbivore to control weeds
  - introducing a parasite
  - introducing sterile males
  - using pheromones

Adaptations of cereals

- Rice is adapted to cultivation in paddy fields because:
  - much of the stem and some of the root tissue is aerenchyma
  - the plant grows rapidly
  - rice is ethanol tolerant
  - additional roots, called nodal roots, develop from submerged regions of the stem
- The adaptations of sorghum include:
  - C4 photosynthesis
  - an extensive root system
  - leaves that roll into tubes to reduce water loss
  - many leaves with a large surface area

- The adaptations of maize include:
  - C4 photosynthesis
  - a low water requirement
  - many leaves with a large surface area

Questions

Multiple-choice

1 Increasing the availability of a limiting factor will:
   A have no effect on the rate of the reaction it influences
   B increase the rate of the reaction it influences
   C decrease the rate of the reaction it influences
   D stop the reaction it influences

2 To synthesise amino acids, plants use:
   A lipids and phosphate ions
   B lipids and nitrate ions
   C carbohydrates and nitrate ions
   D carbohydrates and phosphate ions

3 The rate of photosynthesis is principally influenced by:
   A light intensity, water availability and carbon dioxide concentration
   B light intensity, temperature and carbon dioxide concentration
   C water availability, temperature and carbon dioxide concentration
   D temperature, the availability of water and light intensity

4 Inorganic fertilisers are:
   A slow-release products that improve the structure of the soil
   B quick-release products that improve the structure of the soil
   C quick-release products that do not improve the structure of the soil
   D slow-release products that do not improve the structure of the soil

5 Identify which of the following does *not* occur during rapid eutrophication:
   A nitrate ions are leached into waterways
   B there is an algal bloom
   C algae use up the oxygen in the waterway
   D plants die as a result of lack of light

6 Pesticide resistance involves:
   A a mutation that causes immunity to the pesticide
   B more resistant individuals surviving to reproduce than non-resistant individuals
   C pest resurgence
   D none of the pests being killed by the pesticide

7 Biological control may involve:
   A introducing a parasite
   B using pheromones
   C introducing sterile males
   D any of the above

8 Two adaptations of rice plants are:

A they use C4 photosynthesis and have extensive root systems

B their stems contain aerenchyma and they have many leaves with a large surface area

C they have extensive root systems and show ethanol tolerance

D their stems contain aerenchyma and they show ethanol tolerance

9 Two adaptations of sorghum plants are:

A nodal roots and the use of C4 photosynthesis

B an extensive root system and aerenchyma in the stem

C an extensive root system and leaves that curl into a tube

D ethanol tolerance and many leaves with a large surface area

10 C4 photosynthesis is more efficient than C3 (normal) photosynthesis under conditions of:

A high temperature and high carbon dioxide concentration

B low temperature and high carbon dioxide concentration

C high temperature and low carbon dioxide concentration

D low temperature and low carbon dioxide concentration

Examination-style

1 Organisms that reduce the yield of a crop plant are called pests. They can be controlled using pesticides, by biological control or by integrated crop management.

The graph shows the effects of repeated pesticide applications on a population of pests.

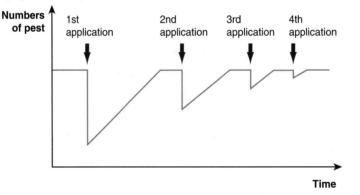

(a) (i) Suggest two reasons why the first application of the pesticide does not reduce the pest population to zero. *(2 marks)*

(ii) Explain the reduction in effect of the pesticide at the second, third and fourth applications. *(3 marks)*

(b) Give one benefit of each of the following in an integrated crop management system:

(i) crop rotation (not growing the same crop in the same field in successive years)

(ii) using organic fertilisers (such as farmyard manure) rather than inorganic fertilisers

    (iii) planting crops that are tolerant of the local soil pH
       conditions   *(3 marks)*

Total: 8 marks

2 (a) Give three ways in which rice is adapted to cultivation
     in paddy fields.   *(3 marks)*

  (b) Cyanobacteria thrive in the anaerobic conditions of the
     waterlogged soil in paddy fields. Cyanobacteria are able
     to fix nitrogen gas to form ammonium ions and then to
     use these in the synthesis of amino acids. How may this
     benefit the rice plants?   *(3 marks)*

Total: 6 marks

3 The graph shows the numbers of pests in an area before and after the
  introduction of a predator to act as a biological control agent.

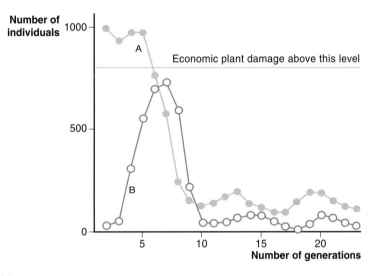

  (a) Which of the two lines, A or B, represents the pest population.
     Give *two* reasons for your answer.   *(3 marks)*

  (b) Describe two other methods of biological control.   *(4 marks)*

  (c) In comparison with biological control, give two advantages and
     two disadvantages of the use of pesticides.   *(4 marks)*

Total: 11 marks

4 (a) Copy and complete the table by writing 'yes' or 'no' in the boxes.

Feature of fertiliser	Inorganic fertiliser	Organic fertiliser
Improves structure of soil		
Improves fertility of soil		
Likely to cause eutrophication		
Slow release of ions		
Aids early germination of seeds		

(2 marks)

(b) Explain why farmers need to apply fertilisers to fields in which crops are grown, whereas areas where crops are not grown do not require fertilisers. *(4 marks)*

(c) Explain why using a crop rotation that includes clover reduces the amount of nitrogen-containing fertiliser that needs to be applied. *(4 marks)*

Total: 10 marks

5 Rice and maize are cereals. They form an important part of the diet of the people in the regions of the world where they are cultivated.

(a) Rice is cultivated in 'paddy fields' in many eastern countries. The crop is grown in fields which frequently become flooded and parts, or sometimes all, of the crop become submerged.

 (i) Explain how the rice crop is able to survive periods of total submergence. *(2 marks)*

 (ii) Give two other features of rice that allow it to grow effectively in the paddy fields. *(2 marks)*

(b) Maize has a specialised method of photosynthesis that is more efficient than the normal method of photosynthesis at high temperatures and low carbon dioxide concentrations. The graph shows the effect of increasing carbon dioxide concentrations on the rate of photosynthesis in plants that use the normal method of photosynthesis.

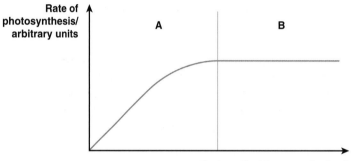

 (i) Suggest two reasons why the rate of photosynthesis remains constant in region B. Give an explanation for each reason you suggest. *(4 marks)*

 (ii) Sketch, on the graph, the curve you would expect if the same experiment had been carried out using either sorghum or maize. *(1 mark)*

(c) Some strains of maize have been genetically engineered to make them resistant to the 'corn borer', an insect that causes serious damage to maize crops. The gene introduced comes from a bacterium and codes for a protein toxic to the insect. Other strains of maize have been engineered to make them tolerant to herbicides. Suggest how combining these two traits in one strain of maize could eventually result in improved crop yields as well as reduced costs for the grower. *(6 marks)*

Total: 15 marks

Chapter 14

Controlling the reproduction of humans and domestic mammals

This chapter covers:
- the nature of the oestrous and menstrual cycles in female mammals
- the functions of the pituitary and ovarian hormones in controlling the oestrous and menstrual cycles
- the role of negative feedback in controlling the levels of hormones
- the use of synthetic hormones to control fertility in humans and in domestic mammals
- in vitro fertilisation and embryo transplantation in domestic mammals

Mammalian reproduction is controlled by hormones, both in the male and in the female. The female hormones determine how a follicle develops, when ovulation takes place, the condition of the uterine lining and its loss in menstruation. Negative feedback systems operate so that the levels of these hormones in the blood plasma are precisely regulated to produce their effects at the right time of the menstrual (or oestrous) cycle.

Doctors and vets can now use synthetic mammalian hormones to alter the fertility of their patients. They can induce multiple ovulations and they can prevent ovulation from occurring. Vets can also ensure that the oestrous cycles of all the members of a flock of sheep coincide. This means that the sheep can all be fertilised together and, therefore, give birth to lambs at about the same time.

Patrick Fox

All the lambs in this flock were born within a short space of time

Reproductive cycles in female mammals

The ovarian cycle

The human female releases an **oocyte** from her ovary about once every 28 days, from puberty to menopause. This is called **ovulation**. Why does it happen every 28 days? What causes it? The answer to the first question is 'because natural selection made it that way'. To understand the causes and regulation of ovulation, it is necessary to understand what happens in the ovarian cycle.

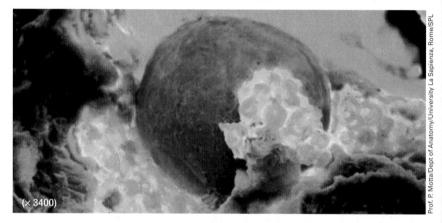

(× 3400)

Prof. P. Motta/Dept of Anatomy/University La Sapienza, Rome/SPL

> Oocytes are immature egg cells, each of which may develop into an ovum that could be fertilised by a sperm. However, the final transformation of oocyte into ovum only takes place when the nucleus of a sperm penetrates the oocyte.

False-colour scanning electron micrograph of ovulation. The oocyte has ruptured the external surface of the ovary

The production of oocytes begins in the ovaries before birth. By the time of puberty, there are tens of thousands of oocytes contained in groups of cells called **primary follicles**, near the outer edge of each ovary. Each month, one (or, occasionally, more) of these follicles is stimulated to develop. It enlarges and becomes a fluid-filled **Graafian follicle**. At this stage of development, ovulation takes place — the follicle bursts and the oocyte is released into one of the Fallopian tubes. The remains of the follicle form a **corpus luteum**, which secretes **progesterone** — a hormone that has an important role to play in maintaining the structure of the lining of the uterus. If an ovum is fertilised, the corpus luteum continues to remain active for approximately 3 months. If there is no **fertilisation** and no **implantation**, the corpus luteum degenerates, a new cycle begins and another follicle starts to mature.

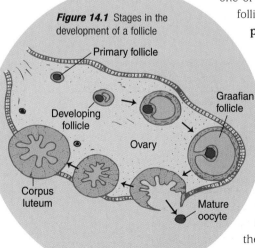

Figure 14.1 Stages in the development of a follicle

Primary follicle

Developing follicle

Graafian follicle

Ovary

Corpus luteum

Mature oocyte

> Implantation is the process by which an embryo becomes embedded in the lining of the uterus.

Figure 14.1 shows the changes *over time* that occur in a single follicle. All these stages of development would not be visible at the same time in one ovary.

The endometrial or menstrual cycle

As the changes of the ovarian cycle are taking place, developments also take place in the lining of the uterus — the **endometrium**. In the first phase of the cycle, before ovulation, the endometrium becomes thicker and more blood vessels develop. This is necessary so that, if implantation occurs, there will be an extensive network of blood vessels to supply the developing embryo with sufficient oxygen and nutrients. Following ovulation, this process continues and the endometrium begins to secrete a nutritive fluid. If implantation does not occur, smooth muscle in the walls of arterioles in the endometrium constricts, reducing the blood supply. This results in tissue death and the loss of the dead tissue in **menstruation**.

◀ The term 'menstrual cycle' is often used to describe the cycle of events that occur in the ovary and in the uterine lining. Strictly, it refers to the latter only.

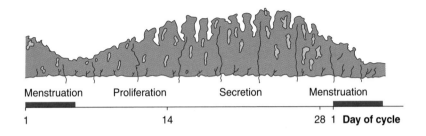

Figure 14.2 Changes in the endometrium during the menstrual cycle

The main events of the ovarian and menstrual cycles are summarised in Table 14.1. Notice how the events of the ovarian and menstrual cycles have given rise to alternative names for some of the stages.

Table 14.1

Stage	Events occurring	
	In ovary (ovarian cycle)	**In uterus (menstrual cycle)**
Menses/menstruation	Primary follicle begins to develop	Endometrium is shed
Follicular/proliferative phase	Follicle develops into a Graafian follicle	New endometrium proliferates (develops more tissue)
Ovulatory phase	Ovulation takes place — oocyte shed into Fallopian tube	Endometrium continues to proliferate
Luteal/secretory phase	Corpus luteum is formed in ovary; degenerates if implantation does not occur	Endometrium secretes nutrients; if implantation does not occur, constriction of arterioles leads to tissue death

The oestrous cycle in non-human mammals

Only female humans and female great apes menstruate. Other mature female mammals go through a similar cycle of changes called the **oestrous cycle**. The main phases are almost identical to those in humans, but there is much less build-up of the endometrium during the follicular/proliferative phase of the cycle. As a result, if there is no implantation, the small amount of extra tissue simply regresses. Therefore, there is no menstruation.

The length of the oestrous cycle varies from animal to animal, as does the period of time during which they take place. For example, in pigs the cycle lasts about 21 days and occurs throughout the year; in sheep the cycle lasts only 16 days and is restricted to the winter months. The time in the cycle when ovulation takes place is called oestrus or heat (the body temperature rises by about 0.5°C). Females will only mate during this period, which may only last for 1 or 2 days.

It is important that a farmer can recognise when a female cow or sheep is in oestrus. This is because the oocytes are only viable for the 2 days of this period — they must be fertilised within this time. Recognising oestrus allows the farmer to introduce the male at the right time to give the best chance of a successful mating. Alternatively, the farmer could arrange for **artificial insemination** to be carried out. There are several indicators of oestrus, other than the rise in temperature. For example, cows that are in oestrus will attempt to mount, and allow themselves to be mounted by, other cows. These are the 'primary indicators' of oestrus. 'Secondary indicators', which are not as reliable as the primary indicators, include butting, licking and head-resting. Other domestic mammals have different indicators of oestrus.

Hormonal control of the ovarian and menstrual cycles

Both the ovarian and menstrual cycles are controlled by hormones. The pituitary gland (just beneath the brain) produces and secretes a number of hormones, some of which induce other glands in the body to secrete their hormones. Two of

Box 14.1 How do hormones target specific organs?

A hormone usually has a specific target organ where it produces its effect. For example, insulin targets the liver, causing increased uptake of glucose and activating enzymes that convert glucose into glycogen. Insulin is a non-steroid hormone and is able to target the liver because receptor molecules in the plasma membrane of liver cells are complementary in shape to the insulin molecule. Binding starts a cascade of reactions that ultimately leads to the conversion of glucose into glycogen.

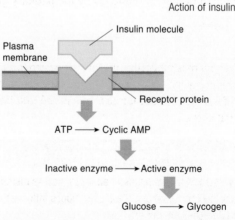

Action of insulin

Both FSH and LH target organs in this way.

Oestrogen and progesterone are steroid hormones and act differently. Being steroids, they are lipid-soluble and can pass through the plasma membrane. They bind with receptors on the nuclear envelope and initiate a cascade of reactions that switches on, or off, certain target genes. Only cells with the appropriate receptors in the nuclear envelope are influenced.

◀ A steroid is a type of lipid.

these hormones (**follicle-stimulating hormone** (FSH) and **luteinising hormone** (LH) are directly involved in controlling the ovarian cycle. By so doing, they also indirectly control the menstrual cycle. As a result of stimulation by the pituitary hormones, the ovaries (in particular the developing follicles) produce other hormones (oestrogen and progesterone) that influence the events of the menstrual cycle.

The pituitary hormones

Follicle stimulating hormone

An increase in the plasma concentration of FSH stimulates follicles to become larger and develop into Graafian follicles. Levels of FSH rise during the first part of the follicular phase of the cycle. FSH also stimulates the follicles to produce oestrogen. As the concentration of oestrogen increases in the blood plasma, it has two effects on the pituitary gland:

- it inhibits the secretion of FSH
- it stimulates the secretion of LH

As a result, the pituitary gland:

- reduces the secretion of FSH, so the plasma concentration of FSH falls
- increases the secretion of LH, so the plasma concentration of LH increases

Luteinising hormone

The levels of LH rise slowly through the initial part of the follicular phase and then sharply towards the end of the phase, typically on days 13–14 of a 28-day cycle. This sharp increase in the concentration of LH triggers ovulation. LH also stimulates the corpus luteum formed at ovulation to secrete increased amounts of progesterone. The increased concentrations of progesterone in the plasma inhibit the secretion of both FSH and LH by the pituitary gland.

The ovarian hormones

Oestrogen

As noted earlier, increasing concentrations of oestrogen inhibit the secretion of FSH by the pituitary gland. Oestrogen also influences the endometrium, causing the initial proliferation of endometrial tissue in the first half (proliferative phase) of the menstrual cycle.

◀ Oestrogen is not actually a single hormone, but a collection of related steroid hormones.

Box 14.2 Oestrogen and breast cancer

Oestrogens are steroid hormones that can cross plasma membranes and bind with receptors in the nuclear envelope. Steroid hormones influence cell activities by switching certain genes on and off.

Some of the effects of oestrogens occur because they cause cells to increase their rate of division. This is what happens in the endometrium. Sometimes, breast cancer cells are 'oestrogen-receptor positive' — they have receptors that cause them to take up oestrogen at a faster rate than is normal. This stimulates the cells to divide and promotes the development of the cancer.

Progesterone

Besides inhibiting the secretion of both FSH and LH by the pituitary gland, progesterone influences the endometrium. It maintains the uterine lining and causes it to become even thicker, ready for an embryo to implant. It also causes the endometrium to become more vascular, as blood vessels continue to develop. If implantation does not occur, the corpus luteum degenerates and the concentration of progesterone in the plasma falls. This means that the maintenance function of progesterone is lost — arterioles in the endometrium constrict, resulting in tissue death and loss in menstruation. As the plasma concentration of progesterone falls, its inhibitory effect on the pituitary gland diminishes. The pituitary begins to increase secretion of FSH again and a new cycle commences.

Negative feedback systems controlling the ovarian and menstrual cycles

Negative feedback is a process that tends to restore levels of a substance to normal when deviations from the norm occur. For example, when the plasma concentration of FSH increases above its normal level, it is brought back to the normal lower level by the inhibitory effect of oestrogen.

The negative feedback systems that control the ovarian and menstrual cycles are summarised in Figures 14.3 and 14.4.

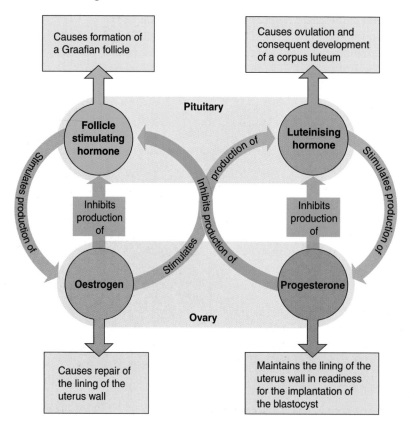

Figure 14.3 Feedback systems that control the secretion of pituitary and ovarian hormones

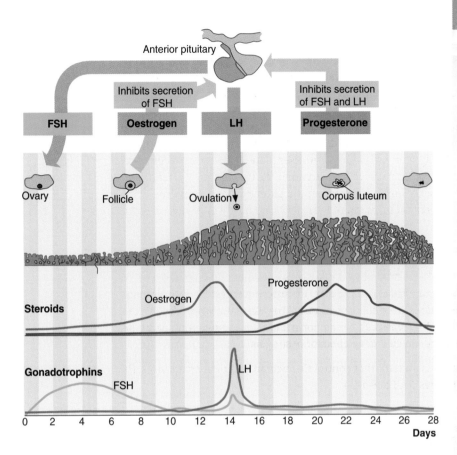

Figure 14.4 A summary of the control of the menstrual and ovarian cycles

Controlling fertility in humans and domestic mammals

Controlling human fertility

For a number of years, it has been possible to prevent ovulation using hormonal treatment — the contraceptive pill has been widely used since the 1960s. More recently, it has become possible to enhance the fertility of women who, for some reason, either do not ovulate at all or ovulate only infrequently.

The contraceptive pill

The key to avoiding an unwanted pregnancy is to prevent ovulation. If no oocytes are released into the Fallopian tubes, fertilisation cannot result from intercourse. Figures 14.3 and 14.4 show how ovulation is controlled and give a clue as to how it may be prevented.

- FSH stimulates ovulation.
- Oestrogen and progesterone both inhibit the secretion of FSH.

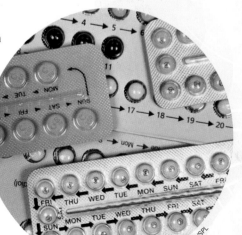

Contraceptive pills

Saturn Stills/SPL

A pill containing oestrogen and progesterone will inhibit the secretion of FSH. If there is no (or very little) FSH in the plasma, no ovarian follicles will develop. Therefore, ovulation cannot occur. However, prolonged exposure to high doses of oestrogen has been linked with a number of health problems, including:

- some types of breast cancer
- heart disease
- strokes

Another type of contraceptive pill contains only progesterone (the 'progesterone only' pill). However, it is less reliable than the combined pill and this must be set against potential health benefits.

Inducing ovulation

Some women have quite regular and otherwise normal menstrual cycles but they either do not ovulate or only ovulate infrequently. This may be caused by lower than normal levels of FSH in the blood plasma. Sometimes, although the level of FSH is too low to cause follicles to develop, it still stimulates them to produce oestrogen. This is a self-perpetuating situation because oestrogen inhibits the secretion of FSH. The fertility drug clomiphene acts by preventing the inhibition of FSH secretion. Therefore, the concentration of plasma FSH increases. This is usually sufficient to stimulate normal ovulation and, sometimes, to cause multiple ovulation. This occurs because it is difficult to regulate the concentration of FSH precisely. If there are no further complications, clomiphene should induce regular ovulation and normal intercourse should be successful. If there are further complications, such as blocked or scarred Fallopian tubes, or ovarian cysts, other procedures may have to be adopted.

Box 14.3 IVF treatment

Sometimes, the clomiphene treatment followed by sexual intercourse is unsuitable, because of the presence of other factors, such as blocked Fallopian tubes. In these cases, in vitro fertilisation (IVF) may be an option. Multiple ovulation is usually induced by injections of synthetic FSH, rather than by using clomiphene to increase natural FSH secretion. Up to ten oocytes are then removed from the Fallopian tubes and are fertilised outside the body by the partner's sperm, where possible. The fertilised ova (often referred to as pre-embryos) are then transferred into the woman's uterus.

Usually no more than two embryos are transferred to the woman's uterus, to avoid the complications of multiple births. What becomes of the remaining fertilised embryos? There are huge ethical issues surrounding the answer to this question. The most common outcome is for the embryos to be frozen. These can be recovered later and transferred to the woman's uterus if she wants more children.

If fertilisation by the partner's sperm is not possible (because of disease or a low sperm count), artificial insemination by donor (AID) may be used.

A new, and still experimental, technique called ICSI (intracytoplasmic sperm injection) involves the injection of a single sperm nucleus into the cytoplasm of an oocyte. This technique could be used when the male has a low sperm count. It has the added benefit that both partners would be the biological parents of the child.

(a) A technician removing a frozen embryo from storage for IVF
(b) Checking to see how many oocytes have been fertilised and have begun to develop into embryos

Controlling fertility in domestic mammals

In farming, the animals that die each year, or are sent for slaughter, must be replaced. A dairy farmer, for example, must have a continuous breeding programme to replace these animals. Moreover, cows only produce milk for the months immediately following calving and so, in order to ensure a regular supply of milk, the cow must calve again as soon as possible.

Induced ovulation and embryo transplantation

Many of the procedures already described in treating female infertility in humans are involved. However, the procedures are used to increase fertility rather than to cure infertility.

If a farmer has one cow in the herd that produces significantly more milk than the others, it would be desirable to breed from this cow to produce a herd with a similar yield. Using conventional breeding methods, it would take many years to produce such a herd. However, with IVF and embryo transplantation, this can be achieved in a much shorter time.

The main stages in the process are as follows:
- Injections of FSH are given to the 'superior' cow to induce **multiple ovulation** (sometimes called 'super-ovulation'). The oocytes are collected and stored in a culture medium that has a similar composition to the fluid in the Fallopian tubes.
- Using IVF, the oocytes are fertilised using semen from a registered bull.
- The fertilised ova are allowed to develop into 4-cell or 8-cell embryos.
- The cells of these embryos are then split, returned to the culture medium and each begins to develop again. The development and splitting is repeated until a sufficient number of embryos has been obtained.
- The embryos are screened for:
  - sex (only female embryos are used)
  - the genes needed to produce the high milk yield
- Each suitable embryo is then transplanted into the uterus of a surrogate cow. A herd of surrogates can carry embryos all derived from just one 'superior' cow. The calves that are born will develop into high-milk-yielding cattle.

◀ Oocytes are produced by meiosis, so they will not be genetically identical.

◀ The cells obtained from one original embryo (no matter how many times splitting has occurred) *will* be genetically identical, because they were formed by mitosis.

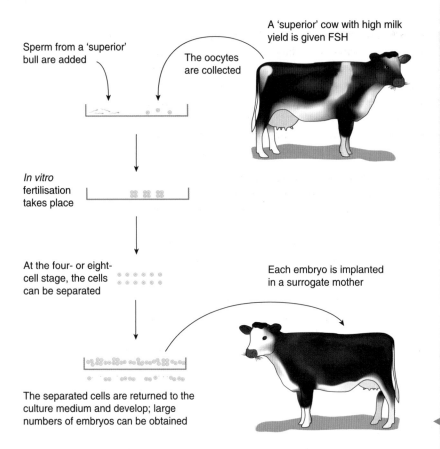

Sperm from a 'superior' bull are added

The oocytes are collected

A 'superior' cow with high milk yield is given FSH

In vitro fertilisation takes place

At the four- or eight-cell stage, the cells can be separated

Each embryo is implanted in a surrogate mother

The separated cells are returned to the culture medium and develop; large numbers of embryos can be obtained

Figure 14.5 IVF and embryo transplantation in cattle

The surrogate cattle need to be at the correct stage of the oestrous cycle to allow implantation to take place. Injections of progesterone can be used to synchronise oestrus.

Box 14.4 Increasing milk yield with BST

Selective breeding is not the only method of increasing the milk yield of cattle. Dairy cattle can be given injections of BST (bovine somatotrophin). This is a growth hormone that has the added effect of increasing milk production and letdown in cattle. Regular injections of BST increase the milk yield significantly. Genetically engineered bacteria produce much of the BST used.

Typical results are shown in the table below.

	Feed/ kg d^{-1}	Milk output/ kg d^{-1}	Milk-to-feed ratio
Without BST	34.1	27.9	0.82
With BST	37.8	37.3	0.99

The milk-to-feed ratio is a measure of productivity. It measures how many kilograms of milk are produced from a kilogram of feed. This is a more important measure than just an increase in yield, since it might require an excessive amount of feed. The figures shown give a 21% increase in milk-to-feed ratio — a 21% increase in real productivity.

Synchronising oestrus in domestic mammals

At lambing time, hundreds of sheep may give birth. All must be checked and, when necessary, given appropriate treatment. A difficult lambing may require expert veterinary assistance. Traditionally, the lambing season may persist over many weeks. **Synchronising oestrus** allows natural or artificial insemination of most of the flock to take place within a few days, with the aim of concentrating most of the lambing into a much shorter period. The basis of this procedure lies in the realisation that, because progesterone inhibits the secretion of FSH and LH, it can be used to suspend the current oestrous cycle and prevent a new one from starting.

The ewes are given daily injections of progesterone for a few days. This quickly suspends their oestrous cycles by suppressing the secretion of the pituitary hormones FSH and LH. When the injections of progesterone are stopped, the inhibition is removed and all the ewes start a new cycle at the same time. This means that they enter oestrus at approximately the same time. If the ewes are all fertilised during this cycle, all the lambs will be born within a few days of each other.

There will be some variation in the timing of lambing because:
- the oestrous cycles of the sheep will vary in length, so the timing of oestrus itself, and therefore of fertilisation, will vary
- the gestation period (period of pregnancy) of different sheep will vary slightly

Summary

Reproductive cycles in female mammals

- Oocytes are contained within a group of cells called a follicle. There are tens of thousands of these towards the outer edge of each ovary.
- Every month, after puberty, one of these follicles enlarges and develops into a Graafian follicle. This eventually bursts, releasing the oocyte into a Fallopian tube; this process is ovulation.
- The development of the follicles is controlled by two pituitary hormones:
  - FSH causes the follicle to enlarge and to secrete oestrogen
  - LH causes ovulation and stimulates the remains of the follicle — the corpus luteum — to secrete progesterone
- Oestrogen inhibits the secretion of FSH, stimulates the secretion of LH and causes the endometrium of the uterus to become thicker and more vascular.
- Progesterone inhibits the secretion of both FSH and LH and maintains the condition of the endometrium.
- If fertilisation and implantation do not occur, the corpus luteum degenerates and the level of plasma progesterone decreases as a consequence. This removes the inhibition of the pituitary gland and a new cycle commences.
- The oestrous cycle in domestic mammals is similar to the menstrual cycle, but there is no menstruation.
- At oestrus, or heat, the temperature of an animal rises by about 0.5°C.
- Standing to be mounted and mounting other animals are primary indicators of oestrus in cattle.

- Recognising oestrus allows a farmer to arrange for mating or artificial insemination to occur during the period when oocytes are still viable.

Controlling fertility in humans and domestic mammals

- The contraceptive pill works by inhibiting the secretion of FSH and preventing ovulation. Some pills contain both oestrogen and progesterone; the 'mini-pill' contains progesterone only.
- The fertility drug clomiphene is used to treat female infertility in humans. It works by removing the inhibition of FSH secretion caused by oestrogen.
- Injections of FSH are given to domestic mammals to induce multiple ovulation.
- The resulting oocytes can be fertilised in vitro (IVF) and the embryos split until there are enough that are suitable for transplantation into surrogate cattle.
- Injections of progesterone are used to synchronise oestrus in domestic mammals. The injections suppress the oestrous cycle. When they are withdrawn, a new cycle starts.
- Injections of BST can increase the productivity of dairy cattle by boosting the milk yield and improving the milk-to-feed ratio.

Questions

Multiple-choice

1 The stages in the development of a follicle in an ovary are:
   A primary follicle → corpus luteum → Graafian follicle
   B Graafian follicle → corpus luteum → primary follicle
   C corpus luteum → primary follicle → Graafian follicle
   D primary follicle → Graafian follicle → corpus luteum
2 Increased secretion of FSH causes:
   A a follicle to develop and increase its secretion of oestrogen
   B a follicle to regress and increase its secretion of progesterone
   C a follicle to regress and increase its secretion of oestrogen
   D a follicle to develop and increase its secretion of progesterone
3 Oestrogen causes:
   A an increase in the thickness of the endometrium and the inhibition of FSH secretion
   B a decrease in the thickness of the endometrium and the inhibition of FSH secretion
   C a decrease in the thickness of the endometrium and the stimulation of FSH secretion
   D an increase in the thickness of the endometrium and the stimulation of FSH secretion
4 In human females, increased secretion of LH causes:
   A ovulation and the secretion of oestrogen by the corpus luteum
   B ovulation and the secretion of progesterone by the corpus luteum
   C menstruation and the secretion of progesterone by the corpus luteum
   D menstruation and the secretion of oestrogen by the corpus luteum

5 Clomiphene can cure some cases of female infertility by:

A increasing FSH secretion by stimulating the pituitary gland

B increasing FSH secretion by blocking the inhibition of the pituitary gland

C increasing LH secretion by blocking the inhibition of the pituitary gland

D increasing LH secretion by stimulating the pituitary gland

6 Before embryo transplantation, embryos can be split and the resulting cells allowed to develop into new embryos. This is possible because:

A each new embryo is produced by meiosis and so there is genetic variation

B each new embryo is produced by mitosis and so there is genetic variation

C each new embryo is produced by mitosis and so all the cells are genetically identical

D each new embryo is produced by meiosis and so all the cells are genetically identical

7 To synchronise oestrus in sheep, the animals are given:

A daily injections of progesterone

B daily injections of oestrogen

C daily injections of FSH

D daily injections of LH

8 The primary indicators of oestrus in cows are:

A standing to be mounted and mounting other animals

B standing to be mounted and butting

C licking and butting

D standing to be mounted and licking

9 In sheep, oocytes are viable:

A for up to 2 days

B during oestrus

C both of the above

D neither of the above

10 Menstruation is caused by:

A a decrease in the level of progesterone causing dilation of arterioles in the endometrium

B a decrease in the level of oestrogen causing dilation of arterioles in the endometrium

C a decrease in the level of oestrogen causing constriction of arterioles in the endometrium

D a decrease in the level of progesterone causing constriction of arterioles in the endometrium

Examination-style

1 (a) The pituitary hormone FSH stimulates follicles in the ovary to secrete oestrogen. A negative feedback system reduces the pituitary secretion of FSH.

(i) Describe *two* effects of oestrogen on the uterine endom etrium. *(2 marks)*

(ii) Use the information concerning secretion of FSH by the pituitary gland to explain what is meant by negative feedback. *(3 marks)*

(b) The table compares the feed requirements and milk output of two herds of cattle. One herd has injections of bovine somatotrophin (BST); the other does not.

	Feed/kg d^{-1}	Milk output/kg d^{-1}
Without BST	32.0	28.0
With BST	37.5	35.0

(i) Calculate the milk-to-feed ratio for each herd. *(2 marks)*

(ii) Use your answer to (b)(i) to explain why it is more profitable for a farmer to use BST. *(2 marks)*

Total: 9 marks

2 It is possible to estimate the levels of the steroid hormones oestrogen and progesterone in the blood by measuring their concentrations in saliva. The procedure is as follows. The patient:

- rinses out her mouth with water
- waits 5 minutes
- collects saliva in a test tube
- stores it for up to 1 week in a refrigerator (if necessary)
- posts it to the laboratory for analysis

(a) Suggest why:

(i) she first rinse out her mouth with water *(1 mark)*

(ii) she must wait 5 minutes before collecting the sample *(2 marks)*

(b) Explain one advantage of this procedure compared with having a doctor take a blood sample. *(1 mark)*

(c) The results from an analysis of one patient's saliva over 70 days are shown in the graph below.

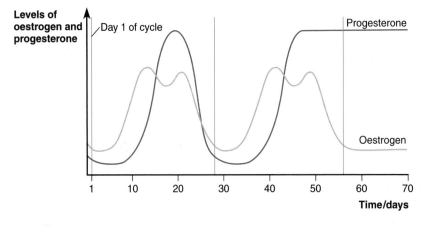

(i) Explain the changes in the concentration of oestrogen from day 7 to day 17. *(2 marks)*

(ii) Did this woman become pregnant during the 70-day period? Give evidence from the graph to support your answer. *(3 marks)*

Total: 9 marks

3 The diagram shows several stages in the development of a follicle.

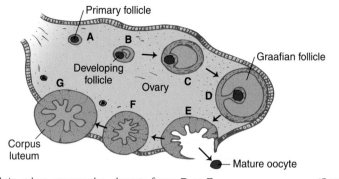

(a) Explain what causes the change from **D** to **E**.   (*2 marks*)
(b) Explain the importance of stage **F** should implantation occur.   (*3 marks*)
(c) Describe the changes occurring in the endometrium that coincide with stages **A** to **E**.   (*2 marks*)

Total: 7 marks

4 (a) Explain how progesterone can be used to synchronise the oestrous cycles of sheep.   (*3 marks*)

(b) Despite synchronising oestrous cycles, lambing can still be spread over several weeks. Suggest two possible explanations for this.   (*2 marks*)

(c) The table shows how the surface on which cattle stand, and their level of general activity, influence mounting activity (as indicated by the mounting index).

Location	Mounting index
Milking parlour	0.1
Holding pen	0.3
Dry concrete alley (stationary)	1.0
Dry concrete alley (moving)	1.1
Dry dirt lot (stationary)	1.6
Dry dirt lot (moving)	1.8

Use the information in the table to describe the influence of freedom to move and the nature of the surface on mounting activity.   (*3 marks*)

Total: 8 marks

5 Read the passage below and answer the questions that follow.

   Biotechnology is being used in a number of ways to increase the milk yield of cattle. It has been possible for some time now to genetically engineer bacteria to produce the hormone bovine somatotrophin (BST). The gene coding for the production of BST is transferred to bacteria, which are then cultured in a large-scale fermenter. The BST they produce is the same as the BST produced by the cattle and acts in the same way — by diverting glucose, fatty acids and body fats to the mammary glands and away from other regions of the body.

More recently, it has become possible to produce large numbers of cattle with a high milk yield by the technique of embryo transplantation. Sperm from an 'excellent' bull of the same breed as the cattle are used to fertilise several eggs from one high-yielding cow, which has been injected with a hormone to cause multiple ovulation. The resulting embryos are implanted into the uteri of other cattle which have been prepared for pregnancy by injections of other hormones.

(a) (i) Why is the bovine somatotrophin produced by the bacteria identical to that produced by the cattle? *(1 mark)*

(ii) Explain how injecting cattle with BST could improve their milk yield. *(2 marks)*

(iii) Describe a likely procedure for transferring the gene coding for the production of BST from cattle cells into bacterial cells. *(6 marks)*

(b) (i) Injections of which hormone would cause multiple ovulation? Explain how this would happen. *(2 marks)*

(ii) Name one of the 'other hormones' that are used to prepare the uterus for pregnancy. Explain how the hormone would act. *(2 marks)*

(iii) Although the bull and the cow are chosen carefully to produce the desired high yield, there can still be considerable variation in the milk yield of the offspring. Explain why. *(2 marks)*

Total: 15 marks

Index